The World's Greatest Literature

THE Masterpieces of the World's Greatest Authors in *History, Biography, Philosophy, Economics, Politics; Epic and Dramatic Literature, History of English Literature, Oriental Literature (Sacred and Profane), Orations, Essays.* Sixty-one Crown Octavo Volumes   ::   ::   ::

ILLUSTRATED WITH FRONTISPIECES, EACH A MASTER WORK OF ART IN PORTRAITURE OR HISTORIC PAINTING

Editors

MOORISH LITERATURE

COMPRISING

ROMANTIC BALLADS, TALES OF THE BERBERS, STORIES OF THE KABYLES, FOLK-LORE, AND NATIONAL TRADITIONS

TRANSLATED INTO ENGLISH FOR THE FIRST TIME

WITH A SPECIAL INTRODUCTION BY
RENÉ BASSET, Ph.D.
OF THE UNIVERSITY OF FRANCE, AND DIRECTOR OF THE
ACADÉMIE D'ALGER

REVISED EDITION

NEW YORK
P. F. COLLIER & SON

SPECIAL INTRODUCTION.

THE region which extends from the frontiers of Egypt to the Atlantic Ocean, and from the Mediterranean to the Niger, was in ancient times inhabited by a people to whom we give the general name of Berbers, but whom the ancients, particularly those of the Eastern portion, knew under the name of Moors. "They were called Maurisi by the Greeks," said Strabo, "in the first century A.D., and Mauri by the Romans. They are of Lybian origin, and form a powerful and rich nation." [1] This name of Moors is applied not only to the descendants of the ancient Lybians and Numidians, who live in the nomad state or in settled abodes, but also to the descendants of the Arabs who, in the eighth century A.D., brought with them Islamism, imposed by the sabre of Ogbah and his successors. Even further was it carried, into Spain, when Berbers and Arabs, reunited under the standard of Moussa and Tarik, added this country to the empire of the Khalifa. In the fifteenth century the Portuguese, in their turn, took the name to the Orient, and gave the name of Moors to the Mussulmans whom they found on the Oriental coast of Africa and in India.

The appellation particularizes, as one may see, three peoples entirely different in origin—the Berbers, the Arabs of the west, and the Spanish Mussulmans, widely divided, indeed, by political struggles, but united since the seventh and eighth centuries in their religious law. This distinction must be kept in mind, as it furnishes the necessary divisions for a study of the Moorish literature.

The term Moorish Literature may appear ambitious applied to the monuments of the Berber language which have come down to us, or are gathered daily either from the lips of singers on the mountains of the Jurgura, of the Aures, or of the Atlas of Morocco; under the tents of the Touaregs

---

[1] Geographica, t. xviii, ch. 3, § ii.

of the desert or the Moors of Senegal; in the oases of the south of Algeria or in Tunis. But it is useless to search for literary monuments such as have been transmitted to us from Egypt and India, Assyria and Persia, ancient Judea, Greece and Rome; from the Middle Ages; from Celt, Slav, and German; from the Semitic and Ouralo-altaïque tongues; the extreme Orient, and the modern literature of the Old and New World.

But the manifestations of thought, in popular form, are no less curious and worthy of study among the Berbers. I do not speak of the treatises on religion which in the Middle Ages and in our day were translated from the Arabic into certain dialects: that borrowed literature, which also exists among the Sonalulis of Eastern Africa and the Haussas and the Peuls of the Soudan, has nothing original. But the popular literature—the stories and songs—has an altogether different importance. It is, above all, the expression of the daily life, whether it relates to fêtes or battles or even simple fights. These songs may be satirical or laudatory, to celebrate the victory of one party or deplore the defeat of the True Believers by the Christians, resounding on the lips of children or women, or shouted in political defiance. They permit us, in spite of a coarse rhythm and language often incorrect, an insight into their manner of life, and to feel as do peoples established for centuries on African soil. Their ancestors, the Machouacha, threatened Egypt in the time of Moses and took possession of it, and more than twenty centuries later, with the Fatimides, converted Spain to the Mussulman faith. Under Arab chiefs they would have overcome all Eastern Europe, had it not been for the hammer of Charles Martel, which crushed them on the field of Poitiers.

The richest harvest of Berber songs in our possession is, without doubt, that in the dialect of the Zouaous, inhabiting the Jurgura mountains, which rise some miles distant from Algiers, their crests covered with snow part of the year.[2] All kinds of songs are represented; the rondeaux of children whose inspiration is alike in all countries:

"Oh, moonlight clear in the narrow streets,
Tell to our little friends

[2] Hanoteau, Poésies Populaires de la Khabylie du Jurgura, Paris, 1867, 8vo.

To come out now with us to play—
To play with us to-night.
If they come not, then we will go
To them with leather shoes.   (Kabkab.)[3]

" Rise up, O Sun, and hie thee forth,
On thee we'll put a bonnet old:
We'll plough for thee a little field—
A little field of pebbles full:
Our oxen but a pair of mice."

" Oh, far distant moon:
Could I but see thee, Ali!
Ali, son of Sliman,
The beard [4] of Milan
Has gone to draw water.
Her cruse, it is broken;
But he mends it with thread,
And draws water with her:
He cried to Ayesha:
'Give me my sabre,
That I kill the merle
Perched on the dunghill
Where she dreams;
She has eaten all my olives.' " [5]

In the same category one may find the songs which are pe-
culiar to the women, " couplets with which they accompany
themselves in their dances; the songs, the complaints which
one hears them repeat during whole hours in a rather slow
and monotonous rhythm while they are at their household
labors, turning the hand-mill, spinning and weaving cloths,
and composed by the women, both words and music." [6]

One of the songs, among others, and the most celebrated in
the region of the Oued-Sahal, belonging to a class called Deker,
is consecrated to the memory of an assassin, Daman-On-Mesal,
executed by a French justice. As in most of these couplets,
it is the guilty one who excites the interest:

" The Christian oppresses. He has snatched away
This deserving young man;
He took him away to Bougre,
The Christian women marvelled at him.
Pardieu! O Mussulmans, you
Have repudiated Kabyle honor." [7]

---

[3] A sort of sandal.   [4] Affectionate term for a child.
[5] Hanoteau, v. 441-443.   [6] Hanoteau, Preface, p. iii.   [7] Hanoteau, p. 94.

With the Berbers of lower Morocco the women's songs are called by the Arab name Eghna.

If the woman, as in all Mussulman society, plays an inferior rôle—inferior to that allowed to her in our modern civilizations —she is not less the object of songs which celebrate the power given her by beauty:

> " O bird with azure plumes,
> Go, be my messenger—
> I ask thee that thy flight be swift;
> Take from me now thy recompense.
> Rise with the dawn—ah, very soon—
> For me neglect a hundred plans;
> Direct thy flight toward the fount,
> To Tanina and Cherifa.

> " Speak to the eyelash-darkened maid,
> To the beautiful one of the pure, white throat;
> With teeth like milky pearls.
> Red as vermillion are her cheeks;
> Her graceful charms have stol'n my reason;
> Ceaselessly I see her in my dreams." [8]

> " A woman with a pretty nose
> Is worth a house of solid stone;
> I'd give for her a hundred reaux,[9]
> E'en if she quitted me as soon.

> " Arching eyebrows on a maid,
> With love the genii would entice,
> I'd buy her for a thousand reaux,
> Even if exile were the price.

> " A woman neither fat nor lean
> Is like a pleasant forest green,
> When she unfolds her budding charms,
> She gleams and glows with springtime sheen." [10]

The same sentiment inspires the Touareg songs, among which tribe women enjoy much greater liberty and possess a knowledge of letters greater than that of the men, and know more of that which we should call literature, if that word were not too ambitious:

> " For God's sake leave those hearts in peace,
> 'Tis Tosdenni torments them so;

[8] Hanoteau, p. 350-357.   [9] Keais.   [10] Hanoteau, pp. 302, 303.

> She is more graceful than a troop
> Of antelopes separated from gazelles;
> More beautiful than snowy flocks, ‑
> Which move toward the tents,
> And with the evening shades appear
> To share the nightly gathering;
> More beautiful than the striped silks
> Enwrapped so closely under the haiks,
> More beautiful than the glossy ebon veil,
> Enveloped in its paper white,
> With which the young man decks himself,
> And which sets off his dusky cheek." [1]

The poetic talent of the Touareg women, and the use they make of this gift—which they employ to celebrate or to rail at, with the accompaniment of their one-stringed violin, that which excites their admiration or inspires them with disdain —is a stimulant for warriors:

> " That which spurs me to battle is a word of scorn,
> And the fear of the eternal malediction
> Of God, and the circles of the young
> Maidens with their violins.
> Their disdain is for those men
> Who care not for their own good names. [2]

> " Noon has come, the meeting's sure.
> Hearts of wind love not the battle;
> As though they had no fear of the violins,
> Which are on the knees of painted women—
> Arab women, who were not fed on sheep's milk;
> There is but camel's milk in all their land.
> More than one other has preceded thee and is widowed,
> For that in Amded, long since,
> My own heart was burned.
> Since you were a young lad I suffered—
> Since I wore the veil and wrapped
> My head in the folds of the haik." [3]

War, and the struggle of faction against faction, of tribe against tribe, of confederation against confederation, it is which, with love, above all, has inspired the Berber men. With the Khabyles a string of love-songs is called " Alamato,"

[1] Masqueray, Observations grammaticales sur la grammaire Touareg et textes de la Tourahog des Tailog, pp. 212, 213. Paris, 1897.
[2] Masqueray, p. 220.
[3] Masqueray, p. 227.

because this word occurs in the first couplet, always with a belligerent inspiration:

> " He has seized his banner for the fight
> In honor of the Bey whose cause he maintains,
> He guides the warriors with their gorgeous cloaks,
> With their spurs unto their boots well fastened,
> All that was hostile they destroyed with violence;
> And brought the insurgents to reason."

This couplet is followed by a second, where allusion is made to the snow which interrupts communication:

> " Violently falls the snow,
> In the mist that precedes the lightning;
> It bends the branches to the earth,
> And splits the tallest trees in twain.
> Among the shepherds none can pasture his flock;
> It closes to traffic all the roads to market.
> Lovers then must trust the birds,
> With messages to their loves—
> Messages to express their passion.

> " Gentle tame falcon of mine,
> Rise in thy flight, spread out thy wings,
> If thou art my friend do me this service;
> To-morrow, ere ever the rise of the sun,
> Fly toward her house; there alight
> On the window of my gracious beauty." [4]

With the Khabyles of the Jurgura the preceding love-songs are the particular specialty of a whole list of poets who bear the Arab name of *T'eballa*, or " tambourinists." Ordinarily they are accompanied in their tours by a little troop of musicians who play the tambourine and the haut-boy. Though they are held in small estimation, and are relegated to the same level as the butchers and measurers of grain, they are none the less desired, and their presence is considered indispensable at all ceremonies—wedding fêtes, and on the birth of a son, on the occasion of circumcision, or for simple banquets.

Another class, composed of *Ameddah*, " panegyrists," or *Fecia*, " eloquent men," are considered as much higher in rank. They take part in all affairs of the country, and their advice is sought, for they dispense at will praise or blame. It is they

---

[4] Hanoteau, pp. 348–350.

who express the national sentiment of each tribe, and in case of war their accents uplift warriors, encourage the brave, and wither the cowardly. They accompany themselves with a Basque drum. Some, however, have with them one or two musicians who, after each couplet, play an air on the flute as a refrain.[5]

In war-songs it is remarkable to see with what rapidity historical memories are lost. The most ancient lay of this kind does not go beyond the conquest of Algiers by the French. The most recent songs treat of contemporary events. Nothing of the heroic traditions of the Berbers has survived in their memory, and it is the Arab annalists who show us the rôle they have played in history. If the songs relating to the conquest of Algeria had not been gathered half a century ago, they would doubtless have been lost, or nearly so, to-day. At that time, however, the remembrance was still alive, and the poets quickly crystallized in song the rapidity of the triumph of France, which represents their civilization:

"From the day when the Consul left Algiers,
The powerful French have gathered their hosts:
Now the Turks have gone, without hope of return,
Algiers the beautiful is wrested from them.

"Unhappy Isle that they built in the desert,
With vaults of limestone and brick;
The celestial guardian who over them watched has withdrawn.
Who can resist the power of God?

"The forts that surround Algiers like stars,
Are bereft of their masters;
The baptized ones have entered.
The Christian religion now is triumphant,
O my eyes, weep tears of blood, weep evermore!

"They are beasts of burden without cruppers,
Their backs are loaded,
Under a bushel their unkempt heads are hidden,
They speak a *patois* unintelligible,
You can understand nothing they say.

"The combat with these gloomy invaders
Is like the first ploughing of a virgin soil,
To which the harrowing implements

⁵ Hanoteau, Introduction.

> Are rude and painful;
> Their attack is terrible.

> " They drag their cannons with them,
> And know how to use them, the impious ones;
> When they fire, the smoke forms in thick clouds:
> They are charged with shrapnel,
> Which falls like the hail of approaching spring.
> Unfortunate queen of cities—
> City of noble ramparts,
> Algiers, column of Islam,
> Thou art like the habitation of the dead,
> The banner of France envelops thee all." [6]

It is, one may believe, in similar terms that these songs, lost to-day, recount the defeat of Jugurtha, or Talfarinas, by the Romans, or that of the Kahina by the Arabs. But that which shows clearly how rapidly these songs, and the remembrance of what had inspired them, have been lost is the fact that in a poem of the same kind on the same subject, composed some fifty years ago by the Chelha of meridional Morocco, it is not a question of France nor the Hussains, but the Christians in general, against whom the poet endeavors to excite his compatriots.

It is so, too, with the declamatory songs of the latest period of the Middle Ages, the dialects more or less precise, where the oldest heroic historical poems, like the Song of Roland, had disappeared to leave the field free for the imagination of the poet who treats the struggles between Christians and Saracens according to his own fantasy.

Thanks to General Hanoteau, the songs relating to the principal events of Khabyle since the French conquest have been saved from oblivion, viz., the expedition of Maréchal Bugeaud in 1867; that of General Pelissier in 1891; the insurrection of Bon Bar'la; those of Ameravun in 1896, and the divers episodes of the campaign of 1897 against the Aith Traten, when the mountains were the last citadel of the Khabyle independence:

> " The tribe was full of refugees,
> From all sides they sought refuge
> With the Aith Traten, the powerful confederation.
> ' Let us go,' said they, ' to a sure refuge,'

[6] Hanoteau, pp. 2, 3, 5, 7, 9, 11.

For the enemy has fallen on our heads,'
But in Arba they established their home." [7]

The unhappy war of 1870, thanks to the stupidity of the
military authorities, revived the hope of a victorious insurrection. Mograne, Bon Mazrag, and the Sheikh Haddad aroused
the Khabyles, but the desert tribes did not respond to their appeal. Barbary was again conquered, and the popular songs
composed on that occasion reproached them for the folly of
their attempt.

Bon Mezrah proclaimed in the mountains and on the plain:

" Come on, a Holy War against the Christians,
He followed his brother until his disaster,
His noble wife was lost to him.
As to his flocks and his children,
He left them to wander in Sahara.
Bon Mezrag is not a man,
But the lowest of all beings;
He deceived both Arabs and Khabyles,
Saying, ' I have news of the Christians.'

" I believed Haddad a saint indeed,
With miracles and supernatural gifts;
He has then no scent for game,
And singular to make himself he tries.

" I tell it to you; to all of you here
(How many have fallen in the battles),
That the Sheikh has submitted.
From the mountain he has returned,
Whoever followed him was blind.
He took flight like one bereft of sense.
How many wise men have fallen
On his traces, the traces of an impostor,
From Babors unto Guerrouma!
This joker has ruined the country—
He ravaged the world while he laughed;
By his fault he has made of this land a desert." [8]

The conclusion of poems of this kind is an appeal to the
generosity of France:

" Since we have so low fallen, [9]
You beat on us as on a drum;

[7] Hanoteau, p. 124.
[8] R. Basset, L'insurrection Algerienne, de 1871 dans les chansons populaires Khabyles Lourain, 1892.
[9] J. D. Luciani, Chansons Khabyles de Ismail Azekkion. Algiers, 1893.

You have silenced our voices.
We ask of you a pardon sincere,
O France, nation of valorous men,
And eternal shall be our repentance.
From beginning to the end of the year
We are waiting and hoping always:
My God! Soften the hearts of the authorities."

With the Touaregs, the civil, or war against the Arabs, re-places the war against the Christians, and has not been less actively celebrated:

"We have saddled the shoulders of the docile camel,
I excite him with my sabre, touching his neck,
I fall on the crowd, give them sabre and lance;
And then there remains but a mound,
And the wild beasts find a brave meal." [10]

One finds in this last verse the same inspiration that is found in the celebrated passage of the Iliad, verses 2 and 5: " Anger which caused ten thousand Achæans to send to Hades numer-ous souls of heroes, and to make food of them for the dogs and birds of prey." It is thus that the Arab poet expresses his ante-Islamic " Antarah ":

"My pitiless steel pierced all the vestments,
The general has no safety from my blade,
I have left him as food for savage beasts
Which tear him, crunching his bones,
His handsome hands and brave arms." [1]

The Scandinavian Skalds have had the same savage accents, and one can remember a strophe from the song of the death of Raynor Lodbrog:

" I was yet young when in the Orient we gave the wolves a bloody repast and a pasture to the birds. When our rude swords rang on the helmet, then they saw the sea rise and the vultures wade in blood." [2]

Robbery and pillage under armed bands, the ambuscade even, are celebrated among the Touaregs with as great pleas-ure as a brilliant engagement:

"Matella! May thy father die!
Thou art possessed by a demon,

[10] Masqueray, pp. 228, 229.   [1] Mo'allagah, v. 49, 50.
        [2] Marmier, Lettres sur l'Islemde.

To believe that the Touaregs are not men.
They know how to ride the camel; they
Ride in the morning and they ride at night;
They can travel; they can gallop:
They know how to offer drink to those
Who remain upon their beasts.
They know how to surprise a
Courageous man in the night.
Happy he sleeps, fearless with kneeling camels;
They pierce him with a lance,
Sharp and slender as a thorn,
And leave him to groan until
His soul leaves his body:
The eagle waits to devour his entrails." [3]

They also show great scorn for those who lead a life relatively less barbarous, and who adorn themselves as much as the Touaregs can by means of science and commerce:

" The Tsaggmaren are not men,
Not lance of iron, nor yet of wood,
They are not in harness, not in saddles,
They have no handsome saddle-bags,
They've naught of what makes mankind proud;
They've no fat and healthy camels,
The Tsaggmaren; don't speak of them;
They are people of a mixed race,
There is no condition not found with them.
Some are poor, yet not in need;
Others are abused by the demon,
Others own nothing but their clubs.
There are those who make the pilgrimage, and repeat it,
There are those who can read the Koran and learn by that
They possess in the pasturage camels, and their little ones,
Besides nuggets of gold all safely wrapped." [4]

Another style, no less sought for among the Berbers inhabiting cities, is the " complaint " which flourished in lower Morocco, where it is known under the Arab name of Lqist (history). When the subject is religious, they call it *Nadith* (tradition). One of the most celebrated is that wherein they tell of the descent into the infernal regions of a young man in search of his father and mother. It will give an idea of this style of composition to recite the beginning:

[3] Hanoteau, Essaie de grammaire de la langue Tamachek, pp. 210, 211. Paris, 1860.
[4] Hanoteau, p. 213.

> " In the name of God, most clement and merciful,
>   Also benediction and homage to the prophet Mohammed,
>   In the name of God, listen to the words of the author,
>   This is what the Talebs tell, according to the august Koran.
>   Let us begin this beautiful story by
>   Invoking the name of God.
>   Listen to this beautiful story, O good man,
>   We will recite the story of a young man
>   In Berbere; O God, give to us perfection;
>   That which we bring to you is found in truthful tradition,
>   Hard as a rock though thy heart be, it will melt;
>   The father and mother of Saba died in his childhood
>   And left him in great poverty;
>   Our compassionate Lord guided him and showed him the way,
>   God led him along toward the Prophet,
>   And gave to him the Koran." [5]

Other poems—for instance, that of Sidi Hammen and that
of Job—are equally celebrated in Morocco. The complaints
on religious subjects are accompanied on the violin, while those
treating of a historical event or a story with a moral have the
accompaniment of a guitar. We may class this kind of poems
among those called *Tandant,* in lower Morocco, which consist
in the enumeration of short maxims. The same class exist
also in Zouaona and in Touareg.

But the inspiration of the Khabyle poets does not always
maintain its exaltation. Their talents become an arm to
satirize those who have not given them a sufficiently large
recompense, or—worse still, and more unpardonable—who
have served to them a meagre repast:

> " I went to the home of vile animals,
>   Ait Rebah is their name;
>   I found them lying under the sun like green figs,
>   They looked ill and infirm.
>   They are lizards among adders,
>   They inspire no fear, for they bite not.
>   Put a sheepskin before them, they
>   Will tear your arms and hands;
>   Their parched lips are all scaly,
>   Besides being red and spotted.
>
> " As the vultures on their dung heaps,
>   When they see carrion, fall upon it,
>   Tearing out its entrails,

⁵ R. Basset, Le Poème de Sabi, p. 15 et suis. Paris 1879.

> That day is for them one of joy.
> Judging by their breeches,
> And the headdresses of their wives,
> I think they are of Jewish origin." [6]

This song, composed by Mohammed Said or Aihel Hadji, is still repeated when one wishes to insult persons from Aith Erbah, who have tried several times to assassinate the poet in revenge.

Sometimes two rival singers find themselves together, and each begins to eulogize himself, which eulogy ends in a satire on the other. But the joust begun by apostrophes and Homeric insults finishes often with a fight, and the natural arm is the Basque drum until others separate the adversaries.[7] We have an example in a dialogue of this kind between Youssuf ou Kassi, of the Aith Djemnad, and Mohand ou Abdalia, of the Aith Kraten. The challenge and the jousts—less the blows—exist among the chellahs of lower Morocco, where they are called *Tamawoucht;* but between man and woman there is that which indicates the greatest liberty of manners. The verses are improvised, and the authors are paid in small money. Here is a specimen:

The woman: " When it thunders and the sky is overcast,
　　　　　　Drive home the sheep, O watchful shepherd."
The man: " When it thunders, and the sky is overcast,
　　　　　　We will bring home the sheep."
The woman: " I wish I had a bunch of switches to strike you with!
　　　　　　May your father be accursed, Sheepkeeper!"
The man: " Oh, God, I thank thee for having created
　　　　　　Old maids to grind meal for the toilers." [8]

Another manifestation, and not less important of the popular Berber literature, consists in the stories. Although no attempt has been made in our days to gather them, many indications permit us to believe that they have been at all times well treasured by these people. In the story of Psyche that Apuleius inserted at the end of the second century A.D., in the romance of Metamorphoses,[9] we read that Venus imposed on Psyche, among other trials, that of sorting out and placing

[6] Hanoteau, Poèmes Populaires de la Khabyle, pp. 179–181, Du Jurgura.
[7] Hanoteau, p. 275 et seq.　　　　[8] Stemme, p. 7, 8.
[9] Hanoteau, Essai de Grammaire Khabyle, p. 282 et seq. Alger.

in separate jars the grains of wheat, oats, millet and poppy pease, lentils and lima beans which she had mixed together. This task, beyond the power of Psyche, was accomplished by the ants which came to her aid, and thus she conquered the task set by her cruel mother-in-law.

This same trial we find in a Berber story. It is an episode in a Khabyle story of the Mohammed ben Sol'tan, who, to obtain the hand of the daughter of a king, separated wheat, corn, oats, and sorghum, which had been mingled together. This trait is not found in Arab stories which have served as models for the greater part of Khabyle tales. It is scarcely admissible that the Berbers had read the " Golden Ass " of Apuleius, but it is probable that he was born at Madaure, in Algeria, and retained an episode of a popular Berber tale which he had heard in his childhood, and placed in his story.

The tales have also preserved the memory of very ancient customs, and in particular those of adoption. In the tales gathered in Khabyle by General Hanoteau,[10] T. Rivière,[1] and Moulieras,[2] also that in the story of Mizab, the hero took upon himself a supernatural task, and succeeded because he became the adopted son of an ogress, at whose breast he nursed.[3] This custom is an ancient one with the Berbers, for on a *bas relief* at Thebes it shows us a chief of the Machouacha (the Egyptian name of the Berbers) of the XXII Dynasty nursed and adopted by the goddess Hathor. Arab stories of Egypt have also preserved this trait—for instance, " The Bear of the Kitchen," [4] and El Schater Mohammed.[5]

During the conquest of the Magreb by the Arabs in the seventh century A.D., Kahina, a Berber queen, who at a given moment drove the Mussulman invaders away and personified national defiance, employed the same ceremony to adopt for son the Arab Khaled Ben Yazed, who was to betray her later.

Assisted by these traits of indigenous manners, we can call to mind ogres and pagans who represent an ancient population, or, more exactly, the sectarians of an ancient religion like the

[10] Hanoteau, p. 266. Le chasseur.
[1] Contes Populaires de la Khabylie du Jurgura, p. 239. Paris, 1892. Le chausseur.
[2] Legendes et contes merveilleuses de la grande Khabylie, p. 20. 2 vols. Tunis, 1893-1898. Le fils du Sultan et le chien des Chrètiens, p. 90. Histoire de Ali et sa mère.
[3] R. Basset, Nouveaux Contes Berbers, p. 18. Paris, 1807. La Pomme de jeunesse.
[4] Spitta-bey, Contes Arabes modernes, p. 12. Ley de 1883.
[5] Arless Pasha, Contes Populaire de la vallée du Nil. Paris, 1895.

Paganism or the Christianity which was maintained on some points of Northern Africa, with the Berbers, until the eleventh century A.D. Fabulous features from the Arabs have slipped into the descriptions of the Djohala, mingled with the confused souvenirs of mythological beings belonging to paganism before the advent of Christianity.

It is difficult to separate the different sources of the Berber stories. Besides those appearing to be of indigenous origin, and which have for scene a grotto or a mountain, one could scarcely deny that the greater part, whether relating to stories of adventure, fairy stories, or comical tales, were borrowed from foreign countries by way of the Arabs. Without doubt they have furnished the larger part, but there are some of which there are no counterparts in European countries. " Half a cock," for instance, has travelled into the various provinces of France, Ireland, Albania, among the Southern Slavs, and to Portugal, from whence it went to Brazil; but the Arabs do not know it, nor do they know Tom Thumb, which with the Khabyles becomes H'ab Sliman. In the actual state of our knowledge, we can only say that there is a striking resemblance between a Berber tale and such or such a version. From thence comes the presumption of borrowed matter. But, for the best results to be gained, one should be in possession of all the versions. When it relates to celebrated personages among the Mussulmans, like Solomon, or the features of a legend of which no trace remains of the names, one can certainly conclude that it is borrowed from the Arabs. It is the same with the greater number of fairy tales, whose first inventors, the Arabs, commenced with the " Thousand and One Nights," and presented us with " The Languages of the Beasts," and also with funny stories.

The principal personage of these last is Si Djeha, whose name was borrowed from a comic narrative existing as early as the eleventh century A.D. The contents are sometimes coarse and sometimes witty, are nearly all more ancient, and yet belong to the domain of pleasantries from which in Germany sprung the anecdotes of Tyll Eulenspiegel and the Seven Suabians, and in England the Wise Men of Gotham. In Italy, and even in Albania, the name of Djeha is preserved under the form of Guifa and Guicha; and the Turks, who possess the richest literature on this person, have made him a Ghadji Sirii Hissar, under the name of Nasr-eddin Hodja (a form altered from Djoha). The traits attributed to such persons as Bon Idhes, Bon Goudous, Bon Kheenpouch, are equally the same as those bestowed upon Si Djeha.

But if the Berbers have borrowed the majority of their tales, they have given to their characters the manners and appearance and names of their compatriots. The king does not differ from the Amir of a village, or an Amanokul of the Touaregs. The palace is the same as all those of a Haddarth, and Haroun al Raschid himself, when he passes into Berber stories, is plucked of the splendor he possesses in the " Thousand and One Nights," and in Oriental stories. This anachronism renders the heroes of the tales more real, and they are real Berbers, who are alive, and who express themselves like the mountaineers of Jurgura, the Arabs of the Atlas; like the men of Ksour, or the nomads of Sahara. In general there is little art in these stories, and in style they are far below other collections celebrated through the entire world.

An important place is given to the fables or stories of animals, but there is little that is not borrowed from foreign lands, and the animals are only such as the Berbers are familiar with. The adventures of the jackal do not differ from those of the fox in European stories. An African trait may be signalled in the prominence which it offers the hare, as in the stories of *Ouslofs* and *Bantous*. Also, the hedgehog, neglected so lamentably in our fables, holds an important place; and if the jackal manages to deceive the lion, he is, in spite of his astute nature, duped by the hedgehog when he tries a fall with him. As to the lion, the serpent, the cock, the frog, the turtle, the hyena, the jackal, the rat, their rôles offer little of the place they play in the Arab tales, or even the Europeans.

If we pass from Berber we find the Arab tongue as spoken among the Magreb, and will see that the literature is composed of the same elements, particularly in the tales and songs. There are few special publications concerning the first, but there are few travellers who have not gathered some, and thus rendered their relations with the people more pleasant. In what concerns the fairy tales it is, above all, the children for whom they are destined, " when at night, at the end of their

wearisome days, the mothers gather their children around them
under the tent, under the shelter of her Bon Rabah, the little
ones demand with tears a story to carry their imaginations far
away." " Kherrfin ya summa " (" Tell us a story "), they say,
and she begins the long series of the exploits of Ah Di Douan.[6]
Even the men do not disdain to listen to the tales, and those
that were gathered from Tunis and Tripoli by Mr. Stemme,[7]
and in Morocco by Messrs. Souin and Stemme,[8] show that the
marvellous adventures, wherein intervene the Djinns, fairies,
ogres, and sorcerers, are no less popular among the Arab people
than among the Berbers.

We must not forget that these last-named have borrowed
much from the first ones, and it is by them that they have
known the celebrated Khalif of Bagdad, one of the principal
heroes of the " Thousand and One Nights," Haroun al Raschid,
whose presence surprises us not a little when figuring in adventures incompatible with the dignity of a successor of the
Prophet.

As in the Berber tales, one finds parallels to the Arab stories
among the folk-lore of Europe, whether they were borrowed
directly or whether they came from India.   One will notice,
however, in the Arab tales a superior editing.   The style is
more ornate, the incidents better arranged.   One feels that, although it deals with a language disdaining the usage of letters,
it is expressed almost as well as though in a cultivated literary
language.   The gathering of the populations must also be
taken into consideration; the citizens of Tunis, of Algiers, and
even in the cities of Morocco, have a more exact idea of civilized life than the Berber of the mountains or the desert.   As
to the comic stories, it is still the Si Djeha who is the hero,
and his adventures differ little with those preserved in Berber,
and which are common to several literatures, even when the
principal person bears another name.

The popular poetry consists of two great divisions, quite
different as to subject.   The first and best esteemed bears the
name of Klam el Djedd, and treats of that which concerns the
Prophet, the saints, and miracles.   A specimen of this class is

[6] Deeplun, Recueil de textes pour l'étude de l'Arabe parlé, v. 12, p. iv. Paris, 1891.
[7] Iumsche Märchen und Gedichte. Leipzig, 1898. 2 vols. Märchen und Gedichte.
Aus der Stadt Tripolis in Nord Afrika. Leipzig.
[8] Zum Arabischen Dialekt. Von Markko. Leipzig, 1893. Vers. 8.

the complaint relative to the rupture of the Dam of St. Denis
of Sig, of which the following is the commencement:

> " A great disaster was fated: [9]
> The cavalier gave the alarm, at the moment of the break;
> The menace was realized by the Supreme Will,
> My God! Thou alone art good.
> The dam, perfidious thing,
> Precipitated his muddy Legions,
> With loud growlings.
> No bank so strong as to hold him in check.

> " He spurred to the right,
> The bridges which could not sustain his shock fell
> Under his added weight;
> His fury filled the country with fear, and he
> Crushed the barrier that would retain him."

As to the class of declamatory poems, one in particular is
popular in Algiers, for it celebrates the conquest of the
Maghreb in the eleventh century by the divers branches of the
Beni-Hilal, from whom descend almost the whole of the Arabs
who now are living in the northwest of Africa. This veritable
poem is old enough, perhaps under its present form, for the
historian, Ten Khaldoun, who wrote at the end of the fourteenth century and the beginning of the fifteenth, has preserved
the resumé of the episode of Djazza, the heroine who abandoned her children and husband to follow her brothers to the
conquest of Thrgya Hajoute. To him are attributed verses
which do not lack regularity, nor a certain rhythm, and also a
facility of expression, but which abound in interpolations and
faults of grammar. The city people could not bear to hear
them nor to read them. In our days, for their taste has changed
—at least in that which touches the masses—the recital of the
deeds of the Helals is much liked in the Arab cafés in Algeria
and also in Tunis. Still more, these recitals have penetrated
to the Berbers, and if they have not preserved the indigenous
songs of the second Arab invasion, they have borrowed the
traditions of their conquerors, as we can see in the episode of
Ali el Hilalien and of Er-Redah.

The names of the invading chiefs have been preserved in
the declamatory songs: Abou Zeid, Hassan ben Serhan, and,
above all, Dyab ben Ghanum, in the mouth of whom the poet

[9] Delphin et Genis. Notes sur la Poesie et la musique Arabes dans le Maghreb Alge-
rien, pp. 14-16. Paris, 1886.

puts at the end of the epic the recital of the exploits of his race:

" Since the day when we quitted the soil and territory of the Medjid,
 I have not opened my heart to joy;
We came to the homes of Chokir and Cherif ben Hachem who pours
 upon thee (Djazzah) a rain of tears;
We have marched against Ed-Dabis ben Monime and we have over-
 run his cities and plains.
We went to Koufat and have bought merchandise from the trades-
 men who come to us by caravan.
We arrived at Ras el Ain in all our brave attire and we mastered all
 the villages and their inhabitants.
We came to Haleb, whose territory we had overrun, borne by our
 swift, magnificent steeds.
We entered the country of the Khazi Mohammed who wore a coat of
 mail, with long, floating ends,
We traversed Syria, going toward Ghaza, and reached Egypt, belong-
 ing to the son of Yakoub, Yousof, and found the Turks with
 their swift steeds.
We reached the land of Raqin al Hoonara, and drowned him in a
 deluge of blood.
We came to the country of the Mahdi, whom we rolled on the earth,
 and as to his nobles their blood flowed in streams.
We came to the iron house of Boraih, and found that the Jewish was
 the established religion.
We arrived at the home of the warrior, El Hashais:
The night was dark, he fell upon us while we slept without anxiety,
He took from us our delicate and honored young girls, beauties whose
 eyes were darkened with kohol.
Abou Zeid marched against him with his sharp sword and left him
 lying on the ground.
Abou So'dah Khalifah the Zemati, made an expedition against us,
 and pursued us with the sword from all sides.
I killed Abou So'dah Khalifah the Zemati, and I have put you in
 possession of all his estates.
They gave me three provinces and So'dah, this is the exact truth that
 I am telling here.
Then came an old woman of evil augur and she threw dissension
 among us, and the Helals left for a distant land.
Then Abou Ali said to me: ' Dyab, you are but a fool.'
I marched against him under the wing of the night, and flames were
 lighted in the sheepfolds.
He sent against me Hassan the Hilali, I went to meet him and said,
 ' Seize this wretched dog.' These are the words of the Zoght Dyab
 ben Ghanem and the fire of illness was lighted in his breast." [10]

[10] R. Basset. Un Episode d'une chanson de geste Arabe sur la seconde conquête de l'Afrique Septentrionale par les Mussulmans. Bulletin de Correspondence Africaine, p. 147. Alger, 1885, in 8vo. See also Stemme. Tripolitanisches Bederinenlieder. Leipzig, 1804, in 8vo.

The second style of modern Arabic poetry is the "Kela-mel hazel." It comprises the pieces which treat of wine, women, and pleasures; and, in general, on all subjects considered light and unworthy of a serious mind. One may find an example in the piece of "Said and Hyza," and in different works of Mr. Stemme cited above. It is particularly among the nomad Arabs that this style is found, even more than the dwellers in cities, on whom rests the reproach of composing verses where the study and sometimes the singularity of expression cannot replace the inspiration, the energy, and even the delicacy of sentiment often found among the nomads:

"The country remains a desert, the days of heat are ended, the trees of our land have borne the attack of Summer, that is my grief.
After it was so magnificent to behold, its leaves are fallen, one by one, before my eyes.
But I do not covet the verdure of a cypress; my sorrow has for its cause a woman, whose heart has captivated mine.
I will describe her clearly; you will know who she is; since she has gone my heart fails me.
Cheika of the eye constantly veiled, daughter of Mouloud, thy love has exhausted me.
I have reached a point where I walk dizzily like one who has drunken and is drunk; still am I fasting; my heart has abandoned me.
Thy thick hair is like the ostrich's plumes, the male ostrich, feeding in the depressions of the dunes; thy eyebrows are like two *nouns* [Arab letters] of a Tlemcen writing.
Thy eyes, my beautiful, are like two gleaming gun barrels, made at Stamboul, city defiant of Christians.
The cheek of Cherikha is like the rose and the poppy when they open under the showers.
Thy mouth insults the emerald and the diamond; thy saliva is a remedy against the malady; without doubt it is that which has cured me." [1]

To finish with the modern literature of the northwest of Africa, I should mention a style of writings which played a grand rôle some five centuries ago, but that sort is too closely connected with those composing the poems on the Spanish Moors, and of them I shall speak later. It remains now to but enumerate the enigmas found in all popular literature, and the satiric sayings attributed to holy persons of the fifteenth century, who, for having been virtuous and having possessed

[1] Joly, Poesie Arnaduno chez les Nomades Algeriennes. Revue Africaine, XLV, pp. 217-219. Alger, 1901, 8vo.

the gift of miracles, were none the less men, and as such bore
anger and spite. The most celebrated of all was Sidi Ahmed
ben Yousuf, who was buried at Miliana. By reason of the
axiom, " They lend but to the rich," they attributed to him all
the satirical sayings which are heard in the villages and among
the tribes of Algeria, of which, perhaps, he did pronounce some.
Praises are rare:

> " He whom you see, wild and tall,
> Know him for a child of Algiers."

> " Beni Menaur, son of the dispersed,
> Has many soldiers,
> And a false heart."

> " Some are going to call you Blida (little village),
> But I have called you Ourida (little rose)."

> " Cherchel is but shame,
> Avarice, and flight from society,
> His face is that of a sheep,
> His heart is the heart of a wolf;
> Be either sailor or forge worker,
> Or else leave the city." [2]

> " He who stands there on a low hill
> All dressed in a small mantle,
> Holding in his hand a small stick
> And calling to sorrow, ' Come and find me,'
> Know him for a son of Medea."

> " Miliana; Error and evil renown,
> Of water and of wood,
> People are jealous of it,
> Women are Viziers there,
> And men the captives."

> " Ténès; built upon a dunghill,
> Its water is blood,
> Its air is poison,
> By the Eternal! Sidi Ahmed will not pass the night here,
> Get out of the house, O cat!"

> " People of Bon Speur,
> Women and men,
> That they throw into the sea."

[2] R. Basset. **Les dictionnaires satiriques attribués à Sidi ben Yousof.** Paris, 1890, 8vo.

" From the Orient and Occident,
   I gathered the scamps,
   I brought them to Sidi Mohammed ben Djellal,
   There they escaped me,
   One part went to Morocco,
   And the rest went down into Eghrès."

" Oran the depraved,
   I sold thee at a reasonable price;
   The Christians have come there,
   Until the day of the resurrection."

" Tlemcen : Glory of the chevaliers ;
   Her water, her air,
   And the way her women veil themselves
   Are found in no other land."

" Tunis : Land of hypocrisy and deceit,
   In the day there is abundance of vagabonds,
   At night their number is multiplied,
   God grant that I be not buried in its soil."

Another no less celebrated in Morocco, Sidi Abdan Rahman
el Medjidont, is, they say, the author of sentences in four
verses, in which he curses the vices of his time and satirizes
the tribes, and attacks the women with a bitterness worthy of
Juvenal :

" Morocco is the land of treason;
   Accursed be its habitants;
   They make guests sleep outside,
   And steal their provisions." [3]

" Deceptive women are deceivers ever,
   I hastened to escape them.
   They girdle themselves with vipers,
   And fasten their gowns with scorpions."

" Let not thyself fall victim to a widow,
   Even if her cheeks are bouquets,
   For though you are the best of husbands,
   She will repeat ceaselessly, ' God, be merciful to the dead.' "

" No river on the mountains,
   No warm nights in the winter,
   No women doing kind actions,
   No generous-hearted enemies."

[1] H. J. Castries. Les Gnomes de Sidi Abdir Rahman El Medjedoub. Paris, 1896.

The battle of the Guadalete, where sank the Visigoth empire, delivered Spain almost defenceless to the Arab and Berber conquest. There developed then a civilization and an intellectual culture far superior to those of the barbarous Christian refugees in the Asturias, where they led a rude and coarse life which but seasoned them for future struggles. Of their literary monuments, there remain to us but mediocre Latin chronicles. The court of the Omayades at Cordova saw a literature blossom which did not disappear even after the fall of the Khalifate. On the contrary, it seemed to regain a new vigor in the small states which surged up about the Iberian Peninsula. The Christians, under the domination of the Mussulmans, allowed themselves to be seduced by the Arabian literature. " They loved to read their poems and romances. They went to great expense and built immense libraries. They scarcely knew how to express themselves in Latin, but when it was necessary to write in Arabic, they found crowds of people who understood that language, wrote it with the greatest elegance, and composed poems even preferable in point of view to the art of the Arab poets themselves." [4]

In spite of the complaints of fanatics like Euloge and Alvaro, the literary history of that time was filled with Christian names, either those of Spanish who had remained faithful to the ancient faith, or renegades, or children of renegades. By the side of the Arab names, like that of the Bishop Arib ben Said of Cordova, are found those of Ibn Guzman (Son of Guzman), Ibn el Goutya (son of Gothe), Ibn Loyon (son of Leon), Ibn er Roumaye (son of the Greek), Ibn Konbaret (son of Comparatus), Ibn Baschkoual (son of Paschal), and all have left a name among letters.

One magnificent period in literature unfolded itself in the eleventh century A.D., in the little courts of Seville, of Murcie, of Malaga, Valence, Toledo, and Badajos. The kings, like El Nis Sasim, El Mo'hadhid, El Mishamed, Hbn Razin, rank among the best poets, and even the women answered with talent to the verses which they inspired. They have preserved the names and the pieces of some of them: Aicha, Rhadia, Fatima, Maryam, Touna, and the Princess Ouallada. Greek antiquity has not left us more elegant verses, nor elegies more

[4] Dozy. Histoire des Mussulmans de l'Espagne, pp. 103-166. Leyden, 1861, in 12mo, 4to.

passionate, than these, of which but a small portion has been saved from forgetfulness in the anthologies of Hbn Khayan, Hbn el Abbar, Hbn Bassam de Turad-eddin, and Ibn el Khatîb el Maggari. They needed the arrival of the Berbers to turn them into Almoran. Those Berbers hastened there from the middle of Sahara and the borders of Senegal to help the cause of Islamism against Spanish rule, as it was menaced through the victories of Alfonso of Castile. The result would have been to stifle those free manifestations of the literary art under a rigorous piety which was almost always but the thin varnish of hypocrisy.

To the Almoravides succeeded the Almohades coming from the Atlas of Morocco. To the Almohades, the Merias coming from Sahara in Algeria, but in dying out each of these dynasties left each time a little more ground under the hands of the Christians, who, since the time in Telage, when they were tracked into the caverns of Covadonga, had not ceased, in spite of ill fortune of all sorts, to follow the work of deliverance. It would have been accomplished centuries before if the internal struggle in Christian Spain in the fourteenth and fifteenth centuries had not accorded some years of respite to the kingdom which was being founded at Granada, and revived, although with less brilliancy, the splendor of the times before the twelfth century.

In the course of the long struggle the independent Christians had not been able to avoid feeling in a certain measure something of the influence of their neighbors, now their most civilized subjects. They translated into prose imitations of the tales such as those of the book of Patronis, borrowing from the general chronicles or in translations like the " Kalila and traditions, legendary or historic, as they found them in the Dimna," or the book of " The Ruses of Women," in verse.

In their oldest romances—for instance, that of the " Children of Sara," [5] and in those to which they have given the name of *romances fronterizos,* or romances of the frontier—they give the facts of the war between the Mussulmans and the Christians.

But they gave the name of Mauresques to another and different class of romances, of which the heroes are chevaliers,

[5] T. Ramon Manendoe Pidal. La legende de les Infantes de Sara. Madrid, 1896. 8vo.

who have nothing of the Mussulman but the name. The talent of certain *littérateurs* of the sixteenth century exercised itself in that class where the persons are all conventional, or the descriptions are all imaginative, and made a portrait of the Mussulman society so exact that the romances of Esplandian, Amadis de Gaul, and others, which evoked the delicious knight-errantry of Don Quixote, can present a picture of the veritable chivalry of the Middle Ages. We possess but few verses of the Mussulmans of Granada. Argot de Moll preserved them in Arabic, transcribed in Latin characters, one piece being attributed to Mouley Abou Abdallah:

> " The charming Alhambra and its palaces weep
> Over their loss, Muley Boabdil (Bon Abdallah),
> Bring me my horse and my white buckler,
> That I may fight to retake the Alhambra;
> Bring me my horse and my buckler blue,
> That I may go to fight to retake my children.

> " My children are at Guadia, my wife at Jolfata;
> Thou hast caused my ruin, O Setti Omm el Fata.
> My children are at Guadia, my wife at Jolfata,
> Thou hast caused my ruin, O Setti Omm el Fata!" [6]

As may be seen, these verses have no resemblance to those called Moorish. These are of a purely Spanish diction.[7]

Some romances, but not of these last-named, have kept traces of the real legends of the Arabs. There is among them one which treats of the adventures of Don Rodrigues, the last king of the Visigoths—" The Closed House of Toledo." [8] " The Seduction of la Cava," " The Vengeance of Count Julien," " The Battle of Guadalete," are brought back in the same fashion by the historians and writers of Mussulman romances.

The romance on the construction of the Alhambra has preserved the character of an Arabic legend which dates from before the prophet.[9] There is also a romance on the conquest of Spain, attributed to an Arab writer, the same man whom Cervantes somewhat later feigned to present as the author of Don Quixote, the Moor, Cid Hamet ben Engels.[10]

[6] A. de Circourt. Histoire des Moors mudijares et des Moresques. Paris, 1846.
[7] T. A. de Circourt. I. iii., p. 327-332.
[8] R. Basset. Legendes Arabes d'Espagne. La Maison fermée de Tolède. Oran, 1898, in 8vo.
[9] R. Basset. D'Alhambra et le Chateau de Khanumag : Revue des traditions populaires. Fairier, 1871, p. 459-465.
[10] Histoire des Conquêtes d'Espagne par les Mores. Par Ali Aven Sufran. Paris, 1720.

It is another style of writing, less seductive, perhaps, than that of the Moorish romances, in spite of their lack of vivacity and their bad taste. But why mark this as the expression of the Mussulman sentiment under Christian domination? Conquered by the Castilians, the Aragons, and the Portuguese, the Moors had lost the use of Arabic, but they had preserved the exterior sign-writing, just as their new converts retained their usages and their national costumes. We possess a complete literature composed in Spanish, but written in Arabic characters. They called it by the name of *Aljaniado*. Its chief characteristic is that it treats of the principal legends of the Mussulmans; those of Solomon and Moses, of Jesus; the birth, childhood, and the marriage of Mohammed; Temins ed Daria, the war of the king El Mohallal, the miracle of the moon, the ascension of Mohammed to heaven, the conversion of Omar, the battle of Yarmouk, the golden castle, the marvels that God showed to Abraham, Ali and the forty young girls, the anti-Christ and the day of judgment,[1] etc.; the legend of Joseph, son of Jacob; that of Alexander the Great,[2] to which could be added the story of the princess Zoraida,[3] without speaking of the pious exhortations, magic formulas, conjurations, and charms.[4]

The Moors held to these documents all the more that they were written in Arabic, and that the fury of the Inquisition was let loose upon them. To save them from the flames, their owners hid them with the greatest care, and but recently, at El Monacid, they found a whole library in Arabic and Aljamiado, hidden more than two centuries between the double walls of an old house.[5] The Mussulman proprietor of these books and his descendants were dead, or had emigrated to Africa, abandoning the treasure which was to see the light in a more tolerant epoch.

Political relations also existed between those of the Moors who remained in Spain as converts and such as had fled from persecution and carried to the populations of the north of Africa the hatred of the Spanish Christians. Thus we find

[1] Guillon Robles. Legendas Moriscas. Madrid, 1885-86. 36 petit in 8vo.
[2] Guillon Robles. La Legenda de Jose, hijo de Jacob, ye do Alexandro Magna. Zaragoza, 1888, en 8vo.
[3] L de Eguilas el Hditz. de La Princess Zoraida. Granada, 1892, 16mo.
[4] P. Gil y Ribera et Mar Sanches. Colleccion el textos Aljamiados. Zaragoza, 1888, 8vo.
[5] Pamo. Las coplas del Peregrino de Puey Monçon. Zaragoza, 1897. Pet. en 8vo.

among the popular literature of the Magreb the same legends, but edited in Arabic. Only a small number has been published.[6] Whether in one language or the other, editing does not offer anything remarkable. The stories have been developed, after the traditions of the Mussulmans, by the *demi-littérateurs,* and by that means they have become easier and more accessible to the multitude.

It is thus that a literature in Spain sadly ends which, during seven centuries, had counted historians and poets, philologists, philosophers and savants, and which the Christian literature replacing it can possibly equal in some points, but never surpass.[7]

René Basset

[6] R. Basset. Les Aventures Merveilleuses de Tunis et Dais. Rome, 1891, en 8vo. L'expédition du Chateau d'or, et la combat d'Ali et du dragon. Rome, 1893, en 8vo. M'lle Florence Groff. Les sept dormants, La ville de Tram, et l'excursion contre la Makke, Alger, 1891, en 8vo.

[7] M. Basset's "Special Introduction" was written in French; the English translation was made by Robert Arnot.

PREFACE

THE Moorish ballads which appear in this volume are selected from a unique department of European literature. They are found in the Spanish language, but their character is oriental; their inspiration comes from the Mahometan conquerors of northern Africa, and while they exhibit a blending of Spanish earnestness and chivalry with the wild and dashing spirit of the Arab, they present a type of literature which is quite unparalleled in the Latin and Teutonic countries of the Mediterranean basin.

Spain is especially rich in ballad literature, infinitely richer than any other civilized nation. These ballads take various forms. By Cervantes and his countrymen they are styled romances, and the romance generally consists in a poem which describes the character, sufferings, or exploits of a single individual. The language is simple; the versification, often artless though melodious, is seldom elaborated into complexity of rhyme. But the heroic Moor is set before us in the most vivid colors. The hues and material of his cloak, his housings, his caftan, and his plumes are given, and quite a vocabulary is exhausted in depicting the color, sex, and breed of his warhorse. His weapons, lance, scimitar, and corslet of steel are dwelt upon with enthusiasm. He is as brave as Mars, and as comely as Adonis. Sometimes he dashes into a bull-ring and slays wild creatures in the sight of fair ladies and envious men. He throws his lance of cane, which is filled with sand, so high that it vanishes in the clouds. He is ready to strike down, in his own house, the Christian who has taken from him and wedded the lady of his choice. He is almost always in love with some lady who is unkind and cold, and for her he wanders at times in dark array, expressing his sombre mood in the device and motto which he paints upon his shield. Some of the ballads picture love more fortunate in the most charm-

ing manner, and the dark tortures of jealousy are powerfully
described in others. The devotion of the Moor to his lady
is scarcely caricatured in the mocking language of Cervantes,
and is not exceeded by anything to be found in the history of
French chivalry. But the god of these ballads is Allah, and
they sometimes reveal a trace of ferocity which seems to be de-
rived from religious fanaticism. Nor can the reader fail to be
struck by the profound pathos which many of them express so
well. The dirges are supremely beautiful, their language
simple and direct, but perfect in descriptive touches and in the
cadence of the reiterated burden.

Beside the ballads of warlike and amorous adventures,
there are sea-songs, songs of captivity, and songs of the galley
slave. The Spanish Moor is seized by some African pirate
and carried away to toil in the mill of his master on some
foreign shore, or he is chained to the rowing-bench of the
Berber galley, thence to be taken and sold when the voyage is
over to some master who leaves him to weep in solitary toil
in the farm or garden. Sometimes he wins the love of his
mistress, who releases him and flies in his company.

All these ballads have vivid descriptions of scenery. The
towers of Baeza, the walls of Granada, the green *vegas* that
spread outside every city, the valley of the Guadalquivir, and
the rushing waters of the Tagus, the high cliffs of Cadiz, the
Pillars of Hercules, and the blue waves of the Mediterranean
make a life-like background to every incident. In the cities
the ladies throng the balconies of curling iron-work or crowd
the plaza where the joust or bull-fight is to be witnessed, or
steal at nightfall to the edge of the *vega* to meet a lover, and
sometimes to die in his arms at the hands of bandits.

There is a dramatic power in these ballads which is one of
their most remarkable features. They are sometimes mere
sketches, but oftener the story is told with consummate art, with
strict economy of word and phrase, and the *dénouement* comes
with a point and power which show that the Moorish minstrel
was an artist of no mean skill and address.

The authors of the Moorish romances, songs, and ballads are
unknown. They have probably assumed their present literary
form after being part of the *répertoire* of successive minstrels,
and some of the incidents appear in more than one version.

The most ancient of them are often the shortest, but they belong to the period when southern Spain under Mahometan rule was at the height of its prosperity, and Arabian learning, art, and literature made her rank among the first countries in Europe. The peninsula was conquered by the Moors in the caliphate of Walid I, 705–715 A.D., and the independent dynasty of the Ommiades was founded by Abderrhaman at Granada in 755 A.D. It was from this latter date that the Spanish Moors began to assume that special character in language, manners, and chivalric enthusiasm which is represented in the present ballads; the spirit of Christian knighthood is here seen blended with Arabian passion, impetuosity, and impulsiveness, and the Spanish language has supplanted, even among Mahometan poets, the oriental idiom. We may roughly estimate the period in which the Moorish romance flourished as comprised in the years between 1100 and 1600 A.D.

The term Moorish is somewhat indefinite, and is used in Spanish history as a synonym of Saracen or Mahometan. It cannot be called a national appellation, though originally in the Augustan age it was applied to the dwellers in Mauretania, with whom the Romans had first come in contact when the war with Hannibal was transferred from Italy and Spain to Africa. In the present day, it may be applied to all the races of northwestern Africa who have accepted Mahometanism; in which case it would include the aborigines of that region, who live not on the coast and in towns, but in the Atlas Mountain and the Sahara Desert. While these races, all Berbers under different local names, are Mussulmans in profession, they are not so highly civilized as their co-religionists who people the coast of the Mediterranean. They live a tribal life, and are blood-thirsty and predatory. They are of course mixed in race with the Arabians, but they are separate in their life and institutions, and they possess no written literature. Their oral literature is, however, abundant, though it is only within quite recent years that it has become known to America and Europe. The present collection of tales and fables is the first which has hitherto been made in the English language. The learned men who collected the tales of the Berbers and Kabyles (who are identical in ethnical origin) underwent many hardships in gathering from half-savage lips the material

for their volume. They were forced to live among the wild
tribesmen, join their nomad life, sit at their feasts, and watch
with them round their camp-fire, while it was with difficulty
they transferred to writing the syllables of a barbarous tongue.
The memory of the Berber story-teller seems to be incredibly
capacious and retentive, and the tales were recited over and
over again without a variation. As is to be expected these tales
are very varied, and many of them are of a didactic, if not
ethical, cast. They are instructive as revealing the social life
and character of these mountain and desert tribes.

We find the spirit of the vendetta pervading these tales
with more than Corsican bitterness and unreasoning cruelty,
every man being allowed to revenge himself by taking the
life or property of another. This private and personal war-
fare has done more than anything else to check the advance
in civilization of these tribesmen. The Berbers and Kabyles
are fanatical Mahometans and look upon Christians and
Jews as dogs and outcasts. It is considered honorable to cheat,
rob, or deceive by lies one who does not worship Allah. The
tales illustrate, moreover, the degraded position of women.
A wife is literally a chattel, not only to be bought, but to be
sold also, and to be treated in every respect as man's inferior—
a mere slave or beast of burden. Yet the tribesmen are pro-
foundly superstitious, and hold in great dread the evil spirits
who they think surround them and to whom they attribute
bodily and mental ills. An idiot is one who is possessed by a
wicked demon, and is to be feared accordingly.

There are found current among them a vast number of fairy
tales, such as equal in wildness and horror the strangest in-
ventions of oriental imagination. Their tales of ogres and
ogresses are unsoftened by any of that playfulness and bon-
homie which give such undying charm to the "Thousand
and One Nights." The element of the miraculous takes many
original forms in their popular tales, and they have more than
their share of the folk-lore legends and traditions such as
Herodotus loved to collect. It was said of old that something
new was always coming out of Africa, and certainly the con-
tribution which the Berbers and Kabyles have made to the fund
of wonder-stories in the world may be looked upon as new, in
more than one sense. It is new, not only because it is novel

and unexpected, but because it is fresh, original and highly interesting.

The fables of these tribes are very abundant and very curious. The great hero of the animal fable in Europe has always been the fox, whose cunning, greed, and duplicity are immortalized in the finest fable the world's literature possesses. The fables of northwest Africa employ the jackal instead of Reynard, whose place the sycophant of the lion not inaptly fills.

There are a number of men among the Kabyles and other Berber tribes who make a profession of reciting poems, tales, and proverbs, and travel from one village or encampment to another in search of an audience. They know the national traditions, the heroic legends, and warlike adventures that pertain to each community, and are honored and welcomed wherever they go. It was from these men that the various narratives contained in this collection were obtained, and the translation of them has engaged the talents and labors of some of the world's foremost oriental scholars.

Epiphanius Wilson. —

CONTENTS

MOORISH BALLADS

ROMANCEROS MORISCOS

—

[*Metrical Translation by Epiphanius Wilson, A.M.*]

MOORISH BALLADS

FATIMA'S LOVE

ON the morn of John the Baptist, just at the break of day,
The Moors upon Granada's fields streamed out in
bright array.
Their horses galloped o'er the sod, their lances flashed in air,
And the banners that their dames had wrought spread out
their colors fair.
Their quivers bright flashed in the light with gold and silk
brocade,
And the Moor who saw his love was there looked best in the
parade,
And the Moor who had no lady love strove hard some love
to gain.
'Mong those who from Alhambra's towers gazed on that war-
rior train,
There were two Moorish ladies there whom love had smit-
ten sore;
Zarifa one, and Fatima the name the other bore.
Knit by warm friendship were their hearts till, filled with jeal-
ous pain,
Their glances met, as one fair knight came prancing o'er the
plain.
Zarifa spoke to Fatima, "How has love marred thy face!
Once roses bloomed on either cheek, now lilies take their place;
And you, who once would talk of love, now still and silent stay.
Come, come unto the window and watch the pageant gay!
Abindarraez is riding by; his train is full in view;
In all Granada none can boast a choicer retinue."
"It is not love, Zarifa, that robs my cheek of rose;
No fond and anxious passion this mournful bosom knows;
My cheeks are pale and I am still and silent, it is true,—
For, ah! I miss my father's face, whom fierce Alabey slew.

3

And did I crave the boon of love, a thousand knights were fain
To fight for me in service true on yonder flowery plain.
And all the love I give to each to give me back again.
And for Abindarraez, whose heart and valiant might,
You praise and from the window watch, with rapturous de-
    light——"
The lady stopped, for at their feet knelt down the well-loved
    knight.

THE BRAGGART REBUKED

" If thou art brave in battle's hour
    As thou art bold in pleasure's rout;
If thou canst make the lances fly
    As thou canst fling thy words about;

" If thou canst in the vega fight
    As thou the ladies' eyes canst praise;
And show on horseback half the skill
    That marks thee in the dance's maze;

" Meet with the briskness of the joust
    The challenge of the deadly lance,
And in the play of scimitars
    Be sprightly as in festive dance;

" If thou art ready in the field
    As thou art nimble on the square;
And canst the front of battle face
    As though thou flirtest with the fair;

" If thou dost don thy shining mail
    As lightly as thy festive suit,
And listenest to the trumpet call
    As though it were thy lady's lute;

" And if, as in the gamesome hour
    Thou flingest round the rattling reed
'Against the foeman's moated camp,
    Thou spurrest on thy thundering steed;

" If, when the foe is face to face,
    Thou boastest as thou oft hast done
When far away his ranks were ranged,
    And the fierce fight had not begun ;—

" Go, Zaide, to the Alhambra go,
    And there defend thy soldier fame ;
For every tongue is wagging there,
    And all, derisive, speak thy name.

" And if thou fear to go alone,
    Take others with thee to thine aid ;
Thy friends are ready at thy beck,
    And Zaide need not be afraid !

" It is not in the palace court,
    Amid the throng of ladies bright,
That the good soldier, by his tongue,
    Proves himself valorous in the fight.

" It is not there his hands can show
    What in the battle he can do ;
But where the shock of onset tests
    The fearless heart, the iron thew.

" Betake thee to the bloody field
    And let thy sword thy praises sing ;
But silence is most eloquent
    Amid the courtiers of the King."

Thus Tarfe wrote, the Moorish knight,
    His heart so filled with furious rage
That where his fiery pen had passed
    It pierced and rent the flimsy page.

He called his varlet to his side,
    " Now seek the Alhambra's hall," said he,
" And privately to Zaide say
    That this epistle comes from me ;

" And whisper, that none else may hear,
    And say that I his coming wait,
Where Genil's crystal torrent laves
    The pillars of yon palace gate."

THE ADMIRAL'S FAREWELL

The royal fleet with fluttering sail is waiting in the bay;
And brave Mustapha, the Admiral, must start at break of day.
His hood and cloak of many hues he swiftly dons, and sets
Upon his brow his turban gay with pearls and amulets;
Of many tints above his head his plumes are waving wide;
Like a crescent moon his scimitar is dangling at his side;
And standing at the window, he gazes forth, and, hark!
Across the rippling waters floats the summons to embark.

>Blow, trumpets; clarions, sound your strain!
>Strike, kettle-drum, the alarum in refrain.
>Let the shrill fife, the flute, the sackbut ring
>A summons to our Admiral, a salvo to our King!

The haughty Turk his scarlet shoe upon the stirrup placed,
Right easily he vaulted to his saddle-tree in haste.
His courser was Arabian, in whose crest and pastern show
A glossy coat as soft as silk, as white as driven snow.
One mark alone was on his flank! 'twas branded deep and
    dark;
The letter F in Arab script, stood out the sacred mark.
By the color of his courser he wished it to be seen
That the soul of the King's Admiral was white and true and
    clean.
Oh, swift and full of mettle was the steed which that day bore
Mustapha, the High Admiral, down to the wave-beat shore!
The haughty Turk sails forth at morn, that Malta he may take,
But many the greater conquest his gallant men shall make;
For his heart is high and his soul is bent on death or victory,
And he pauses, as the clashing sound comes from the distant
    sea;

>Blow, trumpets; clarions, sound your strain!
>Strike, kettle-drum, the alarum in refrain.
>Let fife and flute, and sackbut in accord
>   Proclaim, Aboard! Aboard!
>Thy pinnace waits thee at the slip, lord Admiral,
>   aboard!

And as he hears the summons Love makes for him reply,
" O whither, cruel fortune, wilt thou bid the warrior fly?
Must I seek thee in the ocean, where the winds and billows
 roar?
Must I seek thee there, because in vain I sought thee on the
 shore?
And dost thou think the ocean, crossed by my flashing sail,
With all its myriad waters and its rivers, can avail
To quench the ardent fire of love that rages in my breast,
And soothe the fever of my soul into one hour of rest?
And as he mused, in bitter thought, Mustapha reached in haste
A balcony; till dawn of day before that house he paced,
And all his heart's anxieties he counted o'er and o'er,
And, when the darkness of the night toward opening twilight
 wore,
Upon the balcony there came the cause of all his sighs,
But a smile was on her rosy lips and a light was in her eyes.
" O lovely Zaida," he began, and gazed into her face,
" If my presence at thy window is a burden to thy peace,
One pledge bestow upon me, one pledge of love, I pray,
And let me kiss thy lily hand before I sail away."
" I grieve for thy departure," the lady made reply,
" And it needs no pledge to tell thee I am faithful till I die,
But if one token thou must have, take this ere thou depart;
('Twas fashioned by these hands of mine) and keep it on thy
 heart!"
The Moor rose in his stirrups, he took it from her hand,
'Twas a piece of lace of gold and silk shaped for a helmet
 band.
There was the wheel of fortune with subtile needle drawn,
(Ah, Fortune that had left him there dejected and forlorn!)
And as he paused, he heard the sound tumultuous come again,
'Twas from the fleet, down in the bay, and well he knew the
 strain.

  Blow, trumpets; clarions, sound your strain;
  Strike, kettle-drum, the alarum in refrain.
  Let fife and flute, and sackbut in accord
    Proclaim, Aboard! Aboard!
  Thy pinnace waits thee at the slip, lord Admiral,
    aboard!

Oh, stay my foes, nor in such haste invite me to the field!
Here let me take the triumphs that softer conquests yield!
This is the goal of my desire, the aim of my design,
That Zaida's hand in mine be placed and her heart beat close
    to mine!
Then spake the fair Sultana, and she dropped a tender tear,
" Nay mourn not for the present pain, for future bliss is near.
The wings of Time are swift, and they bear a brighter day;
And when once the longed-for gift is here 'twill never pass
    away!"
Then the Moor's heart beat high with joy; to smiles were
    changed his sighs,
In silent ecstasy he gazed into the lady's eyes.
He rode to meet his waiting fleet, for favoring was the wind,
But while his body went on board, he left his heart behind!

    Blow, trumpets; clarions, sound your strain!
    Strike, kettle-drum, the alarum in refrain.
    Let the shrill fife, the flute, the sackbut ring
    A summons to our Admiral, a salvo to our King.

MORIANA AND GALVAN

'Twas Princess Moriana,
    Upon a castle's height,
That played with Moorish Galvan
    At cards for her delight;
And oft he lost the stakes he set,
    Full many a coin I wis;
When Moriana lost, she gave
    Her hand for him to kiss.
And after hours of pleasure
    Moor Galvan sank to sleep;
And soon the lady saw a knight
    Descend the mountain steep;
His voice was raised in sorrow,
    His eyes with tears were wet,
For lovely Moriana
    His heart could ne'er forget.

For her, upon St. John's Day,
  While she was gathering flowers,
The Moors had made a captive,
  Beneath her father's towers.
And Moriana raised her eyes
  And saw her lover ride,
And on her cheeks her Moorish lord
  The sparkling tears descried.
With anger raged his spirit,
  And thus to her he cried:
" What ails thee, gentle lady?
  Why flows with tears thine eye?
If Moors of mine have done thee wrong,
  I swear that they shall die;
If any of thy maidens
  Have caused thee this distress,
The whip across their shoulders
  Shall avenge their wickedness.
Or, if the Christian countrymen
  Have sorrow for thee made,
I will, with conquering armies,
  Their provinces invade.
The warlike weapons that I don
  Are festal robes to me;
To me the din of battle
  Is sweet tranquillity;
The direst toils the warrior bears
  With steadfast joy I meet;
To me the watch that nightlong lasts
  Is like a slumber sweet."
" No Moors of thine within these halls
  Have caused to me this pain;
No maidens waiting in my bower
  Have showed to me disdain;
Nor have my Christian kinsmen
  To mourn my spirit made,
Provoking thee in vengeance
  Their province to invade.
Vain the deep cause of my distress
  From Galvan's eye to hide—

'Tis that I see down yonder mount
  A knight in armor ride.
'Tis such a sight that does my tears
  From very heart-springs move;
For yonder knight is all to me,
  My husband and my love."
Straight the Moor's cheek with anger flushed,
  Till red eclipsed the brown,
And his clenched fist he lifted
  As if to strike her down.
He gnashed his teeth with passion,
  The fangs with blood were red,
He called his slaves and bade them
  Strike off the lady's head.
He bade them bind and take her
  First to the mountain's height,
That she the doom might suffer
  Within her husband's sight;
But all the lady answered,
  When she was brought to death,
Were words of faith and loyalty
  Borne on her parting breath:
" Behold, I die a Christian,
  And here repeat my vows
Of faithfulness to yonder knight,
  My loved and lawful spouse."

THE BEREAVED FATHER

" Rise up, rise up, thou hoary head,
  What madness causes thy delay?
Thou killest swine on Thursday morn,
  And eatest flesh on fasting day.

" 'Tis now seven years since first I trod
  The valley and the wandering wood;
My feet were bare, my flesh was torn,
  And all my pathway stained in blood.

"Ah, mournfully I seek in vain
  The Emperor's daughter, who had gone
A prisoner made by caitiff Moors,
  Upon the morning of St. John.

"She gathered flowers upon the plain,
  She plucked the roses from the spray,
And in the orchard of her sire
  They found and bore the maid away."

These words has Moriana heard,
  Close nestled in the Moor's embrace;
The tears that welled from out her eyes
  Have wet her captor's swarthy face.

THE WARDEN OF MOLINA

The warden of Molina, ah! furious was his speed,
As he dashed his glittering rowels in the flank of his good
  steed,
And his reins left dangling from the bit, along the white high-
  way,
For his mind was set to speed his horse, to speed and not to
  stay.
He rode upon a grizzled roan, and with the wind he raced,
And the breezes rustled round him like a tempest in the waste.
In the Plaza of Molina at last he made his stand,
And in a voice of thunder he uttered his command:
      To arms, to arms, my captains!
      Sound, clarions; trumpets, blow;
      And let the thundering kettle-drum
      Give challenge to the foe.

"Now leave your feasts and banquetings and gird you in your
  steel!
And leave the couches of delight, where slumber's charm you
  feel;
Your country calls for succor, all must the word obey,
For the freedom of your fathers is in your hands to-day.
Ah, sore may be the struggle, and vast may be the cost;
But yet no tie of love must keep you now, or all is lost.

In breasts where honor dwells there is no room in times like
    these
To dally at a lady's side, kneel at a lady's knees.
> To arms, to arms, my captains!
> Sound, clarions; trumpets, blow;
> And let the thundering kettle-drum
> Give challenge to the foe.

" Yes, in the hour of peril away with pleasure's thrall!
Let honor take the lance and steed to meet our country's call.
For those who craven in the fight refuse to meet the foe
Shall sink beneath the feet of all struck by a bitterer blow;
In moments when fair honor's crown is offered to the brave
And dangers yawn around our State, deep as the deadly grave,
'Tis right strong arms and sturdy hearts should take the sword
    of might,
And eagerly for Fatherland descend into the fight.
> To arms, to arms, my captains!
> Sound, clarions; trumpets, blow;
> And let the thundering kettle-drum
> Give challenge to the foe.

" Then lay aside the silken robes, the glittering brocade;
Be all in vest of leather and twisted steel arrayed;
On each left arm be hung the shield, safe guardian of the breast,
And take the crooked scimitar and put the lance in rest,
And face the fortune of the day, for it is vain to fly,
And the coward and the braggart now alone are doomed to
    die.
And let each manly bosom show, in the impending fray,
A valor such as Mars himself in fury might display.
> To arms, to arms, my captains!
> Sound, clarions; trumpets, blow;
> And let the thundering kettle-drum
> Give challenge to the foe.

He spoke, and at his valiant words, that rang through all the
    square,
The veriest cowards of the town resolved to do and dare;
And stirred by honor's eager fire forth from the gate they
    stream,

And plumes are waving in the air, and spears and falchions
    gleam;
And turbaned heads and faces fierce, and smiles in anger
    quenched,
And sweating steeds and flashing spurs and hands in fury
    clenched,
Follow the fluttering banners that toward the vega swarm,
And many a voice re-echoes the words of wild alarm.
        To arms, to arms, my captains!
        Sound, clarions; trumpets, blow;
        And let the thundering kettle-drum
        Give challenge to the foe.

And, like the timid lambs that crowd with bleatings in the fold,
When they advancing to their throats the furious wolf behold,
The lovely Moorish maidens, with wet but flashing eyes,
Are crowded in a public square and fill the air with cries;
And tho', like tender women, 'tis vain for them to arm,
Yet loudly they re-echo the words of the alarm.
To heaven they cry for succor, and, while to heaven they pray,
They call the knights they love so well to arm them for the
    fray.
        To arms, to arms, my captains!
        Sound, clarions; trumpets, blow;
        And let the thundering kettle-drum
        Give challenge to the foe.

The foremost Moorish nobles, Molina's chosen band,
Rush forward from the city the invaders to withstand.
There marshalled in a squadron with shining arms they speed,
Like knights and noble gentlemen, to meet their country's
    need.
Twelve thousand Christians crowd the plain, twelve thousand
    warriors tried,
They fire the homes, they reap the corn, upon the vega wide;
And the warriors of Molina their furious lances ply,
And in their own Arabian tongue they raise the rallying cry.
        To arms, to arms, my captains!
        Sound, clarions; trumpets, blow;
        And let the thundering kettle-drum
        Give challenge to the foe.

THE LOVES OF BOABDIL AND VINDARAJA

Where Antequera's city stands, upon the southern plain,
The captive Vindaraja sits and mourns her lot in vain.
While Chico, proud Granada's King, nor night nor day can rest,
For of all the Moorish ladies Vindaraja he loves best;
And while naught can give her solace and naught can dry her tear,
'Tis not the task of slavery nor the cell that brings her fear;
For while in Antequera her body lingers still,
Her heart is in Granada upon Alhambra's hill.
There, while the Moorish monarch longs to have her at his side,
More keen is Vindaraja's wish to be a monarch's bride.
Ah! long delays the moment that shall bring her liberty,
A thousand thousand years in every second seem to fly!
For she thinks of royal Chico, and her face with tears is wet,
For she knows that absence oft will make the fondest heart forget.
And the lover who is truest may yet suspicion feel,
For the loved one in some distant land whose heart is firm as steel.
And now to solve her anxious doubts, she takes the pen one day
And writes to royal Chico, in Granada far away.
Ah! long the letter that she wrote to tell him of her state,
In lonely prison cell confined, a captive desolate!
She sent it by a Moorish knight, and sealed it with her ring;
He was warden of Alhambra and stood beside the King,
And he had come sent by the King to Antequera's tower,
To learn how Vindaraja fared within that prison bower.
The Moor was faithful to his charge, a warrior stout and leal,
And Chico took the note of love and trembling broke the seal;
And when the open page he saw and read what it contained,
These were the words in which the maid of her hard lot complained:

The Letter of Vindaraja

" Ah, hapless is the love-lorn maid like me in captive plight,
For freedom once was mine, and I was happy day and night.
Yes, happy, for I knew that thou hadst given me thy love,
Precious the gift to lonely hearts all other gifts above.
Well mightest thou forget me, though 'twere treachery to say
The flame that filled thy royal heart as yet had passed away.
Still, though too oft do lovers' hearts in absent hours repine.
I know if there are faithful vows, then faithful will be thine!
'Tis hard, indeed, for lovers to crush the doubting thought
Which to the brooding bosom some lonely hour has brought.
There is no safety for the love, when languish out of sight
The form, the smile, the flashing eyes that once were love's
    delight;
Nor can I, I confess it, feel certain of thy vow!
How many Moorish ladies are gathered round thee now!
How many fairer, brighter forms are clustered at thy throne,
Whose power might change to very wax the heart of steel or
    stone!
And if, indeed, there be a cause why I should blame thy heart,
'Tis the delay that thou hast shown in taking here my part.
Why are not armies sent to break these prison bars, and bring
Back to her home the Moorish maid, the favorite of the King?
A maid whose eyes are changed to springs whence flow the
    flood of tears,
For she thinks of thee and weeps for thee through all these
    absent years.
Believe me, if 'twere thou, who lay a captive in his chain,
My life of joy, to rescue thee, my heart of blood I'd drain!
O King and master, if, indeed, I am thy loved one still,
As in those days when I was first upon Alhambra's hill,
Send rescue for thy darling, or fear her love may fade,
For love that needs the sunlight must wither in the shade.
And yet I cannot doubt thee; if e'er suspicion's breath
Should chill my heart, that moment would be Vindaraja's
    death.
Nor think should you forget me or spurn me from your arms,
That life for Vindaraja could have no other charms.
It was thy boast thou once did love a princess, now a slave,
I boasted that to thy behest I full obedience gave!

And from this prison should I come, in freedom once again,
To sit and hear thy words of love on Andalusia's plain,
The brightest thought would be to me that thou, the King,
has seen
'Twas right to free a wretched slave that she might be thy
Queen.
Hard is the lot of bondage here, and heavy is my chain,
And from my prison bars I gaze with lamentation vain;
But these are slight and idle things—my one, my sole distress
Is that I cannot see thy face and welcome thy caress!
This only is the passion that can my bosom rend;
'Tis this alone that makes me long for death, my sufferings
end.
The plagues of life are naught to me; life's only joy is this—
To see thee and to hear thee and to blush beneath thy kiss!
Alas! perchance this evening or to-morrow morn, may be,
The lords who hold me here a slave in sad captivity,
May, since they think me wanton, their treacherous measures
take
That I should be a Christian and my former faith forsake.
But I tell them, and I weep to tell, that I will ne'er forego
The creed my fathers fought for in centuries long ago!
And yet I might forswear it, but that that creed divine
'Tis vain I struggle to deny, for, ah, that creed is thine!"
King Chico read his lady's note and silent laid it down;
Then to the window he drew nigh, and gazed upon the town;
And lost in thought he pondered upon each tender line,
And sudden tears and a sigh of grief were his inward sorrow's
sign.
And he called for ink and paper, that Vindaraja's heart
Might know that he remembered her and sought to heal its
smart.
He would tell her that the absence which caused to her those
fears
Had only made her dearer still, through all those mournful
years.
He would tell her that his heart was sad, because she was not
near—
Yes, far more sad than Moorish slave chained on the south
frontier.

And then he wrote the letter to the darling Moorish slave,
And this is the tender message that royal Chico gave:

THE LETTER OF THE KING

"Thy words have done me grievous wrong, for, lovely
  Mooress, couldst thou think
That he who loves thee more than life could e'er to such a
  treachery sink?
His life is naught without the thought that thou art happy in
  thy lot;
And while the red blood at his heart is beating thou art ne'er
  forgot!
Thou woundest me because thy heart mistrusts me as a fickle
  fool;
Thou dost not know when passion true has one apt pupil taken
  to school.
Oblivion could not, could not cloud the image on his soul im-
  pressed,
Unless dark treachery from the first had been the monarch of
  his breast;
And if perhaps some weary hours I thought that Vindaraja's
  mind
Might in some happier cavalier the solace of her slavery find,
I checked the thought; I drove away the vision that with
  death was rife,
For e'er my trust in thee I lost, in battle I'd forego my life!
Yet even the doubt that thou hast breathed gives me no fran-
  chise to forget,
And were I willing that thy face should cease to fill my vision,
  yet
'Tis separation's self that binds us closer though the centuries
  roll,
And forges that eternal chain that binds together soul and
  soul!
And even were this thought no more than the wild vision of
  my mind,
Yet in a thousand worlds no face to change for thine this
  heart could find.
Thro' life, thro' death 'twere all the same, and when to heaven
  our glance we raise,

2

Full in the very heart of bliss thine eyes shall meet my ardent
gaze.
For eyes that have beheld thy face, full readily the truth will
own
That God exhausted, when he made thee, all the treasures of
his throne!
And my trusting heart will answer while it fills my veins with
fire
That to hear of, is to see thee; and to see, is to desire!
Yet unless my Vindaraja I could look upon awhile,
As some traveller in a desert I should perish for her smile;
For 'tis longing for her presence makes the spring of life
to me,
And allays the secret suffering none except her eye can see.
In this thought alone my spirit finds refreshment and delight;
This is sweeter than the struggle, than the glory of the fight;
And if e'er I could forget her heaving breast and laughing
eye,
Tender word, and soft caresses—Vindaraja, I should die!
If the King should bid me hasten to release thee from thy
chain,
Oh, believe me, dearest lady, he would never bid in vain;
Naught he could demand were greater than the price that I
would pay,
If in high Alhambra's halls I once again could see thee gay!
None can say I am remiss, and heedless of thy dismal fate;
Love comes to prompt me every hour, he will not let my zeal
abate.
If occasion call, I yield myself, my soul to set thee free;
Take this offering if thou wilt, I wait thy word on bended
knee.
Dost thou suffer, noble lady, by these fancies overwrought?
Ah, my soul is filled with sorrow at the agonizing thought;
For to know that Vindaraja languishes, oppressed with care,
Is enough to make death welcome, if I could but rescue
her.
Yes, the world shall know that I would die not only for the
bliss
Of clasping thee in love's embrace and kindling at thy tender
kiss.

This, indeed, would be a prize, for which the coward death
    would dare—
I would die to make thee happy, tho' thy lot I might not
    share!
Then, though I should fail to lift the burden on my darling
    laid,
Though I could not prove my love by rescuing my Moorish
    maid,
Yet my love would have this witness, first, thy confidence
    sublime,
Then my death for thee, recorded on the scroll of future time!
Yes, my death, for should I perish, it were comfort but to
    think
Thou couldst have henceforth on earth no blacker, bitterer
    cup to drink!
Sorrow's shafts would be exhausted, thou couldst laugh at
    fortune's power.
Tho' I lost thee, yet this thought would cheer me in my part-
    ing hour.
Yet I believe that fate intends (oh, bear this forecast in thy
    mind!)
That all the love my passions crave will soon a full fruition
    find;
Fast my passion stronger grows, and if of love there meas-
    ure be,
Believe it, dearest, that the whole can find its summary in me!
Deem that thou art foully wronged, whose graces have such
    power to bless,
If any of thy subject slaves to thee, their queen, should offer
    less.
And accept this pledged assurance, that oblivion cannot roll
O'er the image of thy beauty stamped on this enamored soul.
Then dismiss thy anxious musings, let them with the wind
    away,
As the gloomy clouds are scattered at the rising of the day.
Think that he is now thy slave, who, when he wooed thee,
    was thy King;
Think that not the brightest morning can to him contentment
    bring,
Till the light of other moments in thy melting eyes he trace,

And the gates of Paradise are opened in thy warm embrace.
Since thou knowest that death to me and thee will strike an
    equal blow,
It is just that, while we live, our hearts with equal hopes
    should glow.
Then no longer vex thy lover with complaints that he may
    change;
Darling, oft these bitter questions can the fondest love es-
    trange;
No, I dream not of estrangement, for thy Chico evermore
Thinks upon his Vindaraja's image only to adore."

THE INFANTA SEVILLA AND PERANZUELOS

Upon Toledo's loftiest towers
    Sevilla kept the height;
So wondrous fair was she that love
    Was blinded at the sight.

She stood amid the battlements,
    And gazed upon the scene
Where Tagus runs through woodland
    And flowers and glades of green.

And she saw upon the wide highway
    The figure of a knight;
He rode upon a dappled steed,
    And all his arms were bright.

Seven Moors in chains he led with him,
    And one arm's length aloof
Came a dog of a Moor from Morocco's shore
    In arms of double proof.

His steed was swift, his countenance
    In a warlike scowl was set,
And in his furious rage he cursed
    The beard of Mahomet!

He shouted, as he galloped up:
    " Now halt thee, Christian hound;

I see at the head of thy captive band
  My sire, in fetters bound.

" And the rest are brothers of my blood,
  And friends I long to free;
And if thou wilt surrender all,
  I'll pay thee gold and fee."

When Peranzuelos heard him,
  He wheeled his courser round.
With lance in rest, he hotly pressed
  To strike him to the ground;
His sudden rage and onset came
  Swift as the thunder's sound.

The Moor at the first encounter reeled
  To earth, from his saddle bow;
And the Christian knight, dismounting,
  Set heel on the neck of his foe.

He cleft his head from his shoulders,
  And, marshalling his train,
Made haste once more on his journey
  Across Toledo's plain.

CELIN'S FAREWELL

He sadly gazes back again upon those bastions high,
The towers and fretted battlements that soar into the sky;
And Celin, whom the King in wrath has from Granada
    banned
Weeps as he turns to leave for aye his own dear native land;
No hope has he his footsteps from exile to retrace;
No hope again to look upon his lady's lovely face.
Then sighing deep he went his way, and as he went he said:
    " I see thee shining from afar,
    As in heaven's arch some radiant star.
    Granada, queen and crown of loveliness,
    Listen to my lament, and mourn for my distress.

" I see outstretched before my eyes thy green and beauteous
    shore,
Those meadow-lands and gardens that with flowers are
    dappled o'er.
The wind that lingers o'er those glades received the tribute
    given
By many a trembling calyx, wet with the dews of heaven.
From Genil's banks full many a bough down to the water
    bends,
Yon vega's green and fertile line from flood to wall extends;
There laughing ladies seek the shade that yields to them de-
    light,
And the velvet turf is printed deep by many a mounted knight.
  I see thee shining from afar,
  As in heaven's arch some radiant star.
  Granada, queen and town of loveliness,
  Listen to my lament, and mourn for my distress.

" Ye springs and founts that sparkling well from yonder
    mountain-side,
And flow with dimpling torrent o'er mead and garden wide,
If e'er the tears that from my breast to these sad eyes ascend
Should with your happy waters their floods of sadness blend,
Oh, take them to your bosom with love, for love has bidden
These drops to tell the wasting woe that in my heart is hidden.
  I see thee shining from afar,
  As in heaven's arch some radiant star.
  Granada, queen and crown of loveliness,
  Listen to my lament, and mourn for my distress.

" Ye balmy winds of heaven, whose sound is in the rippling
    trees,
Whose scented breath brings back to me a thousand memories,
Ye sweep beneath the arch of heaven like to the ocean surge
That beats from Guadalquivir's bay to earth's extremest
    verge.
Oh, when ye to Granada come (and may great Allah send
His guardian host to guide you to that sweet journey's end!),
Carry my sighs along with you, and breathe them in the ear
Of foes who do me deadly wrong, of her who holds me dear.

Oh, tell them all the agony I bear in banishment,
That she may share my sorrow, and my foe the King relent.
  I see thee shining from afar,
  As in heaven's arch some radiant star.
  Granada, queen and crown of loveliness,
  Listen to my lament, and mourn for my distress."

CELIN'S RETURN

Now Celin would be merry, and appoints a festal day,
When he the pang of absence from his lady would allay:
The brave Abencerrages and Gulanes straight he calls,
His bosom friends, to join him as he decks his stately halls.
And secretly he bids them come, and in secret bids them go;
For the day of merriment must come unnoticed by his foe;
For peering eyes and curious ears are watching high and low,
But he only seeks one happy day may reparation bring
For the foul and causeless punishment inflicted by the King.
  " For in the widest prison-house is misery for me,
   And the stoutest heart is broken unless the hand is
    free."

His followers all he bade them dress in Christian array,
With rude and rustic mantles of color bright and gay;
With silken streamers in their caps, their caps of pointed
  crown,
With flowing blouse, and mantle and gaberdine of brown.
But he himself wore sober robes of white and lion gray,
The emblems of the hopeless grief in which the warrior lay.
And the thoughts of Adalifa, of her words and glancing eyes,
Gave colors of befitting gloom to tint his dark disguise.
And he came with purpose to perform some great and glorious
  deed,
To drive away the saddening thoughts that made the bosom
  bleed.
  " For in the widest prison-house is misery to me,
   And the stoutest heart is broken unless the arm be
    free."

There streams into Granada's gate a stately cavalcade
Of prancing steeds caparisoned, and knights in steel arrayed;
And all their acclamations raise, when Celin comes in sight—
" The foremost in the tournament, the bravest in the fight "—
And Moorish maiden Cegri straight to the window flies,
To see the glittering pageant and to hear the joyous cries.
She calls her maidens all to mark how, from misfortune free,
The gallant Celin comes again, the ladies' knight is he!
They know the story of his fate and undeserved disgrace,
And eagerly they gaze upon the splendor of his face.
Needs not his exploit in the fields, his valorous deeds to tell—
The ladies of Granada have heard and know them well!
    " For in the widest prison-house is misery to me,
        And the stoutest heart must break unless the warrior's
        arm be free."

The beauty of Granada crowds Elvira's gate this night;
There are straining necks and flushing cheeks when Celin
    comes in sight;
And whispered tales go round the groups, and hearts indig-
    nant swell,
As they think what in Granada that hero knight befell.
Now a thousand Moorish warriors to Celin's fame aspire,
And a thousand ladies gaze on him with passionate desire.
And they talk of Adalifa, to whom he made his vow,
Though neither speech nor written page unites them longer
    now.
    " For in the widest prison-house is misery to me,
        And the stoutest heart must break unless the warrior's
        arms be free."

The city waits his coming, for the feast has been prepared,
By rich and poor, by high and low the revel shall be shared;
And there are warriors high in hope to win the jousting prize,
And there are ladies longing for a smile from Celin's eyes.
But when the news of gladness reached Adalifa's ear,
Her loving heart was touched with grief and filled with jealous
    fear;
And she wrote to Celin, bidding him to hold no revel high,
For the thought of such rejoicing brought the tear-drop to
    her eye;

The Moor received the letter as Granada came in sight,
And straight he turned his courser's head toward Jaen's tow-
    ering height,
And exchanged for hues of mourning his robe of festal white.
     " For in the widest prison-house is misery to me,
       And the stoutest heart is broke unless the warrior's
       arm be free."

BAZA REVISITED

Brave Celin came, the valiant son of him the *castelain*
Of the fortress of Alora and Alhama's windy plain.
He came to see great Baza, where he in former days
Had won from Zara's father that aged warrior's praise.
The Moor gazed on that fortress strong, the towers all deso-
    late,
The castle high that touched the sky, the rampart and the
    gate.
The ruined hold he greeted, it seemed its native land,
For there his bliss had been complète while Zara held his
    hand.
And Fortune's cruel fickleness he furiously reviled,
For his heart sent madness to his brain and all his words were
    wild.
" O goddess who controllest on earth our human fate,
How is it I offend thee, that my life is desolate?
Ah! many were the triumphs that from Zara's hands I bore,
When in the joust or in the dance she smiled on me of yore.
And now, while equal fortune incessantly I chase,
Naught can I gather from thy hand but disaster and disgrace.
Since King Fernando brought his host fair Baza to blockade,
My lot has been a wretched lot of anguish unalloyed.
Yet was Fernando kind to me with all his kingly art,
He won my body to his arms, he could not win my heart."
While thus he spoke the mantle that he wore he cast away;
'Twas green, 'twas striped with red and white, 'twas lined with
    dismal gray.
" Best suits my fate, best suits the hue, in this misfortune's
    day;

Not green, not white nor purple, but the palmer's garb of
    gray.
I ask no plumes for helm or cap of nature's living green,
For hope has vanished from my life of that which might have
    been!
And from my target will I blot the blazon that is vain—
The lynx whose eyes are fixed upon the prey that it would
    gain.
For the glances that I cast around meet fortune's foul disdain;
And I will blot the legend, as an accursed screed.
'Twas writ in Christian letters plain that all the world might
    read:
'My good right arm can gain me more altho' its range be
    short,
Then all I know by eye-sight or the boundless range of
    thought.'
The blue tahala fluttering bright upon my armored brow
In brilliant hue assorts but ill with the lot I meet with now.
I cast away this gaudy cap, it bears the purple dye;
Not that my love is faithless, for I own her constancy;
But for the fear that there may be, within the maiden's sight,
A lover worthier of her love than this unhappy knight."
With that he took his lance in hand, and placed it in its rest,
And o'er the plain with bloody spur the mournful Celin
    pressed.
On his steed's neck he threw the reins, the reins hung dangling
    low,
That the courser might have liberty to choose where he would
    go;
And he said: " My steed, oh, journey well, and make thy way
    to find
The bliss which still eludes me, tho' 'tis ever in my mind.
Nor bit nor rein shall now restrain thy course across the lea,
For the curb and the bridle I only use from infamy to flee."

CAPTIVE ZARA

In Palma there was little joy, so lovely Zara found;
She felt herself a slave, although by captive chain unbound.
In Palma's towers she wandered from all the guests apart;
For while Palma had her body, 'twas Baza held her heart.
And while her heart was fixed on one, her charms no less
    enthralled
The heart of this brave cavalier, Celin Andalla called.
Ah, hapless, hapless maiden, for in her deep despair
She did not know what grief her face had caused that knight
    to bear;
And though the Countess Palma strove with many a service
    kind
To show her love, to soothe the pang that wrung the maiden's
    mind,
Yet borne upon the tempest of the captive's bitter grief,
She never lowered the sail to give her suffering heart relief.
And, in search of consolation to another captive maid,
She told the bitter sorrow to no one else displayed.
She told it, while the tears ran fast, and yet no balm did gain,
For it made more keen her grief, I ween, to give another pain.
And she said to her companion, as she clasped her tender
    hand:
" I was born in high Granada, my loved, my native land;
For years within Alhambra's courts my life ran on serene;
I was a princess of the realm and handmaid to a queen.
Within her private chamber I served both night and day,
And the costliest jewels of her crown in my protection lay.
To her I was the favorite of all the maids she knew;
And, ah! my royal mistress I loved, I loved her true!
No closer tie I owned on earth than bound me to her side;
No closer tie; I loved her more than all the world beside.
But more I loved than aught on earth, the gallant Moorish
    knight,
Brave Celin, who is solely mine, and I his sole delight.
Yes, he was brave, and all men own the valor of his brand;
Yes, and for this I loved him more than monarchs of the land.
For me he lived, for me he fought, for me he mourned and
    wept,

When he saw me in this captive home like a ship to the
    breakers swept.
He called on heaven, and heaven was deaf to all his bitter cry,
For the victim of the strife of kings, of the bloody war, was I;
It was my father bade him first to seek our strong retreat.
Would God that he had never come to Baza's castle seat!
Would God that he had never come, an armored knight, to
    stand
Amid the soldiers that were ranked beneath my sire's com-
    mand.
He came, he came, that valiant Moor, beneath our roof to rest.
His body served my father; his heart, my sole behest;
What perils did he face upon that castle's frowning height!
Winning my father's praise, he gained more favor in my
    sight.
And when the city by the bands of Christians was assailed,
My soul 'neath terrors fiercer still in lonely terror quailed.
For I have lost my sire, and I have lost my lover brave,
For here I languish all alone, a subject and a slave.
And yet the Moor, altho' he left with me his loving heart,
I fear may have forgotten that I own his better part.
And now the needle that I ply is witness to the state
Of bondage, which I feel to-day with heart disconsolate.
And here upon the web be writ, in the Arabian tongue,
The legend that shall tell the tale of how my heart is wrung.
Here read: ' If thou hast ta'en my heart when thou didst ride
    away,
Remember that myself, my living soul, behind thee stay.'
And on the other side these words embroidered would I place:
' The word shall never fail that once I spake before thy face.'
And on the border underneath this posy, written plain:
' The promise that I made to thee still constant shall remain.'
And last of all, this line I add, the last and yet the best:
' Thou ne'er shalt find inconstancy in this unchanging breast.'
Thus runs the embroidery of love, and in the midst appears
A phœnix, painted clear, the bird that lives eternal years.
For she from the cold ashes of life at its last wane,
Takes hope, and spreads her wings and soars through skyey
    tracks again.
And there a hunter draws his bow outlined with skilful thread,

And underneath a word which says, ' Nay, shoot not at the
  dead.'
Thus spake the Moorish maiden, and in her eyes were tears of
  grief,
Tho' in her busy needle she seemed to find relief.
And the kindly countess called from far: " Zara, what aileth
  thee?
Where art thou? For I called, and yet thou didst not answer
  me."

THE JEALOUS KING

'Twas eight stout warriors matched with eight, and ten with
  valiant ten,
As Aliatare formed a band allied with Moslem men,
To joust, with loaded canes, that day in proud Toledo's ring,
Against proud Adelifa's host before their lord the King.
The King by proclamation had announced the knightly play,
For the cheerful trumpets sang a truce upon that very day;
And Zaide, high Belchite's King, had sworn that war should
  cease,
And with Tarfe of Valentia had ratified the peace.
But others spread the news, that flew like fire from tongue to
  tongue,
That the King was doting-mad with love, for then the King
  was young;
And had given to Celindaja the ordering of the day.
And there were knights beside the King she loved to see at
  play.
And now the lists are opened and, lo! a dazzling band,
The Saracens, on sorrel steeds leap forth upon the sand;
Their trailing cloaks are flashing like the golden orange rind,
The hoods of green from their shoulders hang and flutter in
  the wind.
They carry targets blazoned bright with scimitars arow,
But each deadly blade is deftly made into a Cupid's bow.
A shining legend can be seen in letters ranged above;
And " Fire and Blood " the motto runs. It speaks of war and
  love.

In double file a company of warriors succeed;
The bold Aliatares come mounted on Arab steeds.
The livery that they wear is dyed in tint of crimson red;
And flower and leaf in white relief its surface overspread.
The globe of heaven, which many a star and constellation
    strow,
Borne upon Atlas' shoulders, is the blazon that they show.
And a Moor of Aliatar this motto does express,
Written upon a streamer, " I Endure through Weariness."
The Adelifas follow; a mighty race are they.
Their armor is more costly, their mantles are more gay.
Of bright carnation is the web, enriched with saffron streaks,
And for favors there are fluttering veils upon their helmet
    peaks.
A globe they blazon on their shields, but it is bruised and broke
By a savage with a bludgeon, who deals it many a stroke;
And a rod, and underneath it this motto tells the tale,
All written in Arabian scrip. It says, " The Strong Prevail."
The eight Azarques following these into the plaza spring,
With air of haughty arrogance they gallop round the ring.
Of blue and purple and pale gold are the mantles that they
    wear,
And for plumes they carry amulets that dangle high in air.
On their left arm are their targets, painted a dazzling green.
The orb of heaven is outlined there on which two hands are
    seen,
The motto, " Green is paramount," is lettered full in view;
Its arrogance explains to all those targets' vivid hue.
Then foams the King in rage to see his doting love was fleered,
And his heart is filled with bitter thought as that proud shield
    appeared.
And he called the warden of his keep, Celin his henchman tried,
And he pointed to Azarque, and, flushed with anger, cried—
" The sun upon that haughty shield myself will bid it set;
It works some mischief upon me, like an evil amulet.
Azarque drew his ready lance, his strong arm hurled it high,
The light shaft soared amid the clouds, and vanished in the sky.
And those whose vision followed it grew dizzy at the sight,
They knew not whither it had flown, nor where it would alight.

The ladies of the burgesses at many a window press
To see the javelin from his hand rise with such readiness,
And those who on the platform were seated with the King
Bent back to see how well the cane that gallant Moor could
    fling.
And as Azarque forward rides, as in retreat he flies,
" Now, Allah guard thee, gallant knight," with shouts the
    people cries.
" My curse upon him; he shall die," the jealous King replies.
But Celindaja paid no heed to all that cavalcade;
Her lips were parched, her throat was dry, her heart was sore
    dismayed.
She asked that they would bring her fruit, but yet she strove
    in vain
With juice of any earthly tree to slake her fevered pain.
" Now let the sport be ended," the angry King decreed.
The joust was late, and every judge in weariness agreed.
And as they closed the empty lists, they heard the King's com-
    mand,
" Now seize, now seize Azarque, a traitor to this land."
The double lines of cavaliers who led the jousting train
Threw down upon the open square the spear of idle cane;
Then swiftly seized the lance of steel and couching it for fight,
According to the royal wish rode down upon the knight.
    For arms and plea must ever bootless prove
    To curb the passions of a king in love.

The other band came forth to save Azarque from his foes,
But the stout Moor waves his hand to them ere they in battle
    close,
Then calmly cries: " Tho' love, it seems, has no respect for
    law,
'Tis right that ye keep peace to-day and from the lists with-
    draw!
Nay, gentlemen, your lances lower before it be too late;
And let our foes their lances raise, in sign of passion's hate;
Thus without blood accorded be a victory and defeat.
'Tis only bloodshed makes the one more bitter or more sweet,
    For arms or reason unavailing prove
    To curb the passions of a king in love."

At last they seize the struggling Moor, the chains are on his
    hands;
And the populace, with anger filled, arrange themselves in
    bands.
They place a guard at every point, in haste to set him free,
But where the brave commander who shall lead to victory?
And where the leader who shall shout and stir their hearts to
    fight?
These are but empty braggarts, but prowlers of the night,
Cut-throats and needy idlers—and so the tumult ends—
Azarque lies in prison, forsaken by his friends.
    For, ah, both arms and reason powerless prove
    To turn the purpose of a king in love.

Alone does Celindaja the coward crowd implore,
" Oh, save him, save him, generous friends, give back to me
    my Moor."
She stands upon the balcony and from that lofty place
Would fling herself upon the stones to save him from disgrace.
Her mother round the weeping girl has flung her withered arm.
" O fool," she whispers in her ear, " in Mary's name be calm!"
Thou madly rushest to thy death by this distracted show.
Surely thou knowest well this truth, if anyone can know,
    How arms and reason powerless prove
    To turn the purpose of a king in love.

Then came a message of the King, in which the monarch said
That a house wherein his kindred dwelt must be a prison made.
Then Celindaja, white with rage: " Go to the King and say
I choose to be my prison-house for many and many a day,
The memory of Azarque, in which henceforth I live:
But the treachery of a monarch my heart will not forgive.
    For the will of one weak woman shall never powerless prove
    To turn the foolish purpose of a king who is in love.

" Alas for thee, Toledo! in former times they said
That they called thee for vengeance upon a traitor's head.
But now 'tis not on traitors, but on loyal men and true
That they call to thee for vengeance, which to caitiff hearts
    are due.

And Tagus gently murmurs in his billows fresh and free
And hastens from Toledo to reach the mighty sea."
E'er she said more, 'they seized the dame, and led her to the
    gate,
Where the warden of the castle in solemn judgment sate.

THE LOVERS OF ANTEQUERA

The brave Hamete reined his steed and from the crupper bent,
To greet fair Tartagona, who saw him with content,
The daughter of Zulema, who had many a foe repelled
From the castle on the hill, which he in Archidora held;
For six-and-thirty years he kept the Christian host at bay,
A watchful warden, fearless of the stoutest foes' array.
And now adown the well-known path, a secret path and sure,
Led by the noble lady, hurried the gallant Moor.
The sentinels beneath the wall were careless, or they slept;
They heeded not Hamete as down the slope he crept.
And when he reached the level plain, full twenty feet away,
He hobbled fast his courser, lest he should farther stray.
Then to the Moorish lady he turned, as if to speak,
Around her waist he flung his arms and kissed her on the
    cheek.
" O goddess of my heart," he said, " by actions I will prove,
If thou wilt name some high emprise, how faithful is my love!
And in Granada I am great, and have much honored been,
Both by the King Fernando and Isabel his Queen.
My name is high, my lineage long, yet none of all my line
Have reached the pitch of glory which men allow is mine.
Narvarez is a knight of name, in love and arms adept,
In Antequera's castle he well the marches kept.
Jarifa was a captive maid, he loved Jarifa well,
And oft the maiden visited within her prison cell.
And, if the thing with honor and virtuous heart may be,
What he did with Jarifa, that would I do with thee."
A star was shining overhead upon the breast of night,
The warrior turned his course, and led the lady by its light.
They reached the foot of one tall rock, and stood within the
    shade,

Where thousand thousand ivy leaves a bower of beauty made.
They heard the genet browsing and stamping as he fed,
And smiling Love his pinions over the lovers spread.
But ere they reached the pleasant bower, they saw before them
    stand,
Armed to the teeth, with frowning face, a strange and savage
    band.
Yes, seventy men with sword in hand surrounded dame and
    knight,
The robbers of the mountain, and they trembled at the sight!
With one accord these freebooters upon Hamete fell,
Like hounds that on the stag at bay rush at the hunter's call,
Burned the Moor's heart at once with wrath, at once with pas-
    sion's flame,
To save the life and, more than life, the honor of his dame.
Straight to his feet he sprung and straight he drew his mighty
    sword,
And plunged into the robber crowd and uttered not a word.
No jousting game was e'er so brisk as that which then he
    waged;
On arm and thigh with deadly blow the slashing weapon raged;
Though certain was his death, yet still, with failing heart, he
    prayed
That till his lady could escape, that death might be delayed.
But, in the dark, a deadly stone, flung with no warning sound,
Was buried in his forehead and stretched him on the ground.
The breath his heaving bosom left and, from his nerveless
    hand,
The sword fell clattering to the ground, before that bloody
    band.
And when the damsel saw herself within those caitiffs' power,
And saw the city mantled in the darkness of the hour,
No grief that ever woman felt was equal to her pain,
And no despair like that of hers shall e'er be known again.
Those villains did not see those locks, that shone like threads
    of gold;
Only the summer sunlight their wondrous beauty told.
They did not mark the glittering chain of gold and jewels fine,
That in the daylight would appear her ivory throat to twine.
But straight she took the scimitar, that once her lover wore,

It lay amid the dewy grass, drenched to the hilt in gore.
And, falling on the bloody point, she pierced her bosom
 through,
And Tartagona breathed her last, mourned by that robber
 crew.
And there she lay, clasping in death her lover's lifeless face,
Her valor's paragon, and she the glass of woman's grace.
And since that hour the tale is told, while many a tear-drop
 falls,
Of the lovers of the vega by Antequera's walls.
And they praise the noble lady and they curse the robber band,
And they name her the Lucretia of fair Andalusia's land.
And if the hearer of the tale should doubt that it be true,
Let him pass along the mountain road, till Ronda comes in
 view,
There must he halt and searching he may the story trace
In letters that are deeply cut on the rocky mountain's face.

TARFE'S TRUCE

" Oho, ye Catholic cavaliers
  Who eye Granada day and night,
 On whose left shoulder is the cross,
  The crimson cross, your blazon bright.

" If e'er your youthful hearts have felt
  The flame of love that brings delight,
 As angry Mars, in coat of steel,
  Feels the fierce ardor of the fight;

" If 'tis your will, within our walls,
  To join the joust, with loaded reed,
 As ye were wont, beneath these towers
  The bloody lance of war to speed;

" If bloodless tumult in the square
  May serve instead of battle's fray,
 And, donning now the silken cloak,
Ye put the coat of steel away;

" Six troops of Saracens are here;
    Six Christian troops, with targe and steed
Be ready, when the day is fixed,
    To join the jousting of the reed.

" For 'tis not right that furious war,
    Which sets the city's roofs in flames,
Should kindle with a fruitless fire
    The tender bosom of our dames.

" In spite of all we suffer here
    Our ladies are with you arrayed,
They pity you in this fierce war,
    This labor of the long blockade.

" Amid the hardships of the siege
    Let pleasure yield a respite brief;
(For war must ever have its truce)
    And give our hardships some relief.

" What solace to the war-worn frame,
    To every soul what blest release,
To fling aside the targe and mail,
    And don one hour the plumes of peace!

" And he who shall the victor be
    Among the jousters of the game,
I pledge my knightly word to him,
    In token of his valorous fame,

" On his right arm myself to bind
    The favor of my lady bright;
'Twas given me by her own white hand,
    The hand as fair as it is white."

'Twas thus that Tarfe, valiant Moor,
    His proclamation wrote at large;
He, King Darraja's favored squire,
    Has nailed the cartel to his targe.

'Twas on the day the truce was made,
    By Calatrava's master bold,

To change the quarters of his camp,
  And with his foes a conference hold.

Six Moorish striplings Tarfe sent
  In bold Abencerraje's train—
His kindred both in race and house—
  To meet the leaguers on the plain.

In every tent was welcome warm;
  And when their challenge they display,
The master granted their request
  To join the joust on Easter day.

In courteous words that cartel bold
  He answered; and a cavalcade
Of Christians, with the Moorish guards,
  Their journey to Granada made.

The guise of war at once was dropped;
  The armory closed its iron door;
And all put on the damask robes
  That at high festival they wore.

The Moorish youths and maidens crowd,
  With joyful face, the city square;
These mount their steeds, those sit and braid
  Bright favors for their knights to wear.

Those stern antagonists in war,
  Like friends, within the town are met;
And peacefully they grasp the hand,
  And for one day the past forget.

And gallant Almarada comes
  (Not Tarfe's self more brave, I ween),
Lord of a lovely Moorish dame,
  Who rules her lover like a queen.

A hundred thousand favors she
  In public or in private gives,
To show her lover that her life
  Is Almarada's while she lives!

And once upon a cloudy night,
   Fit curtain for his amorous mood,
The gallant Moor the high hills scaled
   And on Alhambra's terrace stood.

Arrived, he saw a Moorish maid
   Stand at a window opened wide;
He gave her many a precious gem;
   He gave her many a gift beside.

He spoke and said: " My lady fair,
   Though I have never wronged him, still
Darraja stands upon the watch,
   By fair or foul, to do me ill.

" Those eyes of thine, which hold more hearts
   Than are the stars that heaven displays;
That slay more Moors with shafts of love
   Than with his sword the master slays;

" When will they soften at my smile?
   And when wilt thou, my love, relent?
Let Tarfe go, whose words are big,
   While his sword-arm is impotent!

" Thou seest I am not such as he;
   His haughty words, so seldom true,
Are filled with boasting; what he boasts
   This sturdy arm of mine can do.

" My arm, my lance, ah! well 'tis known
   How oft in battle's darkest hour
They saved Granada's city proud
   From yielding to the Christian's power."

Thus amorous Almarada spoke
   When Tarfe came and caught the word;
And as his ear the message seized,
   His right hand seized upon his sword.

Yet did he deem some Christian troop
   Was in the darkness hovering by;

And at the thought, with terror struck,
  He turned in eager haste to fly!

Darraja roused him at the din;
  And with loud voice to Tarfe spoke;
He knew him from his cloak of blue,
  For he had given the Moor that cloak!

THE TWO MOORISH KNIGHTS

Upon two mares both strong and fleet,
  White as the cygnet's snowy wing,
Beneath Granada's arching gate
  Passed Tarfe and Belchite's King.

Like beauty marks the dames they serve;
  Like colors at their spear-heads wave;
While Tarfe kneels at Celia's feet,
  The King is Dorelice's slave.

With belts of green and azure blue
  The gallant knights are girded fair;
Their cloaks with golden orange glow,
  And verdant are the vests they wear.

And gold and silver, side by side,
  Are glittering on their garment's hem;
And, mingled with the metals, shine
  The lights of many a costly gem.

Their veils are woven iron-gray,
  The melancholy tint of woe—
And o'er their heads the dusky plumes
  Their grief and desolation show.

And each upon his target bears
  Emblazoned badges, telling true
Their passion and their torturing pangs,
  In many a dark and dismal hue.

The King's device shines on his shield—
    A seated lady, passing fair;
A monarch, with a downcast eye,
    Before the dame is kneeling there.

His crown is lying at her feet
    That she may spurn it in disdain;
A heart in flames above is set;
    And this the story of his pain.

" In frost is born this flame of love "—
    Such legend circles the device—
" And the fierce fire in which I burn
    Is nourished by the breath of ice."

Upon her brow the lady wears
    A crown; her dexter hand sustains
A royal sceptre, gilded bright,
    To show that o'er all hearts she reigns.

An orb in her left hand she bears,
    For all the world her power must feel;
There Fortune prostrate lies; the dame
    Halts with her foot the whirling wheel.

But Tarfe's shield is blank and bare,
    Lest Adelifa should be moved
With jealous rage, to learn that he
    Her Moorish rival, Celia, loved.

He merely blazons on his targe
    A peaceful olive-branch, and eyes
That sparkle in a beauteous face,
    Like starlets in the autumn skies.

And on the branch of olive shines
    This legend: " If thy burning ray
Consume me with the fire of love,
    See that I wither not away."

They spurred their horses as they saw
    The ladies their approach surveyed;

And when they reached their journey's end
   The King to Dorelice said:

"The goddesses who reign above
   With envy of thy beauty tell;
When heaven and glory are thy gifts,
   Why should I feel the pangs of hell?

"Oh, tell me what is thy desire?
   And does heaven's light more pleasure bring
Than to own monarchs as thy slaves,
   And be the heiress to a king?

"I ask from thee no favor sweet;
   Nor love nor honor at thy hand;
But only that thou choose me out
   The servant of thy least command.

"The choicest nobles of the realm
   The glory of this office crave;
The lowliest soldier, with delight,
   Would die to prove himself thy slave.

"Each life, each heart is at thy feet;
   Thou with a thousand hearts mayst live;
And if thou wouldst not grant my prayer,
   Oh, take the warning that I give.

"For there are ladies in the court
   To my desires would fain consent,
And lovely Bendarrafa once
   These jealous words but lately sent:

"'Those letters and those written lines,
   Why dost thou not their sense divine?
Are they not printed on thy heart
   As thy loved image is on mine?

"'Why art thou absent still so long?
   It cannot be that thou art dead?'"
Then ceased the King and silent stood,
   While Tarfe to his Celia said:

" Celestial Celia be thy name;
  Celestial calm is on thy brow;
Yet all the radiance of thy face
  Thy cruelty eclipses now.

" A witch like Circe dost thou seem;
  For Circe could o'ercloud the sky;
Oh, let the sun appear once more,
  And bid the clouds of darkness fly!

" Ah, would to God that on the feast,
  The Baptist's consecrated day,
I might my arms about thee fling
  And lead thee from thy home away.

" Yet say not that 'tis in thy power
  To yield or all my hopes to kill;
For thou shalt learn that all the world,
  In leaguer, cannot bend my will.

" And France can tell how many a time
  I fought upon the tented field,
And forced upon their bended knee
  Her loftiest paladins to yield.

" I vanquished many a valiant knight
  Who on his shield the lilies bore;
And on Vandalia's plain subdued
  Of Red Cross warriors many a score.

" The noblest I had brought to yield
  Upon Granada's gory plain,
Did I not shrink with such vile blood
  The honor of my sword to stain."

At this the trumpets called to arms;
  Without one farewell word each knight
Turned from the lady of his heart
  And spurred his steed in headlong flight.

THE KING'S DECISION

Amid a thousand sapient Moors
 From Andalusia came,
Was an ancient Moor, who ruled the land,
 Rey Bucar was his name.

And many a year this sage had dwelt
 With the lady he loved best;
And at last he summoned the Cortes,
 As his leman made request.

The day was set on which his lords
 And commoners should meet,
And they talked to the King of his wide realm's need,
 As the King sat in his seat.

And many the laws they passed that day;
 And among them a law that said
That the lover who took a maid for his love
 The maid of his choice must wed;
And he who broke this ordinance
 Should pay for it with his head.

And all agreed that the law was good;
 Save a cousin of the King,
Who came and stood before him,
 With complaint and questioning;

" This law, which now your Highness
 Has on your lieges laid,
I like it not, though many hearts
 It has exultant made.

" Me only does it grieve, and bring
 Disaster on my life;
For the lady that I love the best,
 Is already wedded wife;

" Wedded she is, wedded amiss;
 Ill husband has she got.

And oft does pity fill my heart
  For her distressful lot.

" And this one thing I tell thee, King,
  To none else has it been told:
If I think her love is silver,
  She thinks my love is gold."

Then spake Rey Bucar in reply,
  This sentence uttered he:
" If thy love be wedded wife, the law
  Hath no penalty for thee."

ALMANZOR AND BOBALIAS

The King Almanzor slept one night,
  And, oh! his sleep was blest;
Not all the seven Moorish kings
  Could dare to break his rest.

The infante Bobalias
  Bethought of him and cried:
" Now rouse thee, rouse thee, uncle dear!
  And hasten to my side.

" And bid them fetch the ladders
  Owned by my sire the King;
And the seven mules that carry them
  Into my presence bring.

" And give to me the seven stout Moors
  Who shall their harness set,
For the love, the love of the countess
  I never can forget."

" Ill-mannered art thou, nephew,
  And never wilt amend;
The sweetest sleep I ever slept,
  Thou bringest to an end."

Now they have brought the ladders
  Owned by his sire the King.
And, to bear the load along the road,
  Seven sturdy mules they bring;

And seven stout Moors, by whom the mules
  In housings are arrayed.
And to the walls of the countess
  Their journey have they made.
There, at the foot of yonder tower,
  They halt their cavalcade.

In the arms of the count Alminique
  The countess lay at rest;
The infante has ta'en her by the hand,
  And caught her to his breast.

THE MOORISH INFANTA AND ALFONZO RAMOS

Beneath the shade of an olive-tree
  Stood the infanta fair;
A golden comb was in her hands,
  And well she decked her hair.

To heaven she raised her eyes, and saw,
  That early morning-tide,
A clump of spears and an armored band
  From Guadalquivir ride.

Alfonzo Ramos with them came,
  The admiral of Castile.
"Now welcome, Alfonzo Ramos!
  Now welcome, steed and steel,
What tidings do you bring of my fleet,
  What tidings of woe or weal?"

"I'll tell thee tidings, lady,
  If my life thou wilt assure."
"Tell on, Alfonzo Ramos,
  Thy life shall be secure."

"Seville, Seville has fallen,
  To the arms of the Berber Moor."

"But for my word thy head this day,
  To the vultures had been tost!"
"If head of mine were forfeited,
  'Tis thine must pay the cost."

THE BULL-FIGHT OF ZULEMA

He was a valorous gentleman, a gay and gallant knight,
Like stars on heaven's fifth circle was the splendor of his might.
In peace, accomplished in the arts of great Apollo's choir,
In war, the brilliant swordsman that Mars might well admire.
His great exploits were written on history's brightest page,
And rightly was he reckoned as the mirror of his age;
Great deeds he did with point of lance and won bright honor's
  crown,
Before the year when each red cheek was clothed in manly
  down.
And such he was through all the world by minstrel harps ex-
  tolled,
Both for the vigor of his arm and for his bearing bold.
His very foes, whom he had made surrender in the fight,
While trembling at his valor, asked blessings on the knight.
And Fame herself, whose pace is swift, whose voice like fire
  can run,
Grew weary with reciting the deeds that he had done.
To tell aright his jeopardies, escapes, and rescues wrought,
A swifter-flying pinion and a louder tongue she sought!
Such was Zulema, such was he, the warrior of renown,
The son of that Zulema who ruled Toledo's town.
Ah! bright the fame the father left, for it shall never die—
The glory of his greater son shall keep its memory.
Now once it happened that he reached a city's towering gate;
'Twas Avila, and there that day the games they celebrate.
The mighty square, when he arrived, was changed into a
  bower;
And every knight wore fluttering plumes and every dame a
  flower.

The scene was strange, because the Moor, in southern cities
    reared,
Had never seen how gay Castile on festal days appeared.
He marked the Adelifas in the King's pavilion stand,
And he asked, and his prayer was granted, to join the cham-
    pion band.
Yet when they gave consent they feared that great Zulema's
    might
Would surely quite excel in joust the best Castilian knight.
But a thousand times they asked that heaven would give to him
    success,
And a thousand times they wondered at his glorious Moorish
    dress.
Full many a lady's beck and smile were on the warrior bent,
And they looked on his manly beauty and they sighed with deep
    content.
But now Zulema by the hand the wardens take and greet,
And 'mid the highest noblemen they yield the knight a seat.
His seat was placed in honor 'mid ladies gay and bright,
Mid warriors of Castile, the first in courage and in might.
Then suddenly, more swift than wind, more wild than comet's
    glare,
Jerama's bull, far famed was he, rushed on the crowded square.
Ah! brave was he in flashing eyes, and fierce was he in heart,
His brow was like a storm-cloud, each horn a giant's dart,
His wide-spread nostrils snorted fire, his neck was short and
    deep,
His skin was black as the thunder-cloud that crowns the moun-
    tain's steep.
Before his coming fled the crowd, until the sunny square
Was emptied of the multitude, and every stone was bare.
Those only who on horseback sat remained to face the foe.
Now trembling with alarm they stand, and now with hope they
    glow.
Good sport they looked to have with him, and lay him in the
    dust,
But the Andalusian hero evaded every thrust.
And sometimes, with a gallant charge he threw them from
    their seat,
He gored them with his savage horn, and trod them with his
    feet!

Ah! great the shame of the vanquished knights; they dared
    not raise their eyes
To the ladies who looked down and smiled from banks and bal-
    conies.
For those soft eyes were fixed no more upon each vanquished
    knight,
But on the monster proud and strong who conquered them in
    fight.
The dames upon the royal seat to Zulema turned their eyes,
And one, the loveliest of them all, who wore a strange disguise,
Yet through her veil such rays she shot that she seemed like
    the sun on high
When he rises, quenching all the stars that filled the midnight
    sky.
She made a sign to him and spoke directly from her heart,
Whose tongue is in a woman's eye. Ah! well it plays its part!
She bade him to redeem the day and avenge each gallant knight
Who had fallen in the dust before the foe in stubborn fight.
And the Moor with gracious mien assents, and from his seat
    descends;
But first with glance and waving scarf a tender message sends
To the lovely Moorish damsel who had called him to the fray,
And had filled his heart with sudden love upon the festal day.
And as he leapt into the sand it was as if he flew,
For love lent wings at his lady's nod, some glorious deed to do.
And when the bull beheld approach, upon the bloody sand,
His bold and tall antagonist, a dagger in his hand,
He roared like thunder, with his hoofs he pawed the dusty
    ground,
The plaza shook, the castle tower re-echoed to the sound!
Long subject to the hand of man, and in subjection born,
He thought to subject human foe to hoof and mighty horn.
Zulema started toward the beast, loud cries would hold him
    back,
But well he knew that victory would follow his attack.
The bull was on him with a bound, and, glaring face to face,
They stood one moment, while a hush fell on the crowded place.
With bold right hand Zulema drew his keen and mighty blade;
Blow after blow 'mid blood and dust upon his foe he laid;
The startled beast retired before such onslaught of his foe,

And the people shouted loud applause and the King himself
  bowed low.
The bull with tossing head roared forth a challenge to the
  knight,
As Zulema turned, and with a bound rushed to the desperate
  fight.
Ah! cruel were the strokes that rained upon that foaming
  flank!
Into the sand that life-blood like a shower of autumn sank.
He roars, he snorts, he spurns the ground, the bloody dust flies
  high,
Now here, now there, in angry pain they see the monster fly.
He turns to see what new-found foe has crossed his path to-day;
But when Zulema faces him he stops to turn away.
For the third time the fight begins; the bull with many a roar
Turns to his foe, while from his lips run mingled foam and
  gore.
The Moor enraged to see the beast again before him stand,
Deals him the deep, the fatal wound, with an unerring hand.
That wound, at last, has oped the gate through which may
  enter death,
And staggering to the dust the beast snorts forth his latest
  breath.
As the bull falls, the crowded square rings with a loud acclaim,
And envy burns in many a knight, and love in many a dame.
The highest nobles of the land the conqueror embrace;
He sees the blush of passion burn on many a damsel's face.
And Fame has blown her trumpet and flies from town to town,
And Apollo takes his pen and writes the hero's title down.

THE RENEGADE

Through the mountains of Moncayo,
  Lo! all in arms arrayed,
Rides pagan Bobalias,
  Bobalias the renegade.

Seven times he was a Moor, seven times
  To Christ he trembling turned;

At the eighth, the devil cozened him
  And the Christian cross he spurned,
And took back the faith of Mahomet,
  In childhood he had learned.

He was the mightiest of the Moors,
  And letters from afar
Had told him how Sevila
  Was marshalling for war.

He arms his ships and galleys,
  His infantry and horse,
And straight to Guadalquivir's flood
  His pennons take their course.

The flags that on Tablada's plain
  Above his camp unfold,
Flutter above three hundred tents
  Of silk brocade and gold.

In the middle, the pavilion
  Of the pagan they prepare;
On the summit a ruby stone is set,
  A jewel rich and rare.

It gleams at morn, and when the night
  Mantles the world at length,
It pours a ray like the light of day,
  When the sun is at its strength.

THE TOWER OF GOLD

Brave Arbolan a prisoner lay
  Within the Tower of Gold;
By order of the King there stood
  Four guards to keep the hold.
'Twas not because against his King
  He played a treacherous part;
But only that Guhala's charms
  Had won the captive's heart.

" Guhala, Guhala,
My longing heart must cry;
    This mournful vow I utter now—
    To see thee or to die."

No longer free those sturdy limbs!
    Revenge had bid them bind
The iron chain on hands and feet;
    They could not chain his mind!
How dolorous was the warrior's lot!
    All hope at last had fled;
And, standing at the window,
    With sighing voice he said:

" Guhala, Guhala,
My longing heart must cry;
    This mournful vow I utter now—
    To see thee or to die."

He turned his eyes to where the banks
    Of Guadalquivir lay;
"Inhuman King!" in grief he cried,
    "Thy mandates I obey;
Thou bidst them load my limbs with steel;
    Thy cruel sentinel
Keeps watch beside my prison door;
    Yet who my crime can tell?

" Guhala, Guhala,
My longing heart must cry;
    This mournful vow I utter now—
    To see thee or to die."

THE DIRGE FOR ALIATAR

No azure-hued tahalia now
Flutters about each warrior's brow;
No crooked scimitars display
Their gilded scabbards to the day.
The Afric turbans, that of yore
Were fashioned on Morocco's shore,
To-day their tufted crown is bare;
There are no fluttering feathers there.
In mourning garments all are clad,
Fit harness for the occasion sad;
But, four by four the mighty throng
In slow procession streams along.
Ah! Aliatar! well he knew
The soldiers of his army true,
The soldiers whose afflicted strain
Gives utterance to their bosom's pain.

Sadly we march along the crowded street,
While trumpets hoarsely blare and drums tempestuous beat.

The phœnix that would shine in gold
On the high banner's fluttering fold,
Scarce can the breeze in gladness bring
To spread aloft its waving wing.
It seemed as if the fire of death
For the first time had quenched her breath.
For tribulation o'er the world
The mantle of despair had furled;
There was no breeze the ground to bless,
The plain lay panting in distress;
Beneath the trailing silken shroud
Alfarez carried through the crowd.

Sadly we march along the crowded street,
While trumpets hoarsely blare and drums tempestuous beat.

For Aliatar, one sad morn,
Mounted his steed and blew his horn;

A hundred Moors behind him rode;
Fleeter than wind their coursers strode.
Toward Motril their course is made,
While foes the castle town blockade;
There Aliatar's brother lay,
Pent by the foes that fatal day.
Woe work the hour, the day, when he
Vaulted upon his saddle-tree!
Ne'er from that seat should he descend
To challenge foe or welcome friend,
Nor knew he that the hour was near,
His couch should be the funeral bier.

Sadly we march along the crowded street,
While trumpets hoarsely blare and drums tempestuous beat.

That day the master's knights were sent,
As if on sport and jousting bent;
And Aliatar, on his way,
By cruel ambush they betray;
With sword and hauberk they surround
And smite the warrior to the ground.
And wounded deep from every vein
He bleeding lies upon the plain.
The furious foes in deadly fight
His scanty followers put to flight,
In panic-stricken fear they fly,
And leave him unavenged to die.

Sadly we march along the crowded street,
While trumpets hoarsely blare and drums tempestuous beat.

Ah sadly swift the news has flown
To Zaida in the silent town;
Speechless she sat, while every thought
Fresh sorrow to her bosom brought;
Then flowed her tears in larger flood,
Than from his wounds the tide of blood.
Like dazzling pearls the tear-drops streak
The pallid beauty of her cheek.

Say, Love, and didst thou e'er behold
A maid more fair and knight more bold?
And if thou didst not see him die,
And Zaida's tears of agony,
The bandage on thine orbs draw tight—
That thou mayst never meet the sight!

Sadly we march along the crowded street,
While trumpets hoarsely blare and drums tempestuous beat.

Not only Zaida's eyes are wet,
For him her soul shall ne'er forget;
But many a heart in equal share
The sorrow of that lady bare.
Yes, all who drink the water sweet
Where Genil's stream and Darro meet,
All of bold Albaicins's line,
Who mid Alhambra's princes shine—
The ladies mourn the warrior high,
Mirror of love and courtesy;
The brave lament him, as their peer;
The princes, as their comrade dear;
The poor deplore, with hearts that bleed,
Their shelter in the time of need.

Sadly we march along the crowded street,
While trumpets hoarsely blare and drums tempestuous beat.

THE SHIP OF ZARA

It was the Moorish maiden, the fairest of the fair,
Whose name amid the Moorish knights was worshipped every-
    where.
And she was wise and modest, as her race has ever been,
And in Alhambra's palace courts she waited on the Queen,
A daughter of Hamete—of royal line was he,
And held the mighty castle of Baja's town in fee.
Now sad and mournful all the day the maiden weeping sat,
And her captive heart was thinking still of the distant caliphat,
Which in the stubborn straits of war had passed from Moslem
    reign,

And now was the dominion of King Ferdinand of Spain.
She thought upon the dreary siege in Baja's desert vale
When the fight was long and the food of beasts and men began
    to fail,
And her wretched father, forced to yield, gave up his castle
    hold,
For falling were the towers, falling fast his warriors bold.
And Zara, lovely Zara, did he give into the care
Of the noble Countess Palma, who loved the maiden fair.
And the countess had to Baja come when Queen Isabella came,
The lovely vega of the town to waste with sword and flame.
And the countess asked of Zara if she were skilled in aught,
The needle, or the 'broidery frame, to Christian damsels taught.
And how she made the hours go by when, on Guadalquivir's
    strand,
She sat in the Alhambra, a princess of the land.
And, while her eyes were full of tears, the Moorish maid re-
    plied:
" 'Twas I the silver tinsel fixed on garments duly dyed;
'Twas I who with deft fingers with gold lace overlaid
The dazzling robes of flowery tint of velvet and brocade.
And sometimes would I take my lute and play for dancers
    there;
And sometimes trust my own weak voice in some romantic air;
But now, this moment, I retain but one, one mournful art—
To weep, to mourn the banishment that ever grieves my heart.
And since 'tis thou alone whose bread, whose roof my life didst
    save,
I weep the bitterest tears of all because I am a slave!
Yet wouldst thou deign, O lady dear, to make more light
    to me
The hours I pass beneath thy roof, in dark captivity,—
I bid thee build for me, if thou approve of the design,
An ocean bark, well fitted to cross the surging brine;
Let it be swift, let it be strong, and leave all barks behind,
When on the surges of the main it feels the favoring wind.
We'll launch it from the sloping shore, and, when the wind
    is high,
And the fierce billows threatening mix their foam-tops with
    the sky,

We'll lower the mainsail, lest the storm should carry us away,
And sweep us on the reefs that lurk in some deep Afric bay.
And on the lofty topmast shall this inscription stand,
Written in letters which they use in every Christian land:
' This ship is tossed in many a storm, it lands on many a shore,
And the wide sea, beneath the wind, it swiftly travels o'er;
'Tis like the human heart which brings no treasure and no gain,
Till, tossed by hard misfortune, it has known the sea of pain.'
And let there be upon the fringe round this inscription hung
Another legend which shall say in the Arabian tongue:
' Oh, might it be that Allah, the merciful, would send
To all my captive miseries a swift and happy end.' "
The countess said: " To build this ship methinks would please
    me well,
Such tasks the sorrows of thy heart might lighten or dispel;
And, Zara, when the summer comes, and winds and floods are
    free,
We'll build our bark, we'll hoist our sail, and start across the
    sea."

HAMETE ALI

Hamete Ali on his way toward the city goes,
His tunic is a brilliant green with stripes of crimson rose,
In sign that no despondency this daring wanderer knows.
His arm, that wears the twisted steel, reflects the sunlight
    sheen,
And bound to it by many a knot is hung his hood of green.
And o'er his bonnet azure-blue, two feathery plumes there fly;
The one is green as the summer and one is blue as sky.
He does not wear these hues to show that he is passion's slave,
They are emblems of the life that beats within his bosom brave.
Yet dusky is his lance's hue and dusky is his shield,
On which are serpents scattered upon a golden field.
Their venomed tongues are quivering and ears before them
    stand,
To show how slanderous hearts can spread their poison o'er
    the land.
A lettered motto in the midst which everyone may read,
Is written in Arabian script, ah! good that all should heed!

" 'Tis naught but innocence of heart can save me from the
blow
With which the slanderous serpents would lay their victim
low."
Upon a piebald colt he rode along the valley's side,
The bravest of the valiant Moors and once Granada's pride.
In furious rage descending from bold Ubeda's steep,
He crossed the vale and mounted to Baza's castle keep.
Defiant still of Fortune's power, his thoughts at last found vent,
For Fortune had been cruel, and in words of discontent,
As if he blamed the serpent upon his shield displayed,
The torrent of his heart broke forth and in wrath the warrior
said:
" O wasters of the brightest hope I knew in years long past!
O clouds by which the blazing sun of bliss is overcast!
O blight of love, O ruin of aspirations pure!
Vile worms, that gnaw and waste away the treasures most
secure!
Attempt no more to banish me from my own native land,
That in my place of honor ye, envious slaves, may stand;
I, too, have friends, whose swords are keen, whose love is
strong and leal.
To them I look for my defence by stratagem or steel.
  And, Fortune, do thy worst; it is not meant,
  By Allah, that his knight should die in banishment.

" Permit it not that in the generous breasts of those whose
blood
Flows in my veins, who by my side as faithful champions
stood,
Those cursed asps, whose effigies my shield's circumference fill,
Could plant the thoughts of villany by which they work me ill.
Just heaven forbids their words should blot the honor of my
name,
For pure and faithful is my heart, howe'er my foes defame;
And Zaida, lovely Zaida, at a word that did me wrong,
Would close her ears in scornful ire and curse the slanderous
tongue.
  And, Fortune, do thy worst; it is not meant,
  By Allah, that his knight should die in banishment.

" Nay, Fortune, turn no more thy wheel, I care not that it rest,
Nor bid thee draw the nail that makes it stand at man's behest
Oh, may I never say to thee, when for thy aid I call,
Let me attain the height of bliss whate'er may be my fall!
And when I roam from those I love, may never cloud arise
To dim my hope of a return and hide me from their eyes.
Yet doubtless, 'tis the absent are oftenest forgot,
Till those who loved when they were near in absence love them
    not.
    And, Fortune, do thy worst; it is not meant,
    By Allah, that his knight should die in banishment.

" And since 'tis my unhappy lot, through slander's cruel wiles,
I should be robbed so many years of Zaida's cheering smiles,
Yet those who say that I am false, and name Celinda's name,
Oh, may they gain no end at length but obloquy and shame!
It is not just that to these words and to these anxious fears,
These wild complaints, the god of love should close his heed-
    less ears!
Yes, I deserve a better fate, the fate that makes more sure;
The fame of those whose slanderous tongue in banishment
    endure.
    And, Fortune, do thy worst; it is not meant,
    By Allah, that his knight should die in banishment."

He spoke, and, lo! before him he saw the city stand,
With walls and towers that frowned in might upon that fertile
    land.
And he saw the glittering banners of Almanzor set on high,
And swaying in the gentle breeze that filled the summer sky.
And those who stood upon the walls, soon as he came in sight,
Streamed forth from the portcullis with welcome for the knight,
For they marvelled at the prancing steed that rushed across
    the plain,
They marvelled at his thundering voice and words of deep
    disdain.
    And, Fortune, do thy worst; it is not meant,
    By Allah, that his knight should die in banishment.

And as he rode into the town and galloped to the square,
Upon the balconies he saw bright dames with faces bare;

They stood, they gazed with eyes of love and gestures of de-
    light,
For they joyed to see among them so stout, so fair a knight.
And all of Baza's people with cries his coming greet,
And follow at his horse's tail from street to crowded street.
His heart with gratitude was filled, his bosom filled with pride,
And with doffed bonnet, lo, he bowed and once again he cried:
    " And, Fortune, do thy worst; it is not meant,
    By Allah, that his knight should die in banishment."

They led him to the warden's house, and there was feasting
    high.
Brave men and beauteous women in crowds were standing by.
The trumpets blew in merry strain, the Moorish horns resound,
And the strain of joy was echoed from every castle round.
And from his colt dismounting he laid his lance aside,
And greeted all the multitude that filled the plaza wide.
Then to the strong tower of the place he hurried from the
    street,
And as he went a thousand times his lips would still repeat:
    " And, Fortune, do thy worst; it is not meant,
    By Allah, that his knight should die in banishment."

ZAIDE'S LOVE

Then Zaide stood enraptured and gazed with placid eye,
For the moment when his heart's desire should be fulfilled was
    nigh.
Propitious was the moment, and happy was the hour,
When all that he had longed for had come into his power.
And he said: " Thrice happy is the wall, and happy is the
    bar,
Tho' from my fond embraces, Zaida, it keeps thee far;
For long as thou shalt live on earth, my Zaida, thou art mine;
And the heart that in my bosom beats, long as it beats, is thine.
And happy is the green, green sod on which thy feet are set,
For the pressure of thy tender foot the grass shall ne'er forget,
Shall ne'er forget the white, white heel that o'er the pathway
    came,

Leaving behind it, everywhere, the print of snow and flame.
But far more happy is the knight, if e'er should Allah send
To this dark separation a bright and peaceful end.
For seems to me the hours that pass, without thy presence
   dear,
Wear the dark robe of sorrow, that orphaned children wear.
I seek to have thee with me, for it is only to the weak
That the happiness is wanting that they do not dare to seek.
And if the doom of death is ours, it will not haste the more
Because we scorn to think of it upon this happy shore.
But ere it come, that doom of death which fills us with alarms,
May Allah grant to me the boon of resting in thine arms!
And if, in that supremest bliss, fate favors my design,
And love is crowned, the lot of life contented I resign.
O darling Zaida, blest is he, 'mid thousands, who can say
That on that bosom, in those arms he for one moment lay!
Come, darling, to thy Zaide's side, and yield to him thy love;
Thou knowest him brave and good and kind, all other knights
   above;
In owning him thy lover true, thou wilt a partner count
Who above all in valor's list is champion paramount.
Thy beauty's sway should be unchecked as death's prevailing
   might,
But, ah, how many worlds would then sink into endless night!
But come, fair Zaida, quickly come to these expectant arms,
And let me win at last the prize of victory o'er thy charms.
It is a debt thou owest me, oh, let the debt be paid."
Then Zaida rose and showed herself in beauty's robe arrayed,
And the Moor cried: "May Allah grant thy sun may ever
   shine,
To light with its full splendor this lonely life of mine!
And tho' my stammering tongue be dumb, and like a broken
   lute,
And in its loudest efforts to speak thy praise be mute,
It can at least announce to thee, loud as the thunder's peal,
The service that I owe to thee, the passion that I feel."
The Moorish lady smiled at this, and spake in tender tone;
"If all this silent tongue of thine has said be loyal shown,
If all thy vows be from thy heart, and all thy heavy sighs
From out a breast unchanging, a constant spirit rise,

I swear that I would grant thy wish and follow thy behest;
But, ah, I fear lest thy fierce love should bring to me no rest,
I fear these honeyed words that from thy lips so lightly fly
At last should prove a serpent's fang to sting me till I die."
Then swore to her the Moor: " If this the end should ever be,
May the firm earth beneath my feet yawn wide and swallow me!
And may the blessed sunlight, the symbol of my hope,
Wither these orbs and leave me in eternal night to grope!"
At this the lovers joined their hands and hearts, and, with a
    kiss,
Sealed all their vows of friendship and promises of bliss—
Their love was strong and solid and constant should remain,
Till death should end their bondage and break the golden
    chain.

ZAIDA'S JEALOUSY.

Kind friend of Bencerraje's line, what judgment dost thou hold
Of all that Zaida's changeful moods before thine eyes unfold?
Now by my life I swear that she to all would yield her will;
Yet by my death I swear that she to all is recreant still.
Come near, my friend, and listen while I show to you this note,
Which to the lovely lady in bitter grief I wrote;
Repeat not what I read to thee, for 'twere a deadly shame,
Since thou her face admirest, should slander smirch her name:
" O Moorish maiden, who like time, forever on the wing,
Dost smiles and tears, with changing charm, to every bosom
    bring,
Thy love is but a masquerade, and thou with grudging hand
Scatterest the crumbs of hope on all the crowds that round
    thee stand.
With thee there is no other law of love and kindliness
But what alone may give thee joy and garland of success.
With each new plume thy maidens in thy dark locks arrange,
With each new tinted garment thy thoughts, thy fancies
    change.
I own that thou art fairer than even the fairest flower
That at the flush of early dawn bedecks the summer's bower.
But, ah, the flowers in summer hours change even till they
    fade,

And thou art changeful as the rose that withers in the shade.
And though thou art the mirror of beauty's glittering train,
Thy bosom has one blemish, thy mind one deadly stain;
For upon all alike thou shed'st the radiance of thy smile,
And this the treachery by which thou dost the world beguile.
I do not plead in my complaint thy loveliness is marred,
Because thy words are cruel, because thy heart is hard;
Would God that thou wert insensible as is the ocean wild
And not to all who meet thee so affable and mild;
Ah, sweetest is the lingering fruit that latest comes in time,
Ah, sweetest is the palm-tree's nut that those who reach must
    climb.
Alas! 'twas only yesterday a stranger reached the town—
Thou offeredst him thy heart and bade him keep it for his own!
O Zaida, tell me, how was this? for oft I heard thee say
That thou wert mine and 'twas to me thy heart was given
    away.
Hast thou more hearts than one, false girl, or is it changeful-
    ness
That makes thee give that stranger guest the heart that I
    possess?
One heart alone is mine, and that to thee did I resign.
If thou hast many, is my love inadequate to thine?
O Zaida, how I fear for thee, my veins with anger glow;
O Zaida, turn once more to me, and let the stranger go.
As soon as he hath left thy side his pledges, thou wilt find,
Were hollow and his promises all scattered to the wind.
And if thou sayst thou canst not feel the pains that absence
    brings,
'Tis that thy heart has never known love's gentle whisperings.
'Tis that thy fickle mind has me relinquished here to pine,
Like some old slave forgotten in this palace court of thine.
Ah, little dost thou reck of me, of all my pleasures flown,
But in thy pride dost only think, false lady, of thine own.
And is it weakness bids me still to all thy faults be blind
And bear thy lovely image thus stamped upon my mind?
For when I love, the slight offence, though fleeting may be
    the smart,
Is heinous as the treacherous stroke that stabs a faithful heart.
And woman by one look unkind, one frown, can bring despair

Upon the bosom of the man whose spirit worships her.
Take, then, this counsel, 'tis the last that I shall breathe to
thee,
Though on the winds I know these words of mine will wasted
be:
I was the first on whom thou didst bestow the fond caress,
And gave those pledges of thy soul, that hour of happiness;
Oh, keep the faith of those young days! Thy honor and re-
nown
Thou must not blight by love unkind, by treachery's heartless
frown.
For naught in life is safe and sure if faith thou shouldst discard,
And the sunlight of the fairest soul is oft the swiftest marred.
I will not sign this letter nor set to it my name;
For I am not that happy man to whom love's message came,
Who in thy bower thy accents sweet enraptured heard that day,
When on thy heaving bosom, thy chosen love, I lay.
Yet well thou'lt know the hand that wrote this letter for thine
eye,
For conscience will remind thee of thy fickle treachery.
Dissemble as thou wilt, and play with woman's skill thy part,
Thou knowest there is but one who bears for thee a broken
heart."
Thus read the valiant castellan of Baza's castle tower,
Then sealed the scrip and sent it to the Moorish maiden's
bower.

ZAIDA OF TOLEDO

Upon a gilded balcony, which decked a mansion high,
A place where ladies kept their watch on every passer-by,
While Tagus with a murmur mild his gentle waters drew
To touch the mighty buttress with waves so bright and blue,
Stands Zaida, radiant in her charms, the flower of Moorish
maids,
And with her arching hand of snow her anxious eyes she
shades,
Searching the long and dusty road that to Ocaña leads,
For the flash of knightly armor and the tramp of hurrying
steeds.

The glow of amorous hope has lit her cheek with rosy red,
Yet wrinkles of too anxious love her beauteous brow o'er-
    spread;
For she looks to see if up the road there rides a warrior tall—
The haughty Bencerraje, whom she loves the best of all.
At every looming figure that blots the vega bright,
She starts and peers with changing face, and strains her
    eager sight;
For every burly form she sees upon the distant street
Is to her the Bencerraje whom her bosom longs to greet.
And many a distant object that rose upon her view
Filled her whole soul with rapture, as her eager eyes it drew;
But when it nearer came, she turned away, in half despair,
Her vision had deceived her, Bencerraje was not there.
" My own, my Bencerraje, if but lately you descried
That I was angry in my heart, and stubborn in my pride,
Oh, let my eyes win pardon, for they with tears were wet.
Why wilt thou not forgive me, why wilt thou not forget?
And I repented of that mood, and gave myself the blame,
And thought, perhaps it was my fault that, at the jousting
    game,
There was no face among the knights so filled with care as
    thine,
So sad and so dejected, yes, I thought the blame was mine!
And yet I was, if thou with thought impartial wilt reflect,
Not without cause incensed with thee, for all thy strange
    neglect.
Neglect that not from falseness or words of mine had sprung
But from the slanderous charges made by a lying tongue;
And now I ask thee pardon, if it be not too late,
Oh, take thy Zaida to thy heart, for she is desolate!
For if thou pardon her, and make her thine again, I swear
Thou never wilt repent, dear love, thou thus hast humored
    her!
It is the law of honor, which thou wilt never break,
That the secret of sweet hours of love thou mayst not com-
    mon make.
That never shouldst thou fail in love, or into coldness fall,
Toward thy little Moorish maiden, who has given thee her
    all."

She spoke; and Bencerraje, upon his gallant bay,
Was calling to her from the street, where he loitered blithe
and gay,
And quickly she came down to him, to give him, e'er they part,
Her rounded arms, her ivory neck, her bosom, and her heart!

ZAIDE REBUKED

See, Zaide, let me tell you not to pass along my street,
Nor gossip with my maidens nor with my servants treat;
Nor ask them whom I'm waiting for, nor who a visit pays,
What balls I seek, what robe I think my beauty most dis-
plays.
'Tis quite enough that for thy sake so many face to face
Aver that I, a witless Moor, a witless lover chase.
I know that thou art a valiant man, that thou hast slaughtered
more,
Among thy Christian enemies, than thou hast drops of gore.
Thou art a gallant horseman, canst dance and sing and play
Better than can the best we meet upon a summer's day.
Thy brow is white, thy cheek is red, thy lineage is renowned,
And thou amid the reckless and the gay art foremost found.
I know how great would be my loss, in losing such as thee;
I know, if I e'er won thee, how great my gain would be:
And wert thou dumb even from thy birth, and silent as the
grave,
Each woman might adore thee, and call herself thy slave.
But 'twere better for us both I turn away from thee,
Thy tongue is far too voluble, thy manners far too free;
Go find some other heart than mine that will thy ways endure,
Some woman who, thy constancy and silence to secure,
Can build within thy bosom her castle high and strong,
And put a jailer at thy lips, to lock thy recreant tongue.
Yet hast thou gifts that ladies love; thy bearing bold and
bright
Can break through every obstacle that bars them from delight.
And with such gifts, friend Zaide, thou spreadest thy banquet
board,
And bidst them eat the dish so sweet, and never say a word!

But that which thou hast done to me, Zaide, shall cost thee
    dear;
And happy would thy lot have been hadst thou no change to
    fear.
Happy if when thy snare availed to make the prize thine own,
Thou hadst secured the golden cage before the bird was flown.
For scarce thy hurrying footsteps from Tarfe's garden came,
Ere thou boastedst of thine hour of bliss, and of my lot of
    shame.
They tell me that the lock of hair I gave thee on that night,
Thou drewest from thy bosom, in all the people's sight,
And gav'st it to a base-born Moor, who took the tresses
    curled,
And tied them in thy turban, before the laughing world.
I ask not that thou wilt return nor yet the relic keep,
But I tell thee, while thou wearest it, my shame is dire and
    deep:
They say that thou hast challenged him, and swearest he shall
    rue
For all the truths he spake of thee—would God they were not
    true!
Who but can laugh to hear thee blame the whispers that re-
    veal
Thy secret, though thy secret thyself couldst not conceal.
No words of thine can clear thy guilt nor pardon win from me,
For the last time my words, my glance, have been addressed
    to thee."
Thus to the lofty warrior of Abencerraje's race
The lady spoke in anger, and turned away her face:
" 'Tis right," she said, " the Moor whose tongue has proved
    to me unkind
Should in the sentence of my tongue fit retribution find."

ZAIDA'S INCONSTANCY

O fairest Zaida, thou whose face brings rapture to mine eyes!
O fairest Zaida, in whose smile my soul's existence lies!
Fairest of Moorish maidens, yet in revengeful mood,
Above all Moorish maidens, stained by black ingratitude.
'Tis of thy golden locks that love has many a noose entwined,
And souls of free men at thy sight full oft are stricken blind;
Yet tell me, proud one, tell me, what pleasure canst thou gain
From showing to the world a heart so fickle and so vain?
And, since my adoration thou canst not fail to know,
How is it that thy tender heart can treat thy lover so?
And art thou not content my fondest hopes to take away,
But thou must all my hope, my life, destroy, in utter ruin
    lay?
My faithful love, sweet enemy! how ill dost thou requite!
And givest in exchange for it but coldness and despite;
Thy promises, thy pledge of love, thou to the gale wouldst
    fling;
Enough that they were thine, false girl, that they should all
    take wing.
Remember how upon that day thou gavest many a sign
Of love and lavished'st the kiss which told me thou wert
    mine.
Remember, lovely Zaida, though memory bring thee pain,
Thy bliss when 'neath thy window I sang my amorous strain.
By day, before the window, I saw my darling move,
At night, upon the balcony, I told thee of my love.
If I were late or absence detained me from thy sight,
Then jealous rage distraught thy heart, thine eyes with tears
    were bright.
But now that thou hast turned from me, I come thy face to
    greet,
And thou biddest me begone, and pass no longer through thy
    street.
Thou biddest me look on thee no more, nor even dare to write
The letter or the *billet-doux*, that caused thee once delight.
Yes, Zaida, all thy favors, thy love, thy vows, are shown
To be but false and faithless, since thou art faithless grown.

But why? thou art a woman, to fickle falseness born;
Thou prizest those who scorn thee—those who love thee thou
    dost scorn.
I change not, thou art changed, whose heart once fondly
    breathed my name;
But the more thy bosom turns to ice, the fiercer burns my
    flame;
For all thy coldness I with love and longing would repay,
For passion founded on good faith can never die away.

ZAIDE'S DESOLATION

It was the hour when Titan from Aurora's couch awoke,
And on the world her radiant face in wonted beauty broke,
When a Moor came by in sad array, and Zaide was his name.
Disguised, because his heart was sad with love's consuming
    flame;
No shield he bore, he couched no lance, he rode no warrior
    steed;
No plume nor mantle he assumed, motto or blazon screed;
Still on the flank of his mantle blank one word was written
    plain,
In the Moorish of the people, " I languish through disdain."
A flimsy cape his shoulders clad, for, when the garb is poor,
Nobility is honored most because 'tis most obscure.
If he in poverty appeared, 'twas love that made him so;
Till love might give the wealth he sought thus mourning
    would he go.
And still he journeys through the hills and shuns the haunts
    of men;
None look upon his misery in field or lonely fen.
Fair Zaida ne'er forgets that he is prince of all the land,
And ruler of the castles that at Granada stand;
But gold or silver or brocade can ne'er supply the lack
Of honor in a noble line whose crimes have stained it black;
For sunlight never clears the sky when night has spread her
    cloak,
But only when the glory of the morning has awoke.
He lives secure from jealous care, holding the priceless dower

Which seldom falls to loving hearts or sons of wealth and
  power.
Poor is his garb, yet at his side a costly blade appears,
'Tis through security of mind no other arms he bears.

'Tis love that from Granada's home has sent him thus to rove,
And for the lovely Zaida he languishes with love—
The loveliest face that by God's grace the sun e'er shone
  above.
From court and mart he lives apart, such is the King's de-
  sire;
Yet the King's friend Alfaqui is the fair maiden's sire.
Friend of the King, the throne's support, a monarch's son
  is he,
And he has sworn that never Moor his daughter's spouse
  shall be.
He has no ease till the monarch sees his daughter's loveliness.
But she has clasped brave Zaide's hand, and smiled to his
  caress,
And said that to be his alone is her sole happiness.
And after many journeys wide, wearied of banishment,
He sees the lofty tower in which his Moorish maid is pent.

ZAIDA'S LAMENT

Now the hoarse trumpets of the morn were driving sleep
  away;
They sounded as the fleeting night gave truce unto the day.
The hubbub of the busy crowd ceased at that dulcet sound,
In which one moment high and low peace and refreshment
  found.
The hoot of the nocturnal owl alone the silence broke,
While from the distance could be heard the din of waking
  folk;
And, in the midst of silence, came the sound as Zaida wept,
For all night long in fear of death she waked while others
  slept.
     And as she sighed, she sang aloud a melancholy strain;
     "And who would wish to die," she said, "though death
  be free from pain?"

For evil tongues, who thought to win her favor with a lie,
Had told her that the bold Gazul ordained that she should die;
And so she donned a Moor's attire, and put her own away,
And on the stroke of midnight from Xerez took her way.
    And as she sighed, she sang aloud a melancholy strain;
      "And who would wish to die," she said, "though death
        be free from pain?"

She rode a nimble palfrey and scarce could great Gazul
Excel the ardent spirit with which her heart was full.
Yet at every step her palfrey took, she turned her head for
    fear,
To see if following on her track some enemy were near.
    And as she went, she sang aloud a melancholy strain;
      "And who would wish to die," she said, "though death
        be free from pain?"

To shun suspicion's eye, at last she left the king's highway,
And took the journey toward Seville that thro' a bypath lay;
With loosened rein her gallant steed right swiftly did she ride,
Yet to her fear he did appear like a rock on the rough way-
    side.
    And as she went, she sang aloud a melancholy strain;
      "And who would wish to die," she said, "though death
        be free from pain?"

So secretly would she proceed, her very breath she held,
Tho' with a rising storm of sighs her snowy bosom swelled.
And here and there she made a halt, and bent her head to
    hear
If footsteps sounded; then, assured, renewed her swift career.
    And as she went, she sang aloud a melancholy strain;
      "And who would wish to die," she said, "though death
        be free from pain?"

Her fancy in the silent air could whispering voices hear;
"I'll make of thee a sacrifice, to Albenzaide dear;"
This fancy took her breath away, lifeless she sank at length,

And grasped the saddle-bow; for fear had sapped her spirit's
   strength.
     And as she went, she sang aloud a melancholy strain;
      "And who would wish to die," she said, "though death
       be free from pain?"

She came in sight of proud Seville; but the darkness bade her
   wait
Till dawn; when she alighted before a kinsman's gate.
Swift flew the days, and when at last the joyful truth she
   learned,
That she had been deceived; in joy to Xerez she returned.
     And as she went, she sang aloud a melancholy strain;
      "And who would wish to die," she said, "though death
       be free from pain?"

ZAIDA'S CURSE

And Zaida Cegri, desolate,
Whom by the cruel cast of fate,
Within one hour, the brandished blade
From wife had mourning widow made,
On Albenzaide's corse was bowed,
Shedding hot tears, with weeping loud.
Bright as the gold of Araby
   Shone out her locks unbound;
And while, as if to staunch the blood,
   Her hand lay on the wound,
She fixed her glances on Gazul,
   Still by his foes attacked.
" 'Twas cruel rage, not jealous love,
   That urged this wicked act."
(Thus she began with trembling voice.)
   "And I to God will pray
That for thy treacherous violence
   Thy dastard life shall pay.
And midway, on thy journey down
To fair Sidonia's castled town,
Mayst thou alone, with no retreat,
The valiant Garci-Perez meet;
And mayst thou, startled at the sight,

Lose all the vigor of thy might;
Thy reins with palsied fingers yield;
And find no shelter in thy shield.
There sudden death or captive shame
Blot all thy valor but the name.
Thy warrior garb thou turnest
    To the livery of the slave;
Thy coat of steel is no cuirass,
    No harness of the brave;
When to Sidonia thou art come,
    To meet thy amorous mate,
May foul suspicion turn her heart
    From love to deadly hate.
Begone! no more the course pursue
Of faithless love and vows untrue.
To remain true to such as thee
Were naught but blackest perjury.
I fear not, hound, thy sword of might;
Turn, traitor, turn and leave my sight,
For thou wert born to change thy mind,
And fling all fealty to the wind.
Ignoble origin is thine,
For lovers of a noble line
Have no such rancorous hearts as thine.
And here I pray that God will bring
    His curse upon thy soul,
That thou in war, in peace, in love
    May meet with failure foul,
And that Sanlucar's lady,
    Whom thou wishest for a bride,
Thee from her castle entrance
    May spurn thee in her pride.
A widowed wife with bleeding heart,
Hear me one moment ere we part!
Thy knightly service I distrust,
I hear thy voice with deep disgust."
Cut to the heart by words so rude,
The Moor within the palace stood;
Say what he could, 'twas but to find
His vain word wasted on the wind.

THE TOURNAMENT OF ZAIDE

By Zaide has a feast been pledged to all Granada's dames,
For in his absence there had been dire lack of festive games,
And, to fulfil the promise the noble man had made,
He called his friends to join him in dance and serenade.
There should be sport of every kind; the youths in white arrayed
Were, to the ladies all unknown, to lead the camisade.
And ere the radiance of dawn could tint the valley-side,
The merry Moor had come abroad, his friends were at his side.
He gathered round a company, they formed a joyous train;
There were fifty gentlemen, the noblest names in Spain.
Before the dawn they sallied forth the ladies to surprise
And all that snowy gowns conceal to see with open eyes.
They bound their brows with garlands of flowerets sweet and bright,
In one hand each a cane-stalk bore, in one a taper white,
And the clarions began to blow, and trump and Moorish horn,
And whoop and shout and loud huzzas adown the street were borne.
From right to left the clamor spread along the esplanade.
And envious Abaicin a thousand echoes made.
The startled horses galloped by, amid the people's yells;
The town to its foundation shook with the jingle of their bells.
Amid the crowd some run, some shout, "Stop, stop!" the elders say;
Then all take order and advance to Alcazaba's way;
Others from Vavataubin to Alpujarra fare,
Down the street of the Gomelas or to Vivarrambla Square.
Now the whole town is on its feet, from wall to towering wall
They surge with shouts or flock around the tower and castle tall.
The ladies who are tenderest and given most to sleep
Awaken at the hubbub and from their windows peep.
And there are seen dishevelled locks clasped by the lily hand;
And snowy throat and bosom bare, revealed in public, stand;
And in their drowsy disarray, and in their anxious fear,

Each Moorish lady is surprised with many a sudden tear;
And many a heart was filled that night with feverish unrest,
As one tall maid looked through the pane with white and
     heaving breast.
And many a Moorish girl was seen by revellers that night
Or running in confusion or halting from affright;
But no one saw fair Zaida, except by memory's sight;
And Zaide in the darkness, with Muza as his guide,
Hurried about the city; what a crowd was at their side!
What racket, and what riot, what shout and prank and play!
It would have had no end unless the sun had brought the day,
And now the leading revellers mustered their ranks once
     more;
To close the frolic with one word; " Go home; the game is
     o'er."

ZAIDE'S COMPLAINT

Brave Zaide paces up and down impatiently the street
Where his lady from the balcony is wont her knight to greet,
And he anxiously awaits the hour when she her face will show
Before the open lattice and speak to him below.
The Moor is filled with desperate rage, for he sees the hour
     is fled
When day by day the dazzling ray of sunlight gilds that head,
And he stops to brood in desperate mood, for her alone he
     yearns
Can aught soothe the fire of fierce desire with which his bosom
     burns.
At last he sees her moving with all her wonted grace,
He sees her and he hastens to their old trysting-place;
For as the moon when night is dark and clouds of tempest fly
Rises behind the dim-lit wood and lights the midnight sky,
Or like the sun when tempests with inky clouds prevail,
He merges for one moment and shows his visage pale;
So Zaida on her balcony in gleaming beauty stood,
And the knight for a moment gazed at her and checked his
     angry mood.
Zaide beneath the balcony with trembling heart drew near;
He halted and with upward glance spoke to his lady dear:

" Fair Moorish maiden, may thy life, by Allah guarded still,
Bring thee the full fruition of that that thou dost will;
And if the servants of thy house, the pages of my hall,
Have lied about thine honor, perdition seize them all;
For they come to me and murmur low and whisper in my ear
That thou wishest to disown me, thy faithful cavalier;
And they say that thou art pledged to one a Moor of wealth
 and pride,
Who will take thee to his father's house and claim thee as his
 bride,
For he has come to woo thee from the wide lands of his sire;
And they say that his scimitar is keen and his heart a flame of
 fire.
And if, fair Zaida, this is true, I kneel before thy feet
Imploring thou wilt tell me true, and fling away deceit;
For all the town is talking, still talking of our love,
And the tongues of slander, to thy blame, to my derision
 move."
The lady blushed, she bowed her head, then to the Moor re-
 plied:
" Dear heart of mine, of all my friends the most undoubted
 friend,
The time has come our friendship should have an early end;
If all, indeed, these tidings know, as you yourself declare,
Pray tell me who of all the town first laid this secret bare.
For if the life that now I lead continue, I shall die.
'Tis cheered by love, but tortured by hopeless agony.
God only knows why I the sport of cruel fate should be.
God only knows the man who says that I am false to thee.
Thou knowest well that Zaida has loved thee long and true,
Tho' her ancient lineage, Moorish knight, is more than is thy
 due,
And thou knowest well the loud expostulations of my sire.
Thou knowest how my mother curses me with curses dire
Because I wait for thee by day, for thee by night I wait.
Tho' far thou comest in the eve, yet dost thou tarry late.
They say to hush the common talk 'tis time that I be wed,
And to his home by some fond Moor in bridal veil be led.
Ah! many are the lovely dames, tall and of beauteous face,
Who are burning in Granada to take my envied place.

They look at thee with loving eyes and from the window call;
And, Zaide, thou deservest well the brightest of them all,
For thou thyself thine amorous eyes have turned and yet will
    turn
Upon the Moorish maidens who for thy embraces burn."
Then with dejected visage the Moor this answer made,
While a thousand thoughts of sorrow his valorous breast in-
    vade:
" Ah, little did I think," he said, " and little did I know
That thou, my lovely Zaida, would ever treat me so;
And little did I think thou wouldst have done this cruel deed
And by thy changeful heart would thus have made my heart
    to bleed.
And this for one unworthy, a man who could not claim
That thou should sacrifice to him thy love, thy life, thy name.
And art thou she who long ago, when evening veiled the sky,
Didst say to me with tender smile from the lofty balcony,
' Zaide, I am thine own, thine own, thine own I still shall
    be,
And thou the darling of my soul art life itself to me ' ? "

GUHALA'S LOVE

The bravest youth that e'er drew rein
Upon Granada's flowery plain,
A courteous knight, of gentle heart,
Accomplished in the jouster's art;
Well skilled to guide the flying steed,
And noted for each warlike deed;
And while his heart like steel was set
When foeman in the battle met,
'Twas wax before his lady's eyes
And melted at her amorous sighs;
And he was like a diamond bright
Amid the sword-thrusts of the fight,
And in the zambra's festive hour
Was gracious as the summer's flower.
In speech he showed the generous mind,
Where wit and wisdom were combined;

And, while his words no envy woke,
He weighed each sentence that he spoke.
And yet his mantle was of blue,
And tinged with sorrow's violet hue;
For fair Guhala, Moorish maid,
Her spell upon his heart had laid;
And thus his cape of saffron bare
The color emblem of despair;
On turban and on tassel lie
The tints that yield an August sky;
For anxious love was in his mind;
And anxious love is ever blind.
With scarce a word did he forsake
The lady pining for his sake;
For, when the festal robe he wore,
Her soul the pall of sorrow wore.
And now he journeyed on his way
To Jaen, for the jousting day,
And to Guhala, left alone,
All relic of delight was gone.
Tho' the proud maid of matchless face
A thousand hearts would fain embrace,
She loved but one, and swiftly ran
And spake her mind to Arbolan.
"O Arbolan, my Moor, my own,
Surely thy love is feeble grown!
The least excuse can bid thee part,
And tear with pain this anxious heart.
Oh, that it once were granted me
To mount my steed and follow thee;
How wouldst thou marvel then to see
That courage of true love in me,
Whose pulse so feebly throbs in thee."
Thus to see Arbolan depart
So fills with grief Guhala's heart.
The Moorish maid, while on he sped,
Lies sickening on her mournful bed.
Her Moorish damsels strive to know
The secret of this sudden blow;
They ask the cause that lays her low;

They seek the sad disease to heal,
Whose cause her feigning words conceal.
And less, indeed, the doubling folds
The Moor within his turban holds,
Than are the wiles Guhala's mind
In search of secrecy can find.
To Zara only, whom she knows,
Sole friend amid a ring of foes,
The sister of her lover leal,
She will the secret cause reveal.
And seeking an occasion meet
To tell with truth and tongue discreet,
While from her eyes the tear-drops start,
She opens thus her bleeding heart:
" O Zara, Zara, to the end,
Thou wilt remain my faithful friend.
How cruel is the lot I bear,
Thy brother's peril makes me fear!
'Tis for his absence that I mourn.
I sicken, waiting his return!"
Such were the words Guhala said.
The love-lorn and afflicted maid
Nor further power and utterance found,
But, fainting, sank upon the ground;
For strength of love had never art
To fill with life a pining heart.

AZARCO OF GRANADA

Azarco left his heart behind
 When he from Seville passed,
And winsome Celindaja
 As hostage held it fast.
The heart which followed with the Moor
 Was lent him by the maid,
And at their tearful parting,
 " Now guard it well," she said.
" O light of my distracted eyes,
 When thou hast reached the fight,

In coat of double-proof arrayed,
   As fits a gallant knight,
Let loyal love and constancy
   Be thy best suit of mail,
In lonely hours of absence,
   When faith is like to fail.
The Moorish girls whom thou shalt meet
   Are dazzling in their grace,
Of peerless wit and generous heart,
   And beautiful of face.
These in the dance may lure thy heart
   To think of me no more,
But none will e'er adore thee
   As I, thy slave, adore.
For to live lonely without thee
   Untouched by jealous fear,
Is more than my poor heart can brook,
   Thou art to me so dear.
If e'er in festal halls thou meet
   Some peril to my peace,
Azarco, turn thy look away,
   And check thine eyes' caprice.
For 'tis by wandering eyes the foes
   Of constancy increase.
May Allah and the prophet
   Make thy pathway safe and clear;
And may one thought be thine abroad
   And Celindaja's here."

AZARCO REBUKED

" Draw rein, draw rein one moment,
   And calm thy hurrying steed,
Who bounds beneath the furious spur
   That makes his flank to bleed.
Here would I, by my grief distraught,
   Upon the very spot,
Remind thee of the happy hours
   Thou, faithless, hast forgot.

When thou, upon thy prancing barb,
　Adown this street would pace,
And only at my window pause
　To gaze into my face.
At thought of all thy cruelty
　A stricken slave I pine;
My heart is burning since it touched
　That frozen breast of thine.
How many pledges didst thou give,
　To win me for thine own!
Our oaths were mutual; I am true,
　Whilst thou art recreant grown.
My eyes, they thrilled thee yesterday,
　To-day thou hast no fears;
For love is not alike two days
　Within a thousand years.
I thought thy name a pledge to me
　Of fondest hope; no less
That thou wouldst take as pledges true
　My kiss and soft caress.
What were thy glowing words but lures
　Thy victim's eyes to blind?
Now safe from treachery's hour I bear
　No rancor in my mind.
But better had I known the truth,
　When I desired to know,
And listened to thy pleading words,
　And read thy written vow.
Nay, give me no excuses vain,
　For none of them I ask,
Plead truth to her thou cozenest now—
　They'll serve thee in the task.
And if my counsel thou wilt take,
　Forget these eyes, this heart,
Forget my grief at thy neglect—
　Forget me—and depart."
Thus to the Moor, Azarco,
　The lovely Zaida cried,
And closed her lattice, overwhelmed
　With sorrow's rising tide.

He spurred his barb and rode away,
  Scattering the dust behind,
And cursed the star that made his heart
  Inconstant as the wind.

ADELIFA'S FAREWELL

Fair Adelifa tore her hair,
Her cheeks were furrowed o'er with care,
When brave Azarco she descried
Ascending the tall galley's side.
She flung the dust upon her head,
She wrung her lily hands and shed
Hot tears, and cursed the bitter day
That bore her heart's delight away.
"Thou, who my glory's captain art,
And general of my bleeding heart,
Guardian of every thought I know,
And sharer of my lot of woe;
Light that illumes my happy face,
The bliss of my soul's dwelling-place;
Why must thou disappear from me,
Thou glass wherein myself I see?
Azarco, bid me understand
What is it thou dost command—
Must I remain and wait for thee?
Ah, tedious will that waiting be.
To war thou farest, but I fear
Another war awaits thee here.
Thou thinkest in some rural nest
Thou'lt set me to be safe at rest.
Ah, if my absence cause thee pain,
My love attend thee on yon plain.
Thy valiant arms' unaided might
Shall win thee victory in the fight.
My faith, Azarco, is thy shield;
It will protect thee in the field.
Thou shalt return with victory,
For victory embarks with thee.

But thou wilt say, Azarco dear,
That women's lightness is to fear.
As with armed soldiers, so you find,
Each woman has a different mind.
And none shall ever, without thee,
Me in the dance or revel see;
Nor to the concert will I roam,
But stay in solitude at home.
The Moorish girls shall never say
I dress in robes of holiday;
'Twere vain to make the body fine
Whose soul is on the sea with thine."
With this Celinda came in sight,
Bahata's sister tall and bright;
This to an end her farewell brought,
But not her dark and anxious thought.

AZARCO'S FAREWELL

" Now saddle me the silver gray,
   The steed of noble race,
And give to me the shield of Fez,
   And my strong corslet lace;
Give me a double-headed lance,
   With points of temper fine;
And, with the casque of stubborn steel,
   That purple cap of mine.
Its plumes unite the saffron's tint
   With heron's crest of snow,
And one long spray of fluttering gray.
   Then give it e'er I go,
And I'll put on the hood of blue
   That Celin's daughter fair,
My Adelifa, best-beloved,
   Once gave to me to wear.
And the square boss of metal bring,
   That circling boughs entwine
With laurels, in whose leaves of gold
   The clustered emeralds shine.

Adonis, hastening to the hunt,
　His heavenly mistress shuns,
The mountain boars before him flee,
　And, ' Die,' the motto runs."
'Twas thus the Moor Azarco spoke,
　Just as the war begun,
To stout Almoralife
　Of Baza, Zelma's son.
Almoralife, brave and wise,
　Full many a minstrel sings,
A knight who in Granada
　Was counted with its kings.
And when they bring the boss of gold
　He heaves a thousand sighs
O'er brave Adonis and his doom,
　Who by the wild boar dies.
" O Adelifa, soul of mine,
　Rejoice, and murmur not,
Up to the end be merry,
　When worms shall be thy lot.
My day of life must needs be short,
　Thy firmness must be long;
Although thou art a woman,
　Unlike thy sex, be strong.
Be not like Venus, tho' in form
　Thou art indeed her peer,
For she forgot in absence,
　And did to death her dear.
And when alone, upon my face
　And likeness fix thine eyes,
And none admit to do me wrong,
　And thy soft heart surprise.
'Twixt sadness and repining
　Love runs his changing way,
The gay he oft makes sorrowful,
　The sorrowful makes gay.
Then, mark, love, in my portrait mark,
　The wide eyes' mute appeal,
For this enchanted painting
　Can speak and breathe and feel.

Think how those eyes shed many a tear,
  When for thy face they yearn;
And let those tears thy patience win
  To tarry my return."
At this Galvano came to say
  That ship and favoring gale
Awaited him, and all his host
  Were eager to set sail.
The Moor went forth to victory,
  He was not pleasure's slave;
His gallant heart was ever prompt
  To keep the pledge he gave.

CELINDA'S COURTESY

Azarco on his balcony
  With humble Cegri stood.
He talked, and Cegri listened
  In a sad and listless mood;
For of his own exploits he read,
  Writ in an open scroll,
But envious Cegri heard the tale
  With rage and bitter dole.
And thro' Elvira's gate, where spreads
  A prospect wide and free,
He marked how Phœbus shot his rays
  Upon the Spanish sea;
And bending to the land his eye
  To notice how the scene
Of summer had its color changed
  To black from radiant green,
He saw that, thro' the gate there passed
  A light that was not day's,
Whose splendor, like a dazzling cloud,
  Eclipsed the solar rays.
That presence changed the tint of earth,
  Drew off the dusky veil,
And turned to living verdure
  The leafage of the dale.

" Till now," Azarco said, " the scene
   Has filled my heart with pain;
'Tis freshened by Celinda's face,
   Or passion turns my brain.
Ah, well may men her beauty praise,
   For its transcendent might
Elates the human spirit,
   And fills it with delight."
And as he saw her coming in,
   The Moor his bonnet doffed,
And bowed to do her honor,
   And spoke in accents soft.
Celinda court'sied to the ground,
   Such favor was not slight,
Her kindly greeting gratified
   The fond hopes of the knight.
And glad and gloomy, each in turn,
   For such a quick success,
He checked a thousand words of love,
   That might his joy express.
And following her with eager eyes—
   " I owe thee much," said he,
" Who dost reward with such a boon
   My merest courtesy.
That favor, tho' unmerited,
   Sweet lady, shall remain
Counted among those choicest gifts
   Our reckoning cannot gain.
Its memory shall suffice to chase
   The grinding pangs of care;
And softening turn the ills of life
   To glory's guerdon rare."
On this Celinda took her leave,
   And vanished from his view,
And, thinking proudly of her smile,
   Azarco straight withdrew.

GAZUL'S DESPONDENCY

Scarce half a league from Gelva the knight dismounted stood,
Leaning upon his upright spear, and bitter was his mood.
He thought upon Celinda's curse, and Zaida's fickle mind,
" Ah, Fortune, thou to me," he cried, " hast ever proved unkind."
And from his valiant bosom burst a storm of angry sighs,
And acts and words of anguish before his memory rise.
" Celinda's loss I count as naught, nor fear her wicked will;
I were a fool, thus cursed by her, to love the lady still."
In rage from out the sod he drew his spear-head, as he spoke,
And in three pieces shivered it against a knotted oak.
He tore away the housings that 'neath his saddle hang,
He rent his lady's favor as with a lion's fang—
The silken ribbon, bright with gold, which in his crest he bore,
By loved Celinda knotted there, now loved by him no more.
He drew, as rage to madness turned, her portrait from his breast:
He spat on it, and to that face derisive jeers addressed.
" Why should I dress in robes of joy, whose heart is wounded sore,
By curses, that requite so ill the duteous love I bore?
Stripped as I am of every hope, 'tis better I go bare,
For the black mantle of my soul is but tormenting care;
I vengeance take on yonder oak, pierced by my lance's steel—
I dote, for, ah! the trees I wound, cannot, like women, feel."
He took the bridle off his steed, " Roam as thou wilt," said he.
" As I gave Zaida her release, I give release to thee."
The swift horse galloped out of sight; in melancholy mood,
The knight, unhorsed and helmetless, his lonely path pursued.

GAZUL IN LOVE

Not greater share did Mars acquire of trophies and renown,
Than great Gazul took with him from Gelva's castled town;
And when he to Sanlucar came his lady welcomed him,
His cup of happiness at last was beaded to the brim.

Alone the joyful lovers stood within a garden glade;
Amid the flowers, those happy hours fled to the evening shade.
With fingers deft Celinda wove a wreath, in which were set
The rose's rudy petals and the scented mignonette.
She plaited him a baldric, with violets circled round,
For violets are for lovers, and with this his waist she bound.
And then the flowery garland she tied upon his head,
" Thy face is delicate and fair as Ganymede's," she said;
" And if great Jove beheld thee now, he'd send his eagle down,
To take thee to the palace halls that high Olympus crown."
The brave Gazul his lady took and kissed her with a smile;
" She could not be so fair," said he, " the girl, who by her guile
Brought ruin on the Trojan realm, and set its towers afire,
As thou art, lady of my heart and queen of my desire."
" If I, indeed, seem fair to thee, then let the bridal rite
Me and the husband of my heart for evermore unite."
" Ah, mine will be the gain," he said, and kissed her with de-
    light.

CELINDA'S INCONSTANCY

Gazul, like some brave bull that stands at bay to meet his fate,
Has fled from fair Celinda's frown and reached Sanlucar's gate.
The Moor bestrides a sorrel mare, her housings are of gray,
The desperate Moor is clad in weeds that shall his grief dis-
    play.
The white and green that once he wore to sable folds give room,
Love's purple tints are now replaced by those of grief and
    gloom.
His Moorish cloak is white and blue, the blue was strewn with
    stars,
But now a covering like a cloud the starry radiance mars.
And from his head with stripes of black his silken streamers
    flow,
His bonnet blue he dyes anew in tints of grief and woe.
Alone are seen the tints of green upon his sword-belt spread,
For by that blade the blood of foes in vengeance shall be shed.
The color of the mantle which on his arm he bore
Is like the dark arena's dust when it is drenched in gore.

Black as the buskins that he wears, and black his stirrup's steel,
And red with rust of many a year the rowels at his heel.
He bears not lance or headed spear, for that which once he bore
Was shivered into splinters beside Celinda's door.
He bears a rounded target, whose quarterings display
The full moon darting through the clouds her ineffectual ray.
For though her orb be full the clouds eclipse her silver light;
The motto: " Fair but cruel, black-hearted though so bright."
And as Celinda stripped the wings which on adventure brave
Sustained his flight—no more shall plume above his helmet
wave.
'Twas noon one Wednesday when Gazul to Gelva's portal
came,
And straight he sought the market-place to join the jousting
game;
The ruler of the city looked at him with surprise,
And never lady knew the knight, so dark was his disguise.
As they had been as soft as wax, he pierced the targets through
With javelins of the hollow cane that in the vega grew;
Not one could stand before the Moor; the tilters turned and
fled,
For by his exploits was revealed the warrior's name of dread.
The lists were in confusion, but calm was on his brow,
As, lifting up his eyes to heaven, he breathed a desperate vow;
" Would God the malediction of Celinda had come true!
And the spears of my assailant had pierced my bosom through!
And that the dames who pitied me had cursed me where I
stand!
And bravely falling I became a hero of the land!
That never succor came to me, for that were rapture high
To her the angry lioness who prays that I may die!"
He spoke, he spurred his courser fleet, and started for the
plain,
And swore within Celinda's sight he'd ne'er return again.

THE BULL-FIGHT

The zambra was but ended, and now Granada's King
Abdeli called his court to sit on Vivarrambla's ring;
Of noble line the bride and groom whose nuptials bade pre-
 pare,
The struggle between valiant knights and bulls within the
 square.
And, when on the arena the mighty bull was freed,
Straight to the deadly conflict one warrior spurred his steed;
His mantle was of emerald of texture damascene,
And hope was in his folded hood as in his mantle green;
Six squires went with him to the ring beside their lord to stand;
Their livery was brilliant green, so did their lord command.
Hope was the augury of his love; hope's livery he wore;
Yet at his side each squire of his a trenchant rapier bore.
Each rapier true was black in hue and sheathed in silver ore;
At once the people knew the knight from his audacious mien—
Gazul the brave was recognized as soon as he was seen!
With graceful dignity he took his station on the sand,
And like a second Mars he seized his rapier in his hand;
With courage strong he eyed the bull, who pawed the ground
 till high
The dust of the arena was mingled with the sky.
All at the sight were terrified, and now with deadly speed,
His horns as keen as points of steel, he rushes at the steed.
The brave Gazul was on the watch, to ward the threatened
 blow,
And save his steed, and with one stroke to lay the assailant low.
The valiant bull, with lowered head advancing to the strife,
Felt from skilled hand the tempered brand pierce to his very
 life.
Deep wounded to the gory ground, where he had stoutly stood,
The hornèd warrior sank at last, bathed in his own heart's
 blood.
Still, on his ruddy couch he lay, his courage quenched at last.
At this exploit the plaudits of the assembly filled the blast;
They hailed the knight whose bravery and skill had done the
 deed,

And slain the hero of the ring, and saved his goodly steed,
And done such pleasure to the King, and to Celinda fair,
To the Queen of Spain and all her train who sat assembled
  there.

LOVERS RECONCILED

Soon as in rage Celinda had closed her lattice fast
And scorned the Moor ungrateful for his service in the past,
Her passion with reflection turns and in repentance ends;
She longs to see the Moor again and make to him amends;
For in the dance of woman's love through every mood they
  range
And those whose hearts are truest are given most to change.
And when she saw the gallant knight before the people all
Shiver his lance to splinters against her palace wall,
And when she saw his cloak of green was changed to mourn-
  ing gray,
She straightway took her mantle with silver buttons gay,
She took her hood of purple pleached with the gold brocade,
Whose fringes and whose borders were all in pearls arrayed,
She brought a cap with sapphires and emeralds bespread;
The green was badge of hope, the blue of jealous rancor dead.
With waving plumes of green and white she decked a snowy
  hood,
And armed with double heads of steel a lance of orange-
  wood—
For colors of the outer man denote the inner mood.
A border too of brilliant green around a target set,
The motto this, " 'Tis folly a true lover to forget."
And first she learned where bold Gazul was entertained that
  day,
And they told her how his coming had put off the tilters' play,
And at her pleasure-house she bade him meet her face to face;
And they told him how Celinda longed for his loved embrace,
And thrice he asked the messenger if all were not a jest,
For oft 'tis dangerous to believe the news we love the best,
For lovers' hopes are often thorns of rancor and unrest.
They told him that the words were true; and without further
  speech

The glory of his lady's eyes he sallied forth to reach.
He met her in a garden where sweet marjoram combined
With azure violets a scent that ravished every wind.
The musk and jasmine mingled in leaf and branch and flower,
Building about the lovers a cool and scented bower.
The white leaf matched her lily skin, the red his bounding
    heart.
For she was beauty's spotless queen, he valor's counterpart.
For when the Moor approached her he scarcely raised his eye,
Dazed by the expectation that she had raised so high.
Celinda with a trembling blush came forth and grasped his
    hand;
They talked of love like travellers lost in a foreign land.
Then said the Moor, " Why give me now love's sweetest paths
    to trace,
Who in thy absence only live on memories of thy face?
If thou should speak of Xerez," he said with kindling eye,
" Now take my lance, like Zaida's spouse this moment let me
    die,
And may I some day find thee in a rival's arms at rest,
And he by all thy arts of love be tenderly caressed;
Unless the Moor whose slander made me odious in thy eyes
In caitiff fraud and treachery abuse thine ear with lies."
The lady smiled, her heart was light, she felt a rapture new;
And like each flower that filled their bower the love between
    them grew,
For little takes it to revive the love that is but true;
And aided by his lady's hand he hastes her gems to don,
And on his courser's back he flings a rich caparison,
A head-stall framed of purple web and studded o'er with gold;
And purple plumes and ribbons and gems of price untold;
He clasped the lady to his heart, he whispered words of cheer,
And then took horse to Gelva to join the tilting there.

CALL TO ARMS

What time the sun in ocean sank, with myriad colors fair,
And jewels of a thousand hues tinted the clouds of air,
Brave Gazul at Acala, with all his host, drew rein—
They were four hundred noblemen, the stoutest hearts in
　Spain—
And scarcely had he reached the town when the command was
　given:
" Now let your shots, your cross-bows, sound to the vault of
　heaven!
Let kettle-drums and trumpets and clarions blend their strain;
Zulema, Tunis' King, now lands upon the coast of Spain,
And with him ride, in arms allied, Marbello and his train."

And though at night he entered no torch or lamp he hath,
For glorious Celinda is the sun upon his path;
And as he enters in the town at once the word is given:
" Now let your shots, your cross-bows, sound to the vault of
　heaven!
Let kettle-drums and trumpets and clarions blend their
　strain;
Zulema, Tunis' King, now lands upon the coast of Spain,
And with him ride, in arms allied, Marbello and his train."

Gazul dismounted from his steed and hastened to his bride;
She sat there mournful and alone and at his sight she sighed;
He flung his arms about the girl; she shrank from his embrace,
And while he looked in wonder, she hid her blushing face;
He said, " And can it be that thou should'st shrink from my
　embrace?"
Before she answered with one voice the air around was riven—
" Now let your shots, your cross-bows, sound to the vault of
　heaven!
Let kettle-drums and trumpets and clarions blend their
　strain;
Zulema, Tunis' King, now lands upon the coast of Spain,
And with him ride, in arms allied, Marbello and his train."

" Ah, traitor," she replied to him, " four months wert thou
    away,
And I in vain expected some tidings day by day."
And humbly did the Moor reply, " Do I deserve the blame?
Who drops the lance to take the pen, he does a deed of shame."
They sank into each other's arms just as the word was given:
" Now let your shots, your cross-bows, sound to the vault of
    heaven!
Let kettle-drums and trumpets and clarions blend their
    strain;
Zulema, Tunis' King, now lands upon the coast of Spain,
And with him ride, in arms allied, Marbello and his train."

GAZUL CALUMNIATED

Gazul, despairing, issues
    From high Villalba's gate,
Cursing the evil fortune
    That left him desolate.
Unmoved he in Granada saw
    What feuds between the foes
The great Abencerrajes
    And the Andallas rose.
He envied not the Moors who stood
    In favor with the King!
He did not crave the honors
    That rank and office bring.
He only cared that Zaida,
    Her soft heart led astray
By lying words of slander,
    Had flung his love away.
And thinking on her beauteous face,
    Her bearing proud and high,
The bosom of the valiant Moor
    Heaved with a mournful sigh.
" And who has brought me this disdain,
    And who my hope betrayed,
And thee, the beauteous Zaida,
    False to thy purpose made?

'And who has caused my spoils of war,
　　The palm and laurel leaf,
To wither on my forehead, bowed
　　Beneath the load of grief?
'Tis that some hearts of treachery black
　　With lies have crossed thy way,
And changed thee to a lioness,
　　By hunters brought to bay.
O tongues of malediction!
　　O slanderers of my fame!
Thieves of my knightly honor!
　　Ye lay up naught but shame.
Ye are but citadels of fraud,
　　And castles of deceit;
When ye your sentence pass, ye tread
　　The law beneath your feet.
May Allah on your cruel plots
　　Send down the wrath divine,
That ye my sufferings may feel,
　　In the same plight as mine.
And may ye learn, ye pitiless,
　　How heavy is the rod
That brings on human cruelty
　　The chastisement of God.
Ye who profess in word and deed
　　The path of truth to hold
Are viler than the nightly wolves
　　That waste the quiet fold."
So forth he rode, that Moorish knight,
　　Consumed by passion's flame,
Scorned and repulsed by Zaida,
　　The lovely Moorish dame.
Then spake he to the dancing waves
　　Of Tagus' holy tide,
" Oh, that thou hadst a tongue, to speak
　　My story far and wide!
That all might learn, who gaze on thee
　　At evening, night, or morn,
Westward to happy Portugal,
　　The sufferings I have borne."

GAZUL'S DESPAIR

Upon Sanlucar's spacious square
  The brave Gazul was seen,
Bedecked in brilliant array
  Of purple, white, and green.
The Moor was starting for the joust,
  Which many a warrior brings
To Gelva, there to celebrate
  The truce between the kings.
A fair Moor maiden he adored,
  A daughter of the brave,
Who struggled at Granada's siege;
  Granada was their grave.
And eager to accost the maid,
  He wandered round the square;
With piercing eyes he peered upon
  The walls that held the fair.
And for an hour, which seemed like years,
  He watched impatient there;
But when he saw the lady mount
  Her balcony, he thought,
That the long hour of waiting
  That vision rendered short.
Dismounting from his patient steed,
  In presence of his flame,
He fell upon his knees and kissed
  The pavement in her name.
With trembling voice he spoke to her,
  " I cannot, cannot meet,
In any joust where you are near,
  Disaster and defeat.
Of yore I lived without a heart,
  Kinsmen, or pedigree;
But all of these are mine, if thou
  Hast any thought of me.
Give me some badge, if not that thou
  Mayst recognize thy knight,
At least to deck him, give him strength,

And succor in the fight."
Celinda heard in jealous doubt;
   For some, with envious art,
Had told her that fair Zaida still
   Ruled o'er the warrior's heart.
She answered him in stormy rage:
" If in the joust thou dost engage
With such success as I desire,
And all thy broken oaths require,
Thou wilt not reach Sanlucar's square
So proud as when thou last wert there.
But there shalt meet, disconsolate,
Eyes bright with love and dark with hate.
God grant that in the deadly joust
The enemies that thou hast roused,
May hurl at thee the unparried dart
And pierce thee, liar, to the heart.
Thy corpse within thy mantle bound
May horses trail along the ground.
Thou comest thy revenge to seek,
But small the vengeance thou shalt wreak.
Thy friends shall no assistance yield;
Thy foes shall tread thee in the field;
For thou the woman-slayer, then,
Shall meet thy final fate from men.
Those damsels whom thou hast deceived
   Shall feel no pang of grief;
Their aid was malediction,
   Thy death is their relief.
The Moor was true in heart and soul,
   He thought she spake in jest.
He stood up in his stirrups,
   Her hand he would have pressed.
" Lady," he said, " remember well
That Moor of purpose fierce and fell
On whom my vengeance I did wreak
Hast felt the curse that now you speak.
And as for Zaida, I repent
That love of mine on her was spent.
Disdain of her and love of thee

Now rule my soul in company.
The flame in which for her I burned
To frost her cruelty has turned.
Three cursed years, to win her smile,
  In knightly deeds I wrought,
And nothing but her treachery
  My faithful service brought,
She flung me off without a qualm,
  Because my lot was poor,
And gave, because the wretch was rich,
  Her favor to a Moor."
Celinda as these words she heard
Impatiently the lattice barred,
And to the lover's ardent sight
It seemed that heaven was quenched in night.
A page came riding up the street,
Bringing the knight his jennets fleet,
With plumes and harness all bedight
And saddled well with housings bright;
The lance which he on entering bore
Brandished the knight with spirit sore,
  And dashed it to the wall,
And head and butt, at that proud door,
  In myriad fragments fall.
He bade them change from green to gray,
  The plumes and harness borne that day
By all the coursers of his train.
  In rage disconsolate,
He rode from Gelva, nor drew rein
  Up to Sanlucar's gate.

VENGEANCE OF GAZUL

Not Rodamont the African,
  The ruler of Argel,
And King of Zarza's southern coast,
  Was filled with rage so fell,
When for his darling Doralice
  He fought with Mandricard,

As filled the heart of bold Gazul
   When, past Sidonia's guard,
He sallied forth in arms arrayed,
   With courage high prepared
To do a deed that mortal man
   Never before had dared.
It was for this he bade them bring
   His barb and coat of mail;
A sword and dusky scabbard
   'Neath his left shoulder trail;
In Fez a Christian captive
   Had forged it, laboring
At arms of subtile temper
   As bondsman of the King.
More precious 'twas to bold Gazul
   Than all his realms could bring.
A tawny tinted *alquizel*
   Beneath his arms he wore;
And, to conceal his thoughts of blood,
   No towering spear he bore.
He started forth for Jerez,
   And hastening on his course,
Trampled the vega far and wide
   With hoof-prints of his horse.
And soon he crossed the splashing ford
   Of Guadelate's tide,
Hard by the ancient haven
   Upon the valley-side.
They gave the ford a famous name
   The waters still retain,
Santa Maria was it called,
   Since Christians conquered Spain.
The river crossed, he spurred his steed,
   Lest he might reach the gate
Of Jarez at an hour unfit,
   Too early or too late.
For Zaida, his own Zaida,
   Had scorned her lover leal,
Wedding a rich and potent Moor
   A native of Seville;

The nephew of a castellan,
  A Moorish prince of power,
Who in Seville was seneschal
  Of castle and of tower.
By this accursed bridal
  Life's treasure he had lost;
The Moor had gained the treasure,
  And now must pay the cost.
The second hour of night had rung
  When, on his gallant steed,
He passed thro' Jerez' gate resolved
  Upon a desperate deed.
And lo! to Zaida's dwelling
  With peaceful mien he came,
Pondering his bloody vengeance
  Upon that house of shame.
For he will pass the portal,
  And strike the bridegroom low;
But first must cross the wide, wide court,
  Ere he can reach his foe.
And he must pass the crowd of men,
  Who in the courtyard stand,
Lighting the palace of the Moor,
  With torches in their hand.
And Zaida in the midst comes forth,
  Her lover at her side;
He has come, amid his groomsmen,
  To take her for his bride.
And bold Gazul feels his heart bound
  With fury at the sight;
A lion's rage is in his soul,
  His brow is black as night.
But now he checks his anger,
  And gently on his steed
Draws near, with smile of greeting,
  That none may balk the deed.
And when he reached the bridal,
  Where all had taken their stand,
Upon his mighty sword-hilt
  He sudden laid his hand;

'And in a voice that all could hear
 " Base craven Moor," said he,
" The sweet, the lovely Zaida
 Shall ne'er be bride to thee.
'And count me not a traitor, I
 Defy thee face to face,
Lay hand upon thy scimitar
 If thou hast heart of grace."
'And with these words he dealt one stroke,
 A cruel stroke and true,
It reached the Moor, it struck his heart
 And pierced it through and through.
Down fell the wretch, that single stroke
 Had laid him with the dead—
" Now let him die for all his deeds,"
 The assembled people said.
Gazul made bravely his defence,
 And none could check his flight;
He dashed his rowels in his steed,
 And vanished in the night.

GAZUL AND ALBENZAIDE

" Tho' thou the lance can hurl as well
 As one a reed might cast,
Talk not of courage for thy crimes
 Thy house's honor blast.
Seek not the revel or the dance,
 Loved by each Moorish dame.
The name of valor is not thine,
 Thou hast a coward's name;
'And lay aside thy mantle fair
 Thy veil and gaberdine,
'And boast no more of gold and gems—
 Thou hast disgraced thy line.
'And see thine arms, for honor fit,
 Are cheap and fashioned plain;
Yet such that he whose name is lost
 May win it back again.

'And Albenzaide keep thy tastes
   Proportioned to thy state;
For oft from unrestrained desires
   Spring hopes infatuate.
Flee from thy thoughts, for they have wings,
   Whose light ambition lifts
Thy soul to empty altitudes,
   Where purpose veers and drifts.
Fling not thyself into the sea,
   From which the breezes blow
Now with abrupt disdain, and now
   With flattering whispers low.
For liberty once forfeited
   Is hard to be regained,
And hardest, when the forfeit falls
   On heart and hand unstained."
Thus spake Gazul, the Moorish lord
   Of fame and honor bright;
Yet, as a craven beggar,
   Fair Zaida scorned the knight.

GAZUL'S ARMS

" Now scour for me my coat of mail,
   Without delay, my page,
For, so grief's fire consumes me,
   Thy haste will be an age;
And take from out my bonnet
   The verdant plumes of pride,
Which once Azarco gave me,
   When he took to him his bride.
And in their place put feathers black,
   And write this motto there:
' Heavy as lead is now his heart,
   Oppressed with a leaden care.'
And take away the diamonds,
   And in their place insert
Black gems, that shall to all proclaim
   The deed that does me hurt,

For if thou take away those gems
  It will announce to all
The black and dismal lot that does
  Unfortuned me befall.
And give to me the buskins plain,
  Decked by no jewels' glow,
For he to whom the world is false
  Had best in mourning go.
And give to me my lance of war,
  Whose point is doubly steeled,
And, by the blood of Christians,
  Was tempered in the field.
For well I wish my goodly blade
  Once more may burnished glow;
And if I can to cleave in twain
  The body of my foe.
And hang upon my baldric,
  The best of my ten swords.
Black as the midnight is the sheath,
  And with the rest accords.
Bring me the horse the Christian slave
  Gave to me for his sire,
At Jaen; and no ransom
  But that did I require.
And even though he be not shod,
  Make haste to bring him here;
Though treachery from men I dread,
  From beasts I have no fear.
The straps with rich enamel decked
  I bid you lay aside;
And bind the rowels to my heel
  With thongs of dusky hide."
Thus spake aloud the brave Gazul,
  One gloomy Tuesday night;
Gloomy the eve, as he prepared
  For victory in the fight.
For on that day the news had come
  That his fair Moorish maid
Had wedded with his bitterest foe,

The hated Albenzaide.
The Moor was rich and powerful,
    But not of lineage high,
His wealth outweighed with one light maid
    Three years of constancy.
Touched to the heart, on hearing this,
    He stood in arms arrayed,
Nor strange that he, disarmed by love,
    'Gainst love should draw his blade.
And Venus, on the horizon,
    Had shown her earliest ray
When he Sidonia left, and straight
    To Jerez took his way.

THE TOURNAMENT

His temples glittered with the spoils and garlands of his love,
When stout Gazul to Gelvas came, the jouster's skill to prove.
He rode a fiery dappled gray, like wind he scoured the plain;
Yet all her power and mettle could a slender bit restrain;
The livery of his pages was purple, green, and red—
Tints gay as was the vernal joy within his bosom shed.
And all had lances tawny gray, and all on jennets rode,
Plumes twixt their ears; adown their flanks the costly housings flowed.
Himself upon his gallant steed carries the circling shield,
And a new device is blazoned upon its ample field.
The phœnix there is figured, on flaming nest it dies,
And from its dust and ashes again it seems to rise.
And on the margin of the shield this motto is expressed:
" 'Tis hard to hide the flames of love once kindled in the breast."
And now the ladies take their seats; each jouster mounts his steed;
From footmen and from horsemen flies fast the loaded reed.
And there appears fair Zaida, whom in a luckless day
The Moor had loved, but since, that love in loathing passed away.

Her treachery had grieved his heart, and she who did the
    wrong
Mourned with repentant heart amid that gay and happy
    throng.
And with her was Zafira, to whom her husband brings
More bliss and happiness than reign amid Granada's kings.
And when she looked at brave Gazul his deeds her grief re-
    new;
The more she sees, the more her heart is ravished at the view.
And now she blushes with desire, now grows with envy pale;
Her heart is like the changing beam that quivers in the scale.
Alminda sees the lovely dame with sudden anguish start,
And speaks with hope she may reveal the secret of her heart.
And troubled Zaida makes reply, " A sudden thought of ill
Has flashed across my mind and caused the anguish that I
    feel."
" 'Twere better," said Alminda, " to check thy fancy's flight,
For thought can rob the happiest hours of all their deep de-
    light."
Then said the maid of Xerez, " To me thou showest plain
Thou hast not felt black envy's tooth nor known what is dis-
    dain.
To know it, would thy spirit move to pity my despair,
Who writhe and die from agony, in which thou hast no share."
Zafira seized the lady's hand, and silence fell around,
As mixed in loud confusion brushed the jousters to the
    ground.
In came the Berber tribesmen, in varied cloaks arrayed;
They ranged themselves in companies against the palisade.
The sound of barbarous trumpets rang, the startled horses
    reared,
And snort and neigh and tramp of hoofs on every side was
    heard,
Then troop meets troop, and valiant hearts the mimic fight
    pursue;
They hurl their javelins o'er the sand and pierce the bucklers
    through.
Long time the battling hosts contend, until that festive day,
The shout, the clash, the applauding cry, in silence die away.

They fain had prayed that time himself would stop Apollo's
    car.
They hate to see the sunset gloom, the rise of evening's star.
And even when the sun is set, he who a foe discerns,
With no less vigor to his targe the loaded javelin turns,
The onset joined, each lance discharged, the judge's voice is
    heard;
He bids the heralds sound a truce, and the wide lists are
    cleared.

ABENUMEYA'S LAMENT

The young Abenumeya, Granada's royal heir,
Was brave in battle with his foe and gallant with the fair.
By lovely Felisarda his heart had been ensnared,
The daughter of brave Ferri, the captain of the guard.
He through the vega of Genil bestrode his sorrel steed,
Alone, on melancholy thoughts his anxious soul to feed,
The tints that clothed the landscape round were gloomy as
    the scene
Of his past life, wherein his lot had naught but suffering been.
His mantle hue was of iron gray bestrewn with purple flowers,
Which bloomed amid distress and pain, like hope of happier
    hours.
And on his cloak were columns worked, (his cloak was saffron
    hued,)
To show that dark suspicion's fears had tried his fortitude;
His shield was blazoned with the moon, a purple streak above,
To show that fears of fickleness are ever born with love.
He bore an azure pennant 'neath the iron of his spear,
To show that lovers oft go wrong deceived by jealous fear.
The hood he wore was wrought of gold and silk of crimson
    clear;
His bonnet crest was a heron plume with an emerald stone
    beneath;
And under all a motto ran, " Too long a hope is death."
He started forth in such array, but armed from head to heel
With tempered blade and dagger and coat of twisted steel.
And hangling low at his saddle-bow was the helmet for his
    head;

And as he journeyed on his way the warrior sighed and said:
"O Felisarda, dearest maid, him in thy memory keep
Who in his soul has writ thy name in letters dark and deep.
Think that for thee in coat of mail he ever rides afield,
In his right hand the spear must stand, his left must grasp the
    shield.
And he must skirmish in the plain and broil of battle brave,
And wounded be, for weapons ne'er from jealousy can save."
And as he spoke the lonely Moor from out his mantle's fold
With many a sigh, that scorched the air, a lettered page un-
    rolled.
He tried in vain to read it but his eyes with tears were blind,
And mantling clouds of sorrow hid the letters from his mind.
The page was moistened by the tears that flowed in plenteous
    tide,
But by the breath of sighs and sobs the softened page was
    dried.
Fresh wounds he felt at sight of it, and when the cause he
    sought,
His spirit to Granada flew upon the wings of thought.
He thought of Albaicin, the palace of the dame,
With its gayly gilded capitals and its walls of ancient fame.
And the garden that behind it lay in which the palm was seen
Swaying beneath the load of fruit its coronet of green.
"O mistress of my soul," he said, "who callest me thine own,
How easily all bars to bliss thy love might trample down!
But time, that shall my constancy, thy fickleness will show,
The world shall then my steadfast heart, thy tongue of
    treachery know.
Woe worth the day when, for thy sake, I fair Granada sought,
These anxious doubts may cloud my brow, they cannot guard
    thy thought.
My foes increase, thy cruelty makes absence bitterer still,
But naught can shake my constancy, and none can do me ill."
On this from Alpujarra the tocsin sounded high.
He rushed as one whose life is staked to save the maid or die.

THE DESPONDENT LOVER

He leaned upon his sabre's hilt,
  He trod upon his shield,
Upon the ground he threw the lance
  That forced his foes to yield.
His bridle hung at saddle-bow,
  And, with the reins close bound,
His mare the garden entered free
  To feed and wander round.
Upon a flowering almond-tree
  He fixed an ardent gaze;
Its leaves were withered with the wind
  That flowers in ruin lays.
Thus in Toledo's garden park,
  Did Abenamar wait,
Who for fair Galliana
  Watched at the palace gate.
The birds that clustered on the towers
  Spread out their wings to fly,
And from afar his lady's veil
  He saw go floating by.
And at this vision of delight,
  Which healed his spirit's pain,
The exiled Moor took courage,
  And hope returned again.
" O Galliana, best beloved,
  Whom art thou waiting now?
And what has treacherous rendered
  My fortune and thy vow?
Thou swearedst I should be thine own,
  Yet 'twas but yesterday
We met, and with no greeting
  Thou wentest on thy way.
Then, in my silence of distress,
  I wandered pondering—
If this is what to-day has brought,
  What will to-morrow bring?
Happy the Moor from passion free,

In peace or turmoil born,
Who without pang of hate or love,
Can slumber till the morn.
O almond-tree, thou provest
That the expected hours
Of bliss may often turn to bane,
As fade thy dazzling flowers.
A mournful image art thou
Of all that lays me low,
And on my shield I'll bear thee
As blazon of my woe.
For thou dost bloom in many a flower,
Till blasted by the wind,
And 'tis of thee this word is true—
' The season was not kind.' "
He spoke and on his courser's head
He slipped the bridle rein,
And while he curbed his gentle steed
He could not curb his pain,
And to Ocana took his course,
O'er Tagus' verdant plain.

LOVE AND JEALOUSY

" Unless thou wishest in one hour
Thine April hope shouldst blighted be,
Oh, tell me, Tarfe, tell me true,
How I may Zaida chance to see.
I mean the foreigner, the wife
New wedded, her with golden hair,
And for each lock a charm besides
She counts—for she is passing fair.
Her, whom the Moorish nobles all
To heaven in their laudation raise,
Till the fine ladies of the land
Are left to languish in dispraise.
The mosque I visit every day,
And wait to see her come in sight;
I wait to see her, where the rout
And revel lengthen out the night.

However, cost me what it may,
  I cannot meet the lovely dame.
Ah, now my eyes are veiled in tears,
  Sure witness of my jealous flame.
And tell me, Tarfe, that my rage
  Has cause enough, for since I've been
Granada's guest (and would to God
  Granada I had never seen!)
My lord forsakes me every night,
  Nor till the morning comes again;
He shuns as painful my caress,
  My very presence brings him pain;
Little indeed he recks of me,
  If only he may elsewhere reign.
For if we in the garden meet,
  Or if we in the chamber be,
His actions his estrangement prove,
  He has not even words for me.
'And if I say to him, ' My life!'
  He answers me, ' My dearest dear,'
Yet with a coldness that congeals
  My very heart with sudden fear.
And all the while I strive to make
  His soul reveal a traitorous thought,
He turns his back on me, as if
  To him my trembling fear was naught.
And when about his neck I cling,
  He drops his eyes and bows his face,
As if, from thought of other arms
  He longed to slip from my embrace.
His bosom heaves with discontent,
  Deep as from hell the sigh is wrenched;
My heart with dark suspicion beats,
  And all my happiness is quenched.
And if I ask of him the cause,
  He says the cause in me is found;
That I am vain, the rover I,
  And to another's bosom bound.
As if, since I have known his love,
  I at the window show my face,

Or take another's hand in mine,
    Or seek the bull-ring, joust, or race;
Or if my footsteps have been found
    To wander a suspected place,
The prophet's curse upon me fall,
    Unless to keep the nuptial pact
And serve the pleasure of my lord.
    I kept the Koran's law exact!
But wherefore should I waste the time
    These tedious questions to recall?
Thou knowest the chase on which he hies,
    And yet in silence hidest all.
Nay, swear not—I will naught believe;
    Thine oaths are but a fowler's net,
And woe betide the dame who falls
    Into the snare that thou hast set.
For men are traitors one and all;
    And all their promises betray;
Like letters on the water writ,
    They vanish, when love's fires decay.
For to fulfil thy promise fair,
    What hours thou hast the whole day long,
What chances on the open road,
    Or in the house when bolts are strong.
O God! but what a thought is this?
    I strangle, in the sudden thrall
Of this sharp pang of agony,
    Oh, hold me, Tarfe, lest I fall."
Thus Adelifa weeping cried
    At thought of Abenamar's quest:
In Moorish Tarfe's arms she fell,
    And panting lay upon his breast.

THE CAPTIVE OF TOLEDO

Upon the loftiest mountain height
   That rises in its pride,
And sees its summits mirrored
   In Tagus' crystal tide,
The banished Abenamar,
   Bound by a captive chain,
Looks on the high-road to Madrid
   That seams the dusty plain.
He measures, with his pining eyes,
   The stretching hills that stand
Between his place of banishment
   And his sweet native land.
His sighs and tears of sorrow
   No longer bear restraint,
And thus in words of anguish
   He utters his complaint:
"Oh, dismal is the exile
   That wrings the heart with woes
And locks the lips in silence,
   Amid unfeeling foes.

O road of high adventure,
   That leadest many a band
To yon ungrateful country where
   My native turrets stand,
The country that my valor
   Did oft with glory crown,
The land that lets me languish here,
   Who won for her renown.
Thou who hast succored many a knight,
   Hast thou no help for me,
Who languish on Toledo's height
   In captive misery?
'Tis on thy world-wide chivalry
   I base my word of blame,
'Tis that I love thee most of all,
   Thy coldness brings me shame.

Oh, dismal is the exile,
  That wrings my heart with woes,
And locks my lips in silence
  Among unfeeling foes.

The warden of fierce Reduan
  With cruelty more deep
That that of a hidalgo,
  Has locked this prison keep;
And on this frontier set me,
  To pine without repose,
To watch, from dawn to sunset,
  Over his Christian foes.
Here like a watch-tower am I set
  For Santiago's lord,
And for a royal mistress
  Who breaks her plighted word.
And when I cry with anguish
  And seek in song relief,
With threats my life is threatened,
  Till silence cloak my grief.
Oh, dismal is the exile,
  That wrings my heart with woes,
And locks my lips in silence
  Among unfeeling foes.

And when I stand in silence,
  Me dumb my jailers deem,
And if I speak, in gentle words,
  They say that I blaspheme.
Thus grievously perverting
  The sense of all I say,
Upon my lips the raging crowd
  The gag of silence lay.
Thus heaping wrong on wrong my foes
  Their prisoner impeach,
Until the outrage of my heart
  Deprives my tongue of speech.
And while my word the passion
  Of my sad heart betrays,

My foes are all unconscious
   Of what my silence says.
Now God confound the evil judge
   Who caused my misery,
And had no heart of pity
   To soften his decree.
Oh, dismal is the exile,
   That wrings my heart with woes,
And locks my lips in silence
   Among unfeeling foes.

THE BLAZON OF ABENAMAR

By gloomy fortune overcast,
   Vassal of one he held in scorn,
Complaining of the wintry world,
   And by his lady left forlorn,
The wretched Abenamar mourned,
   Because his country was unkind,
Had brought him to a lot of woe,
   And to a foreign home resigned.
A stranger Moor had won the throne,
   And in Granada sat in state.
Many the darlings of his soul
   He claimed with love insatiate,
He, foul in face, of craven heart,
   Had won the mistress of the knight;
Her blooming years of beauteous youth
   Were Abenamar's own by right.
But royal favor had decreed
   A foreign tyrant there should reign,
For many a galley owned him lord
   And master, in the seas of Spain.
Oh, haply 'twas that Zaida's self,
   Ungrateful like her changing sex,
Had chosen this emir, thus in scorn
   Her Abenamar's soul to vex.
This was the thought that turned to tears
   The eyes of the desponding knight,

As on his sufferings past he thought,
   His labors and his present plight;
His hopes, to disappointment turned;
   His wealth, now held in alien hands,
His agony o'er love betrayed,
   Lost honor, confiscated lands.
And as his loyalty had met
   Such ill requital from the King,
He called his page and bade him straight
   A limner deft before him bring.
For he would have him paint at large,
   In color, many a new device
And write his sufferings on his shield.
   No single blazon would suffice.
And first a green field parched and seared;
   A coal, in myriad blazes burned,
And like his ardent hopes of yore,
   At length to dust and ashes turned.
And then a miser, rich in gold,
   Who locks away some jewel bright,
For fear the thief a gem may steal,
   Which yet can yield him no delight.
A fair Adonis done to death
   Beneath the wild boar's cruel tusk.
A wintry dawn on pallid skies,
   A summer's day that turns to dusk.
A lovely garden green and fair
   Ravaged and slashed by strokes of steel;
Or wasted in its trim parterres
   And trampled by the common heel.
So spake the brave heart-broken Moor;
   Until his tears and struggling sighs
Turned to fierce rage; the painting then
   He waited for with eager eyes.
He asks that one would fetch a steed,
   Of his good mare no more he recks,
For womankind have done him wrong,
   And she is woman in her sex.
The plumes of yellow, blue, and white
   From off his bonnet brim he tears,

He will no longer carry them;
    They are the colors Zaida wears.
He recks no more of woman's love,
    His city now he bids farewell,
And swears he will no more return
    Nor in Granada seek to dwell.

WOMAN'S FICKLENESS

A stout and valorous gentleman,
    Granada knew his worth,
And rich with many a spoil of love,
    Went Abenamar forth.
Upon his bonnet, richly dyed,
    He bore a lettered scroll,
It ran, " 'Tis only love that makes
    The solace of my soul."
His bonnet and his brow were hid
    Beneath a hood of green,
And plumes of violet and white
    Above his head were seen.
And 'twixt the tassel and the crown
    An emerald circlet shone.
The legend of the jewel said,
    " Thou art my hope alone."
He rode upon a dappled steed
    With housings richly dight,
And at his left side clanking hung
    A scimitar of might.
And his right arm was sleeved in cloth
    Of tawny lion's hue,
And at his lance-head, lifted high,
    A Turkish pennon flew.
And when he reached Daraja's camp
    He saw Daraja stand
Beside his own perfidious love,
    And clasp her by the hand.
He made to her the wonted sign,
    Then lingered for a while,

For jealous anguish filled his heart
  To see her tender smile.
He spurred his courser to the blood;
  One clattering bound he took,
The Moorish maiden turned to him.
  Ah, love was in her look!
Ah, well he saw his hopeless fate,
  And in his jealous mood
The heart that nothing feared in fight
  Was whelmed in sorrow's flood.
"O false and faithless one," he said,
  "What is it that I view?
Thus the foreboding of my soul
  I see at last come true;
Shame that a janizary vile,
  Of Christian creed and race,
A butt of bright Alhambra's feasts,
  Has taken now my place.
Where is the love thou didst avow,
  The pledge, the kiss, the tear,
And all the tender promises
  Thou whisperedst in my ear?
Thou, frailer than the withered reed,
  More changeful than the wind,
More thankless than the hardest heart
  In all of womankind;
I marvel not at what I see,
  Nor yet for vengeance call;
For thou art woman to the core,
  And in that name is all."
The gallant Moor his courser checked,
  His cheek with anger burned,
Men saw, that all his gallant mien
  To gloom and rage was turned.

KING JUAN

" Abenamar, Abenamar," said the monarch to the knight,
" A Moor art thou of the Moors, I trow, and the ladies' fond
delight,
And on the day when first you lay upon your mother's breast,
On land and sea was a prodigy, to the Christians brought un-
rest;
The sea was still as a ruined mill and the winds were hushed
to rest.
And the broad, broad moon sank down at noon, red in the
stormy west.
If thus thou wert born thou well mayst scorn to ope those lips
of thine,
That out should fly a treacherous lie, to meet a word of mine."
" I have not lied," the Moor replied, and he bowed his haughty
head
Before the King whose wrath might fling his life among the
dead.
" I would not deign with falsehood's stain my lineage to betray;
Tho' for the truth my life, in sooth, should be the price I pay.
I am son and squire of a Moorish sire, who with the Christians
strove,
And the captive dame of Christian name was his fair wedded
love;
And I a child from that mother mild, who taught me at her
knee
Was ever told to be true and bold with a tongue that was frank
and free,
That the liar's art and the caitiff heart would lead to the house
of doom;
And still I must hear my mother dear, for she speaks to me
from the tomb.
Then give me my task, O King, and ask what question thou
mayst choose;
I will give to you the word that is true, for why should I refuse? "
" I give you grace for your open face, and the courteous words
you use.

What castles are those on the hill where grows the palm-tree
    and the pine?
They are so high that they touch the sky, and with gold their
    pinnacles shine."
" In the sunset's fire there glisten, sire, Alhambra's tinted tiles;
And somewhat lower Alijire's tower upon the vega smiles,
And many a band of subtile hand has wrought its pillared
    aisles.
The Moor whose thought and genius wrought those works for
    many moons
Received each day a princely pay—five hundred gold doub-
    loons—
Each day he left his labor deft, his guerdon was denied;
Nor less he lost than his labor cost when he his hand applied.
And yonder I see the Generalifé with its orchard green and
    wide;
There are growing there the apple and pear that are Granada's
    pride.
There shadows fall from the soaring wall of high Bermeja's
    tower;
It has flourished long as a castle strong, the seat of the Soldan's
    power."
The King had bent and his ear had lent to the words the war-
    rior spoke,
And at last he said, as he raised his head before the crowd of
    folk:
" I would take thee now with a faithful vow, Granada for my
    bride,
King Juan's Queen would hold, I ween, a throne and crown of
    pride;
That very hour I would give thee dower that well would suit
    thy will;
Cordova's town should be thine own, and the mosque of proud
    Seville.
Nay, ask not, King, for I wear the ring of a faithful wife and
    true;
Some graceful maid or a widow arrayed in her weeds is the
    wife for you,
And close I cling to the Moorish King who holds me to his
    breast,
For well I ween it can be seen that of all he loves me best."

ABENAMAR'S JEALOUSY

Alhambra's bell had not yet pealed
Its morning note o'er tower and field;
Barmeja's bastions glittered bright,
O'ersilvered with the morning light;
When rising from a pallet blest
With no refreshing dews of rest,
For slumber had relinquished there
His place to solitary care,
Brave Abenamar pondered deep
How lovers must surrender sleep.
And when he saw the morning rise,
While sleep still sealed Daraja's eyes,
Amid his tears, to soothe his pain,
He sang this melancholy strain:
 " The morn is up,
  The heavens alight,
 My jealous soul
  Still owns the sway of night.
Thro' all the night I wept forlorn,
Awaiting anxiously the morn;
And tho' no sunlight strikes on me,
My bosom burns with jealousy.
The twinkling starlets disappear;
Their radiance made my sorrow clear;
The sun has vanished from my sight,
Turned into water is his light;
What boots it that the glorious sun
From India his course has run,
To bring to Spain the gleam of day,
If from my sight he hides away?
 The morn is up,
  The heavens are bright,
 My jealous soul
  Still owns the sway of night."

ADELIFA'S JEALOUSY

Fair Adelifa sees in wrath, kindled by jealous flames,
Her Abenamar gazed upon by the kind Moorish dames.
And if they chance to speak to him, or take him by the hand,
She swoons to see her own beloved with other ladies stand.
When with companions of his own, the bravest of his race,
He meets the bull within the ring, and braves him to his face,
Or if he mount his horse of war, and sallying from his tent
Engages with his comrades in tilt or tournament,
She sits apart from all the rest, and when he wins the prize
She smiles in answer to his smile and devours him with her
eyes.
And in the joyous festival and in Alhambra's halls,
She follows as he treads the dance at merry Moorish balls.
And when the tide of battle is rising o'er the land,
And he leaves his home, obedient to his honored King's com-
mand,
With tears and lamentation she sees the warrior go
With arms heroic to subdue the proud presumptuous foe.
Though 'tis to save his country's towers he mounts his fiery
steed
She has no cheerful word for him, no blessing and godspeed;

And were there some light pretext to keep him at her side,
In chains of love she'd bind him there, whate'er the land be-
tide.
Or, if 'twere fair that dames should dare the terrors of the
fight,
She'd mount her jennet in his train and follow with delight.
For soon as o'er the mountain ridge his bright plume dis-
appears,
She feels that in her heart the jealous smart that fills her eyes
with tears.
Yet when he stands beside her and smiles beneath her gaze,
Her cheek is pale with passion pure, though few the words
she says.
Her thoughts are ever with him, and they fly the mountain o'er
When in the shaggy forest he hunts the bristly boar.

In vain she seeks the festal scene 'mid dance and merry song,
Her heart for Abenamar has left that giddy throng.
For jealous passion after all is no ignoble fire,
It is the child of glowing love, the shadow of desire.
Ah! he who loves with ardent breast and constant spirit must
Feel in his inmost bosom lodged the arrows of distrust.
And as the faithful lover by his loved one's empty seat
Knows that the wind of love may change e'er once again they
    meet,
So to this sad foreboding do fancied griefs appear
As he who has most cause to love has too most cause for fear.
And once, when placid evening was mellowing into night,
The lovely Adelifa sat with her darling knight;
And then the pent-up feeling from out her spirit's deeps
Rose with a storm of heavy sighs and trembled on her lips:
" My valiant knight, who art, indeed, the whole wide world
    to me,
Clear mirror of victorious arms and rose of chivalry,
Thou terror of thy valorous foe, to whom all champions yield,
The rampart and the castle of fair Granada's field,
In thee the armies of the land their bright example see,
And all their hopes of victory are founded upon thee;
And I, poor loving woman, have hope in thee no less,
For thou to me art life itself, a life of happiness.
Yet, in this anxious trembling heart strange pangs of fear arise,
Ah, wonder not if oft you see from out these faithful eyes
The tears in torrents o'er my cheek, e'en in thy presence flow.
Half prompted by my love for thee and half by fears of woe,
These eyes are like alembics, and when with tears they fill
It is the flame of passion that does that dew distil.
And what the source from which they flow, but the sorrow and
    the care
That gather in my heart like mist, and forever linger there.
And when the flame is fiercest and love is at its height,
The waters rise to these fond eyes, and rob me of my sight,
For love is but a lasting pain and ever goes with grief,
And only at the spring of tears the heart can drink relief.
Thus fire and love and fear combined bring to my heart dis-
    tress,
With jealous rage and dark distrust alarm and fitfulness.

These rage within my bosom; they torment me till I'd weep.
By day and night without delight a lonely watch I keep.
By Allah, I beseech thee, if thou art true to me,
That when the Moorish ladies turn round and gaze on thee,
Thou wilt not glance again at them nor meet their smiling eye,
Or else, my Abenamar, I shall lay me down and die.
For thou art gallant, fair, and good; oh, soothe my heart's
    alarms,
And be as tender in thy love as thou art brave in arms.
And as they yield to thee the prize for valor in the field
Oh, show that thou wilt pity to thy loving lady yield."
Then Abenamar, with a smile, a kiss of passion gave.
" If it be needful," he replied, " to give the pledge you crave
To tell thee, Adelifa, that thou art my soul's delight
And lay my inmost bosom bare before thy anxious sight,
The bosom on whose mirror shines thy face in lines of light,
Here let me ope the secret cell that thou thyself may see,
The altar and the blazing lamp that always burn for thee.
And if perchance thou art not thus released from torturing
    care,
Oh, see the faith, the blameless love that wait upon thee there.
And if thou dost imagine I am a perjured knight,
I pray that Allah on my head may call down bane and blight,
And when into the battle with the Christian I go
I pray that I may perish by the lances of the foe;
And when I don my armor for the toils of the campaign,
That I may never wear the palm of victory again,
But as a captive, on a shore far from Granada, pine,
While the freedom that I long to have may never more be
    mine.
Yes, may my foes torment me in that sad hour of need;
My very friends, for their own ends, prove worthless as a reed.
My kin deny, my fortune fly, and, on my dying day,
My very hopes of Paradise in darkness pass away.
Or if I live in freedom to see my love once more,
May I meet the fate which most I hate, and at my palace door
Find that some caitiff lover has won thee for his own,
And turn to die, of mad despair, distracted and alone.
Wherefore, my life, my darling wife, let all thy pain be cured;
Thy trust in my fidelity be from this hour assured.

No more those pearly tears of thine fall useless in the dust
No more the jealous fear distract thy bosom with mistrust.
Believe me by the oath I swear my heart I here resign,
And all I have of love and care are, Adelifa, thine.
Believe that Abenamar would his own life betray
If he had courage thus to throw life's choicest gem away."
Then Adelifa smiled on him and at the words he said,
Upon his heaving bosom her blushing cheek she laid.
And from that hour each jealous thought far from her mind
    she thrust
And confidence returned again in place of dark distrust.

FUNERAL OF ABENAMAR

The Moors of haughty Gelves have changed their gay attire.
The caftan and the braided cloak, the brooch of twisted wire,
The gaudy robes, the mantles of texture rich and rare,
The fluttering veils and tunic bright the Moors no longer wear.
And wearied is their valorous strength, their sinewy arms
    hang down;
No longer in their lady's sight they struggle for the crown.
Whether their loves are absent or glowing in their eyes,
They think no more of jealous feud nor smile nor favor prize;
For love himself seems dead to-day amid that gallant train
And the dirge beside the bier is heard and each one joins the
    strain,
And silently they stand in line arrayed in mourning black
For the dismal pall of Portugal is hung on every back.
And their faces turned toward the bier where Abenamar lies,
The men his kinsmen silent stand, amid the ladies' cries
And thousand thousands ask and look upon the Moorish
    knight,
By his coat of steel they weeping kneel, then turn them from
    the sight.
And some proclaim his deeds of fame, his spirit high and brave,
And the courage of adventure that had brought him to the
    grave.
Some say that his heroic soul pined with a jealous smart,
That disappointment and neglect had broke that mighty heart;
That all his ancient hopes gave way beneath the cloud of grief,

Until his green and youthful years were withered like a leaf;
And he is wept by those he loved, by every faithful friend,
And those who slandered him in life speak evil to the end.
They found within his chamber where his arms of battle hung
A parting message written all in the Moorish tongue:
"Dear friends of mine, if ever in Gelves I should die,
I would not that in foreign soil my buried ashes lie.
But carry me, and dig my grave upon mine own estate,
And raise no monument to me my life to celebrate,
For banishment is not more dire where evil men abound,
Than where home smiles upon you, but the good are never
    found."

BALLAD OF ALBAYALDOS

Three mortal wounds, three currents red,
    The Christian spear
Has oped in head and thigh and head—
    Brave Albayaldos feels that death is near.

The master's hand had dealt the blow,
    And long had been
And hard the fight; now in his heart's blood low
    He wallows, and the pain, the pain is keen.

He raised to heaven his streaming face
    And low he said:
"Sweet Jesus, grant me by thy grace,
    Unharmed to make this passage to the dead.

"Oh, let me now my sins recount,
    And grant at last
Into thy presence I may mount,
    And thou, dear mother, think not of my past.

"Let not the fiend with fears affright
    My trembling soul;
Though bitter, bitter is the night
    Whose darkling clouds this moment round me roll.

" Had I but listened to your plea,
　　I ne'er had met
Disaster; though this life be lost to me,
　　Let not your ban upon my soul be set.

" In him, in him alone I trust,
　　To him I pray,
Who formed this wretched body from the dust.
　　He will redeem me in the Judgment Day.

" And Muza, one last service will I ask,
　　Dear friend of mine :
Here, where I died, be it thy pious task
　　To bury me beneath the tall green pine.

" And o'er my head a scroll indite, to tell
　　How, on this sod,
Fighting amid my valiant Moors, I fell.
　　And tell King Chico how I turned to God,

" And longed to be a Christian at the last,
　　And sought the light,
So that the accursed Koran could not cast
　　My soul to suffer in eternal night."

THE NIGHT RAID OF REDUAN

Two thousand are the Moorish knights that 'neath the banner
　　stand
Of mighty Reduan, as he starts in ravage thro' the land.
With pillage and with fire he wastes the fields and fruitful
　　farms,
And thro' the startled border-land is heard the call to arms;
By Jaen's towers his host advance and, like a lightning flash,
Ubeda and Andujar can see his horsemen dash,
　　　While in Baeza every bell
　　　Does the appalling tidings tell,
　　　　" Arm! Arm!"
　　　Rings on the night the loud alarm.

So silently they gallop, that gallant cavalcade,
The very trumpet's muffled tone has no disturbance made.
It seems to blend with the whispering sound of breezes on
    their way,
The rattle of their harness and the charger's joyous neigh.
But now from hill and turret high the flaming cressets stream
And watch-fires blaze on every hill and helm and hauberk
    gleam.
From post to post the signal along the border flies
And the tocsin sounds its summons and the startled burghers
    rise,
   While in Baeza every bell
    Does the appalling tidings tell,
    " Arm! Arm! "
    Rings on the night the loud alarm.

Ah, suddenly that deadly foe has fallen upon the prey,
Yet stoutly rise the Christians and arm them for the foe,
And doughty knights their lances seize and scour their coats
    of mail,
The soldier with his cross-bow comes and the peasant with his
    flail.
And Jaen's proud hidalgos, Andujar's yeomen true,
And the lords of towered Ubeda the pagan foes pursue;
And valiantly they meet the foe nor turn their backs in flight,
And worthy do they show themselves of their fathers' deeds
    of might,
   While in Baeza every bell
    Does the appalling tidings tell,
    " Arm! Arm! "
    Rings on the night the loud alarm.

The gates of dawn are opened and sunlight fills the land,
The Christians issuing from the gates in martial order stand,
They close in fight, and paynim host and Christian knights of
    Spain,
Not half a league from the city gate, are struggling on the
    plain.
The din of battle rises like thunder to the sky,
From many a crag and forest the thundering echoes fly,

'And there is sound of clashing arms, of sword and rattling
    steel,
Moorish horns, the fife and drum, as the scattering squadrons
    reel,
'And the dying moan and the wounded shriek for the hurt that
    none can heal,
        While in Baeza every bell
           Does the appalling tidings tell,
           " Arm! Arm! "
        Rings on the night the loud alarm.

SIEGE OF JAEN

Now Reduan gazes from afar on Jaen's ramparts high,
And tho' he smiles in triumph yet fear is in his eye,
And vowed has he, whose courage none charged with a de-
    fault,
That he would climb the ramparts and take it by assault,
Yet round the town the towers and walls the city's streets im-
    pale,
And who of all his squadrons that bastion can scale?
He pauses until one by one his hopes have died away,
And his soul is filled with anguish and his face with deep dis-
    may.
He marks the tall escarpment, he measures with his eye
The soaring towers above them that seem to touch the sky.
Height upon height they mount to heaven, while glittering
    from afar
Each cresset on the watch-towers burns like to a baleful star.
His eyes and heart are fixed upon the rich and royal town,
And from his eye the tear of grief, a manly tear, flows down.
His bosom heaves with sighs of grief and heavy discontent,
As to the royal city he makes his sad lament:
" Ah, many a champion have I lost, fair Jaen, at thy gate,
Yet lightly did I speak of thee with victory elate,
The prowess of my tongue was more than all that I could do,
And my word outstripped the lance and sword of my squadron
    strong and true.
And yet I vowed with courage rash thy turrets I would bring
To ruin and thy subjects make the captives of my King.

That in one night my sword of might, before the morrow's sun,
Would do for thy great citadel what centuries have not done.
I pledged my life to that attempt, and vowed that thou shouldest
　　fall,
Yet now I stand in impotence before thy castle tall.
For well I see, before my might shall win thee for my King,
That thou, impregnable, on me wilt rout and ruin bring,
Ah, fatal is the hasty tongue that gives such quick consent,
And he who makes the hasty vow in leisure must repent.
Ah! now too late I mourn the word that sent me on this quest,
For I see that death awaits me here whilst thou livest on at rest,
For I must enter Jaen's gates a conqueror or be sent
Far from Granada's happy hills in hopeless banishment;
But sorest is the thought that I to Lindaraja swore:
If Jaen should repulse me I'd return to her no more;
No more a happy lover would I linger at her side,
Until Granada's warrior host had humbled Jaen's pride."
Then turning to his warriors, the Moorish cavalier
Asks for their counsel and awaits their answer while with fear.
Five thousand warriors tried and true the Moors were stand-
　　ing near,
All armed with leathern buckler, all armed with sword and
　　spear.
"The place," they answer, "is too strong, by walls too high
　　'tis bound,
Too many are the watch-towers that circle it around.
The knights and proud hidalgos who on the wall are seen,
Their hearts are bold, their arms are strong, their swords and
　　spears are keen.
Disaster will be certain as the rising of the day,
And victory and booty are a slippery prize," they say,
"It would be wise in this emprise the conflict to forego;
Not all the Moors Granada boasts could lay proud Jaen low."

THE DEATH OF REDUAN

He shrank not from his promise, did Reduan the brave,
The promise to Granada's King with daring high he gave;
And when the morning rose and lit the hills with ruddy glow,
He marshalled forth his warriors to strike a final blow.
With shouts they hurry to the walls, ten thousand fighting
    men—
Resolved to plant the crescent on the bulwarks of Jaen.
The bugle blast upon the air with clarion tone is heard,
The burghers on the city wall reply with scoffing word;
And like the noise of thunder the clattering squadrons haste,
And on his charger fleet he leads his army o'er the waste.
In front of his attendants his march the hero made,
He tarried not for retinue or clattering cavalcade,
And they who blamed the rash assault with weak and coward
    minds
Deserted him their leader bold or loitered far behind.
And now he stands beneath the wall and sees before him rise
The object of the great campaign, his valor's priceless prize;
He dreams one moment that he holds her subject to his arms,
He dreams that to Granada he flies from war's alarms,
Each battlement he fondly eyes, each bastion grim and tall,
And in fancy sees the crescents rise above the Christian wall.
But suddenly an archer has drawn his bow of might,
And suddenly the bolt descends in its unerring flight,
Straight to the heart of Reduan the fatal arrow flies,
The gallant hero struck to death upon the vega lies.
And as he lies, from his couch of blood, in melancholy tone,
Thus to the heavens the hero stout, though fainting, makes his
    moan,
And ere his lofty soul in death forth from its prison breaks,
Brave Reduan a last farewell of Lindaraja takes:
" Ah, greater were the glory had it been mine to die,
Not thus among the Christians and hear their joyful cry,
But in that happy city, reclining at thy feet,
Where thou with kind and tender hands hast wove my wind-
    ing-sheet.
Ah! had it been my fate once more to gaze upon thy face,

And love and pity in those eyes with dying glance to trace,
Altho' a thousand times had death dissolved this mortal frame,
Soon as thy form before me in radiant beauty came,
A thousand times one look of thine had given me back my
    breath,
And called thy lover to thy side even from the gate of death.
What boots it, Lindaraja, that I, at Jaen's gate,
That unsurrendered city, have met my final fate?
What boots it, that this city proud will ne'er the Soldan own,
For thee and not for Jaen this hour I make my moan;
I weep for Lindaraja, I weep to think that she
May mourn a hostage and a slave in long captivity.
But worse than this that some proud Moor will take thee to
    his heart,
And all thy thoughts of Reduan new love may bid depart.
And dwelling on thy beauty he will deem it better far,
To win fair Lindaraja than all the spoils of war,
Yet would I pray if Mahomet, whose servant I have been,
Should ever from the throne of God look on this bloody scene,
And deem it right to all my vows requital fit to make,
And for my valor who attacked the town I could not take,
That he would make thy constancy as steadfast as the tower
Of Jaen's mighty fortress, that withstood the Moorish power;
Now as my life be ebbing fast, my spirit is oppressed,
And Reduan the warrior bold is sinking to his rest,
Oh, may my prayers be answered, if so kind heaven allow,
And may the King forgive me for the failure of my vow,
And, Lindaraja, may my soul, when it has taken its flight,
And for the sweet Elysian fields exchange these realms of
    night,
Contented in the joys and peace of that celestial seat,
Await the happy moment when we once more shall meet."

THE AGED LOVER

'Twas from a lofty balcony Arselia looked down
On golden Tagus' crystal stream that hemmed Toledo's town;
And now she watched the eddies that dimpled in the flood
And now she landward turned her eye to gaze on waste and
    wood,
But in all that lay around her she sought for rest in vain,
For her heart, her heart was aching, and she could not heal the
    pain.
'Tis of no courtly gallant the Moorish damsel dreams,
No lordly emir who commands the fort by Tagus' streams,
'Twas on the banks of Tornes stood the haughty towers of
    note
Where the young alcayde loved by the maid from cities dwelt
    remote.
And never at Almanzor's court had he for honor sought,
Though he dwelt in high Toledo in fair Arselia's thought;
And now she dreams of love's great gift, of passion's deep de-
    light,
When far away from her palace walls a stranger came in sight.
It was no gallant lovelorn youth she saw approaching fast,
It was the hero Reduan whose vernal years were past.
He rode upon a sorrel horse and swiftly he came nigh,
And stood where the dazzling sun beat down upon her balcony;
And with a thoughtful air upon the maiden turned his eye,
For suddenly the aged knight feels all his heart on fire,
And all the frost of his broken frame is kindling with desire.
And while he fain would hide his pain he paces up and down
Before the palace turrets that Toledo's rampart crown.
With anger glows the maiden's mind, " Now get thee gone,"
    she cries,
" For can it be that love of me in blood like thine can rise?
I sicken at the very thought; thy locks, old man, are gray,
Thy baldness and thy trembling hand a doting age betray.
Ah, little must thou count my years of beauty and of bloom,
If thou wouldst wed them with a life thus tottering to the tomb,
Decrepitude is now thy lot, and wherefore canst thou dare
To ask that youthful charms these vile infirmities should
    share?"

And Moorish Reduan heard her words, and saw the meaning
   plain.
Advancing to the balcony he answered her again:
" The sun is king of everything, o'er all he holds his sway,
And thou art like the sun—thy charms I own and I obey;
Thy beauty warms my veins again, and in its rays, forsooth,
I feel the blithe, courageous mood of long-forgotten youth;
Sure love of mine can harm thee not, as sunlight is not lost
When its kind radiance dissolves the fetters of the frost."
Then turning round, a parchment did Reduan unfold,
And on it was a writing in characters of gold;
The meaning of the posy at once the maiden caught:
" Since I can venture, I can have; as yet, I am not naught."
He shows upon his shield a sun, circled with burning rays;
And on the rim was written a little verse which says,
" Two suns, one on my shield, and one in beauty's eyes, I
   trace."
Then at the cold disdain he saw upon her lovely face,
He covered with a gauzy veil the blazon of his shield,
" The sun upon my targe," he cried, " before thy light must
   yield."
But as the maid still pouted and eyed him with disdain,
" The mimic sun," continued he, " which here is blazoned plain,
Is overcast and hides itself from the true orb of day,
And I by beauty's radiance eclipsed must ride away."
And as he spoke the Moor struck deep the rowels in his steed,
And rode away from Tagus' side across the grassy mead.
The Moorish maiden recked not if he were far or near,
Her thoughts returned to fancies sweet of her absent cavalier.

FICKLENESS REBUKED

While in the foeman's ruddy gore
   I waded to the breast,
And for mine own, my native shore
   Fought braver than the best,
While the light cloak I laid aside,
   And doffed the damask fold,
And donned my shirt of mail, the spoil
   Of foeman brave and bold,

Thou, fickle Mooress, puttest on
   Thine odorous brocade,
And hand in hand with thy false love
   Wert sitting in the shade.
Thus on the scutcheon of thy sires
   Thou plantest many a stain;
The pillars of thine ancient house
   Will ne'er be firm again.
But, oh, may Allah vengeance take
   For thine unkind deceit,
And sorely weeping mayst thou pay
   The vengeance that is meet.
Thus shalt thou pay—thy lover's bliss
   Thou shalt not, canst not share,
But feel the bitter mockery
   Thy day-long shame must bear.
And what revenge 'twill be to note
   When thou dost kiss his brow,
How thy gold tresses, soft and light,
   Blend with his locks of snow;
And what revenge to hear him
   To thee his loves recount,
Praising some Moorish lass, or mark
   His sons thy staircase mount.
Yes, thou shalt pay the penalty,
   When, from sweet Genil's side,
Thou passest to the stormy waves
   Of Tagus' rushing tide;
Abencerrajes are not there,
   And from thy balcony
Thou shalt not hear the horsemen
   With loud hoof rushing by.
Thoughts of lost days shall haunt thee then
   And lay thy spirit waste,
When thy past glories thou shalt see
   All faded and effaced;
All gone, those sweet, seductive wiles—
   The love note's scented scroll—
The words, and blushing vows, that brought
   Damnation to thy soul.

Thus the bright moments of the past
  Shall rise to memory's eye,
Like vengeance-bearing ministers
  To mock thy misery.
For time is father of distress;
  And he whose life is long
Experiences a thousand cares,
  A thousand shapes of wrong.
Thou shalt be hated in the court,
  And hated in the stall,
Hated in merry gathering,
  In dance and festival.
Thou shalt be hated far and wide;
  And, thinking on this hate,
Wilt lay it to the black offence
  That thou didst perpetrate.
Then thou wilt make some weak defence,
  And plead a father's will,
That forced thee shuddering to consent
  To do the act of ill.
Enjoy then him whom thus constrained
  Thou choosest for thine own;
But know, when love would have his way,
  He scorns a father's frown.

THE GALLEY-SLAVE OF DRAGUT

Ah, fortune's targe and butt was he,
  On whom were rained the strokes from hate
From love that had not found its goal,
  From strange vicissitudes of fate.
A galley-slave of Dragut he,
  Who once had pulled the laboring oar,
Now, 'mid a garden's leafy boughs,
  He worked and wept in anguish sore.
"O Mother Spain! for thy blest shore
  Mine eyes impatient yearn;
For thy choicest gem is bride of mine,
  And she longs for my return.

They took me from the galley bench;
   A gardener's slave they set me here,
That I might tend the fruit and flowers
   Through all the changes of the year;
Wise choice, indeed, they made of me!
   For when the drought has parched the field,
The clouds that overcast my heart
   Shall rain in every season yield.
O mother Spain! for thy blest shore
   Mine eyes impatient yearn;
For thy choicest gem is bride of mine,
   And she longs for my return.

They took me from the galley's hold;
   It was by heaven's all-pitying grace,
Yet, even in this garden glade,
   Has fortune turned away her face.
Though lighter now my lot of toil,
   Yet is it heavier, since no more
My tear-dimmed eyes, my heart discern,
   Across the sea, my native shore.
O mother Spain! for thy blest shore
   Mine eyes impatient yearn;
For thy choicest gem is bride of mine,
   And she longs for my return.

And you, ye exiles, who afar
   In many a foreign land have strayed;
And from strange cities o'er the sea
   A second fatherland have made—
Degenerate sons of glorious Spain!
   One thing ye lacked to keep you true,
The love no stranger land could share;
   The courage that could fate subdue.
O mother Spain! for thy blest shore
   Mine eyes impatient yearn;
For thy choicest gem is bride of mine,
   And she longs for my return."

THE CAPTIVE'S LAMENT

Where Andalusia's plains at length end in the rocky shore,
And the billows of the Spanish sea against her boundaries roar,
A thousand ruined castles, that were once the haughty pride
Of high Cadiz, in days long past, looked down upon the tide.
And on the loftiest of them all, in melancholy mood,
A solitary captive that stormy evening stood.
For he had left the battered skiff that near the land wash lay,
And here he sought to rest his soul, and while his grief away,
    While now, like furies, from the east the gale began to
       blow,
    And with the crash of thunder the billows broke below.

Ah, yes, beneath the fierce levant, the wild white horses
    pranced;
With rising rage the billows against those walls advanced;
But stormier were the thoughts that filled his heart with bitter
    pain,
As he turned his tearful eyes once more to gaze upon the main.
" O hostile sea," these words at last burst from his heaving
    breast;
" I know that I return to die, but death at least is rest.
Then let me on my native shore again in freedom roam,
For here alone is shelter, for here at last is home."
    And now, like furies, from the east the gale began to
       blow,
    And with the crash of thunder the billows broke below.

'Twas Tagus' banks to me a child my home and nurture gave;
Ungrateful land, that lets me pine unransomed as a slave.
For now to-day, a dying man, am I come back again,
And I must lay my bones on this, the farthest shore of Spain.
It is not only exile's sword that cuts me to the heart;
It is not only love for her from whom they bade me part;
Nor only that I suffer, forgot by every friend,
But, ah! it is the triple blow that brings me to my end."
    And now, like furies, from the east the gale began to
       blow,
    And with the crash of thunder the billows broke below.

" The fire with which my bosom burns, alas! thy coolest breeze
Can never slake, nor can its rage thy coolest wave appease;
The earth can bring no solace to the ardor of my pain,
And the whole ocean waters were poured on it in vain.
For it is like the blazing sun that sinks in ocean's bed,
And yet, with ardor all unquenched, next morning rears its
head.
Thus from the sea my suffering's flame has driven me once
more,
And here I land, without a hope, upon this arid shore."
      And now, like furies, from the east the gale began to
      blow,
      And with the crash of thunder the billows broke below.

Oh, call me not, oh, call me not, thou voice of other years,
The fire that flames within my heart has dried the spring of
tears.
And, while my eyes might well pour forth those bitter drops
of pain,
The drought of self-consuming grief has quenched the healing
rain.
Here, let me cry aloud for her, whom once I called mine own,
For well I wot that loving maid for me has made her moan.
'Tis for her sake my flight I urge across the sea and land,
And now 'twixt shore and ocean's roar I take my final stand."
      And now, like furies, from the east the gale began to
      blow,
      And with the crash of thunder the billows broke below.

Then stooping to the earth he grasped the soil with eager
hand,
He kissed it, and with water he mixed the thirsty sand.
" O thou," he said, " poor soil and stream, in the Creator's
plan
Art the end and the beginning of all that makes us man!
From thee rise myriad passions, that stir the human breast,
To thee at last, when all is o'er, they sink to find their rest.
Thou, Earth, hast been my mother, and when these pangs are
o'er,

Thou shalt become my prison-house whence I can pass no
    more."
            And now, like furies, from the east the gale began to
                blow,
            And with the crash of thunder the billows broke below.

And now he saw the warring winds that swept across the bay
Had struck the battered shallop and carried it away.
" O piteous heaven," he cried aloud, " my hopes are like yon
    bark :
Scattered upon the storm they lie and never reach their mark."
And suddenly from cloudy heavens came down the darkling
    night
And in his melancholy mood the captive left the height.
He gained his boat, with trembling hand he seized the laboring
    oar
And turning to the foaming wave he left his native shore.
" Ah, well I wot on ocean's breast when loud the tempest blows
Will rest be found when solid ground denies the heart repose.
Now let the hostile sea perceive no power of hers I dread,
But rather ask her vengeance may fall upon my head."
Into the night the shallop turned, while floated far behind
The captive's lamentation like a streamer on the wind.
            And now, like furies, from the east the gale began to
                blow,
            And with the crash of thunder the billows broke below.

STRIKE SAIL!

A Turkish bark was on the sea, the sunny sea of Spain,
In sight of cliffs that Hercules made boundaries of the main;
And one, Celimo's captive slave, as fierce the billows grew,
Was listening as the ship-master this order gave the crew:
            " Strike sail! Strike sail! The furious gale
                Is rising fast! Strike sail!"

Fierce fell on them the opposing winds, the ship was helpless
    driven;
And with the ocean's flood were blent the thunder-drops of
    heaven.

And as the inky clouds were rent, the fiery lightning flared,
And 'mid the terror-stricken crew one voice alone was heard:
  "Strike sail! Strike sail! The furious gale
   Is rising fast! Strike sail!"

And one there sat upon the deck, in captive misery,
Whose tears ran mingling with the flood, the flood of sky and
  sea.
Lost in the tempest of his thoughts, he fondly breathed a prayer,
Whose mournful words were echoed by the mount of his de-
  spair:
  "Strike sail! Strike sail! The furious gale
   Is rising fast! Strike sail!"

"If I am captive and a slave, the time shall come when God
Will bring me freed, to tread once more my own, my native
  sod!
Then all my ancient glory shall return to me for aye.
Till then, my soul, be patient and wait that happy day!"
  "Strike sail! Strike sail! The furious gale
   Is rising fast! Strike sail!"

THE CAPTIVE'S ESCAPE

The fair Florida sat at ease, upon a summer's day,
Within a garden green and fair that by the river lay,
And gayly asked that he her spouse would tell his darling
  wife
The cause of his captivity, the history of his life.
"Now tell me, dearest husband, I pray thee tell me true,
Who were thy parents, and what land thy birth and nurture
  knew?
And wherefore did they take thee a captive from that place,
And who has given thee liberty, thy homeward path to trace?"
"Yes, I will tell thee, gentle wife, and I will tell thee true,
For tender is the light I see within thine eyes of blue.
In Ronda did my father raise his castle on the height;
And 'twas in Antequera first my mother saw the light.
Me, to this dark captivity, the dastard Moors ensnared,
Just as the peace had ended and war was not declared.

They took me off in fetters, to barter me for gold,
Velez-de-la-Gomèra was the town where I was sold.
Seven weary days, and for each day a long and weary night,
They set me on the auction-block, before the people's sight.
Yet not a Moorish gentleman and not a Moorish wife
A maravedi offered for the mournful captive's life.
At last there came a Moorish dog, in rich attire, and gave
A thousand golden pieces to have me for his slave.
He led me to his lofty house, and bade me there remain,
Mocked by his lowest underlings, and loaded with a chain.
Ah! vile the life he led me, and deep revenge I swore;
Ah! black the life he gave me, and hard the toils I bore!
By day I beat the piled-up hemp cut from the vega plain;
By night, within the darkened mill, I ground for him the grain.
And though the very corn I ground, I longed to take for meat,
He placed a bridle on my mouth that I should nothing eat!
Therefore, it pleased the God who rules the heavens, the land,
the sea,
That the mistress of that mighty house looked tenderly on me.
And when the Moor a-hunting went, one happy autumn day,
She came into my prison-house and took my chains away;
She bade me sit upon her lap, I answered with delight;
Ah, many a gallant present she made to me that night!
She bathed me and she washed my wounds, and garments
fresh she gave,
Far brighter than were fit to deck the body of a slave;
And love's delight we shared that night, for I grew gay and
bold!
And in the morn she gave to me a hundred crowns of gold.
She oped the gates, she bade me, with smiles, once more be
free;
We fled, for fear that Moorish hound would slay both her and
me.
And so it pleased the God who rules the earth and heavens
above,
To prove his deep compassion and the greatness of his love;
And thus my sad captivity, my days of wandering, o'er,
Florida, in thy loving arms I nestle as of yore!

THE SPANIARD OF ORAN

Right gallant was that gentleman, the warlike knight of Spain,
Who served the King in Oran, with sword and lances twain;
But, with his heart's devotion and passion's ardent fire,
He served a gentle Afric maid of high and noble sire.
And she was fair as noble, and well could she requite
The devotion of a lover and the courage of a knight.
And when one summer evening they paid their vows again,
They heard the alarum ring to arms across the darkling plain;
For the foes' approach had roused the watch and caused the
    war-like sound.
The silver moon had shed its ray upon their targes round,
The targes shot the message to the silent watch-towers by,
And watch-towers sent their tidings by flames that lit the sky;
And the fires had called the bells on high to ring their clear
    alarms—
That tocsin roused the lover locked in the lady's arms.
Ah, sorely felt he in his heart the spur of honor prick,
But love's appeal that held him, it pierced him to the quick.
'Twas cowardice to dally and shrink that foe to face,
But, ah, it was ingratitude to leave her in that case.
And hanging round her lover's neck, she saw that he turned
    pale,
And seized his sword and cast one glance upon his coat of
    mail;
And, with a burst of sighs and tears she bowed her beauteous
    head;
" Oh, rise, my lord, gird on thy arms, and join the fray," she
    said;
Oh, let my tears this couch bedew; this couch of joy shall be
As dolorous as the dreary field of battle, without thee!
Arm, arm thyself and go to war! Hark, hark! the foes ap-
    proach.
Thy general waits; oh, let him not thy knightliness reproach!
Oh, direly will he visit thee for cowardice to-day,
For dire the crime in any clime of soldiers who betray.
Well canst thou glide unnoticed to the camp, without thy
    sword;

Wilt thou not heed my tears, my sighs—begone without a
    word!
Thy bosom is not made of flesh, for, ah! thou canst not feel,
Thou hast no need of arms in fight, for it is hard as steel."
The Spaniard gazed upon her, his heart was full of pride;
She held him fast and even her words retained him at her side.
"Lady," he said, and kissed her, "spite of thy words unwise,
Thou art as sweet as ever in thy lover's faithful eyes.
And since to love and honor this night thou hast appealed,
I take my arms and go, for right it is to thee I yield;
I go into the battle and my body seeks the fight,
But my soul behind me lingers in thy bosom of delight;
Oh, grant me, Lord and Master, to seek the camp below,
Oh, let me take the name to-night and I will cheerful go,
Bearing the sword, the lance, and coat of mail against the
    foe!"

MOORISH ROMANCES

—

[*Metrical Translation by J. Lockhart*]

MOORISH ROMANCES

THE BULL-FIGHT OF GAZUL

[Gazul is the name of one of the Moorish heroes who figure in the " *Historia de las Guerras Civiles de Granada.*" The following ballad is one of very many in which the dexterity of the Moorish cavaliers in the bull-fight is described. The reader will observe that the shape, activity, and resolution of the unhappy animal destined to furnish the amusement of the spectators, are enlarged upon, just as the qualities of a modern race-horse might be among ourselves : nor is the bull without his name. The day of the Baptist is a festival among the Mussulmans, as well as among Christians.]

KING ALMANZOR of Granada, he hath bid the trumpet sound,
He hath summonded all the Moorish lords, from the hills and plains around ;
From vega and sierra, from Betis and Xenil,
They have come with helm and cuirass of gold and twisted steel.

'Tis the holy Baptist's feast they hold in royalty and state,
And they have closed the spacious lists beside the Alhambra's gate ;
In gowns of black and silver laced, within the tented ring,
Eight Moors to fight the bull are placed in presence of the King.

Eight Moorish lords of valor tried, with stalwart arm and true,
The onset of the beasts abide, as they come rushing through ;
The deeds they've done, the spoils they've won, fill all with hope and trust,
Yet ere high in heaven appears the sun they all have bit the dust.

Then sounds the trumpet clearly, then clangs the loud tambour,
Make room, make room for Gazul—throw wide, throw wide
the door;
Blow, blow the trumpet clearer still, more loudly strike the
drum,
The Alcaydé of Algava to fight the bull doth come.

And first before the King he passed, with reverence stooping
low,
And next he bowed him to the Queen, and the Infantas all
a-row;
Then to his lady's grace he turned, and she to him did throw
A scarf from out her balcony was whiter than the snow.

With the life-blood of the slaughtered lords all slippery is the
sand,
Yet proudly in the centre hath Gazul ta'en his stand;
And ladies look with heaving breast, and lords with anxious
eye,
But firmly he extends his arm—his look is calm and high.

Three bulls against the knight are loosed, and two come roaring
on,
He rises high in stirrup, forth stretching his rejón;
Each furious beast upon the breast he deals him such a blow
He blindly totters and gives back, across the sand to go.

" Turn, Gazul, turn," the people cry—the third comes up be-
hind,
Low to the sand his head holds he, his nostrils snuff the wind;
The mountaineers that lead the steers, without stand whispering
low,
" Now thinks this proud alcaydé to stun Harpado so? "

From Guadiana comes he not, he comes not from Xenil,
From Gaudalarif of the plain, or Barves of the hill;
But where from out the forest burst Xarama's waters clear,
Beneath the oak-trees was he nursed, this proud and stately
steer.

Dark is his hide on either side, but the blood within doth boil,
And the dun hide glows, as if on fire, as he paws to the turmoil.
His eyes are jet, and they are set in crystal rings of snow;
But now they stare with one red glare of brass upon the foe.

Upon the forehead of the bull the horns stand close and near,
From out the broad and wrinkled skull, like daggers they appear;
His neck is massy, like the trunk of some old knotted tree,
Whereon the monster's shaggy mane, like billows curled, ye see.

His legs are short, his hams are thick, his hoofs are black as night,
Like a strong flail he holds his tail in fierceness of his might;
Like something molten out of iron, or hewn from forth the rock,
Harpado of Xarama stands, to bide the alcaydé's shock.

Now stops the drum—close, close they come—thrice meet, and thrice give back;
The white foam of Harpado lies on the charger's breast of black—
The white foam of the charger on Harpado's front of dun—
Once more advance upon his lance—once more, thou fearless one!

Once more, once more;—in dust and gore to ruin must thou reel—
In vain, in vain thou tearest the sand with furious heel—
In vain, in vain, thou noble beast, I see, I see thee stagger,
Now keen and cold thy neck must hold the stern alcaydé's dagger!

They have slipped a noose around his feet, six horses are brought in,
And away they drag Harpado with a loud and joyful din.
Now stoop thee, lady, from thy stand, and the ring of price bestow
Upon Gazul of Algava, that hath laid Harpado low.

THE ZEGRI'S BRIDE

[The reader cannot need to be reminded of the fatal effects which were produced by the feuds subsisting between the two great families, or rather races, of the Zegris and the Abencerrages of Granada. The following ballad is also from the " *Guerras Civiles.*"]

Of all the blood of Zegri, the chief is Lisaro,
To wield rejón like him is none, or javelin to throw;
From the place of his dominion, he ere the dawn doth go,
From Alcala de Henares, he rides in weed of woe.

He rides not now as he was wont, when ye have seen him speed
To the field of gay Toledo, to fling his lusty reed;
No gambeson of silk is on, nor rich embroidery
Of gold-wrought robe or turban—nor jewelled tahali.

No amethyst nor garnet is shining on his brow,
No crimson sleeve, which damsels weave at Tunis, decks him
     now;
The belt is black, the hilt is dim, but the sheathed blade is
     bright;
They have housened his barb in a murky garb, but yet her hoofs
     are light.

Four horsemen good, of the Zegri blood, with Lisaro go out;
No flashing spear may tell them near, but yet their shafts are
     stout;
In darkness and in swiftness rides every armed knight—
The foam on the rein ye may see it plain, but nothing else is
     white.

Young Lisaro, as on they go, his bonnet doffeth he,
Between its folds a sprig it holds of a dark and glossy tree;
That sprig of bay, were it away, right heavy heart had he—
Fair Zayda to her Zegri gave that token privily.

And ever as they rode, he looked upon his lady's boon.
" God knows," quoth he, " what fate may be—I may be
     slaughtered soon;

Thou still art mine, though scarce the sign of hope that
    bloomed whilere,
But in my grave I yet shall have my Zayda's token dear."

Young Lisaro was musing so, when onward on the path,
He well could see them riding slow; then pricked he in his
    wrath.
The raging sire, the kinsmen of Zayda's hateful house,
Fought well that day, yet in the fray the Zegri won his spouse.

THE BRIDAL OF ANDALLA

[The following ballad has been often imitated by modern poets, both in
    Spain and in Germany :

            " *Pon te a las rejas azules, dexa la manga que labras,*
              Melancholica Xarifa, veras al galan Andalla," etc.]

" Rise up, rise up, Xarifa, lay the golden cushion down;
Rise up, come to the window, and gaze with all the town.
From gay guitar and violin the silver notes are flowing,
And the lovely lute doth speak between the trumpet's lordly
    blowing,
And banners bright from lattice light are waving everywhere,
And the tall, tall plume of our cousin's bridegroom floats
    proudly in the air:
      Rise up, rise up, Xarifa, lay the golden cushion down;
      Rise up, come to the window, and gaze with all the town.

" Arise, arise, Xarifa, I see Andalla's face,
He bends him to the people with a calm and princely grace,
Through all the land of Xeres and banks of Guadalquivir
Rode forth bridegroom so brave as he, so brave and lovely
    never.
Yon tall plume waving o'er his brow of purple mixed with
    white,
I guess 'twas wreathed by Zara, whom he will wed to-night;
      Rise up, rise up, Xarifa, lay the golden cushion down;
      Rise up, come to the window, and gaze with all the town.

" What aileth thee, Xarifa, what makes thine eyes look down?
Why stay ye from the window far, nor gaze with all the town?

I've heard you say on many a day, and sure you said the truth,
Andalla rides without a peer, among all Granada's youth.
Without a peer he rideth, and yon milk-white horse doth go
Beneath his stately master, with a stately step and slow;
    Then rise, oh, rise, Xarifa, lay the golden cushion down;
    Unseen here through the lattice, you may gaze with all
       the town."

The Zegri lady rose not, nor laid her cushion down,
Nor came she to the window to gaze with all the town;
But though her eyes dwelt on her knee, in vain her fingers
   strove,
And though her needle pressed the silk, no flower Xarifa
   wove;
One bonny rose-bud she had traced, before the noise drew
   nigh—
That bonny bud a tear effaced, slow drooping from her eye.
    "No—no," she sighs—"bid me not rise, nor lay my
      cushion down,
    To gaze upon Andalla with all the gazing town."

"Why rise ye not, Xarifa, nor lay your cushion down?
Why gaze ye not, Xarifa, with all the gazing town?
Hear, hear the trumpet how it swells, and how the people cry!
He stops at Zara's palace gate—why sit ye still—oh, why?"
"At Zara's gate stops Zara's mate; in him shall I discover
The dark-eyed youth pledged me his truth with tears, and was
   my lover?
    I will not rise, with dreary eyes, nor lay my cushion down,
    To gaze on false Andalla with all the gazing town!"

ZARA'S EAR-RINGS

"My ear-rings! my ear-rings! they've dropped into the well,
And what to say to Muça, I cannot, cannot tell."
'Twas thus, Granada's fountain by, spoke Albuharez' daughter,
"The well is deep, far down they lie, beneath the cold blue
    water—
To me did Muça give them, when he spake his sad farewell,
And what to say when he comes back, alas! I cannot tell.

" My ear-rings! my ear-rings! they were pearls in silver set,
That when my Moor was far away, I ne'er should him forget,
That I ne'er to other tongue should list, nor smile on other's
    tale,
But remember he my lips had kissed, pure as those ear-rings
    pale—
When he comes back, and hears that I have dropped them in
    the well,
Oh, what will Muça think of me, I cannot, cannot tell.

" My ear-rings! my ear-rings! he'll say they should have been,
Not of pearl and of silver, but of gold and glittering sheen,
Of jasper and of onyx, and of diamond shining clear,
Changing to the changing light, with radiance insincere—
That changeful mind unchanging gems are not befitting well—
Thus will he think—and what to say, alas! I cannot tell.

" He'll think when I to market went, I loitered by the way;
He'll think a willing ear I lent to all the lads might say;
He'll think some other lover's hand, among my tresses noosed,
From the ears where he had placed them, my rings of pearl un-
    loosed;
He'll think, when I was sporting so beside this marble well,
My pearls fell in,—and what to say, alas! I cannot tell.

" He'll say, I am a woman, and we are all the same;
He'll say I loved when he was here to whisper of his flame—
But when he went to Tunis my virgin troth had broken,
And thought no more of Muça, and cared not for his token.
My ear-rings! my ear-rings! O luckless, luckless well,
For what to say to Muça, alas! I cannot tell.

" I'll tell the truth to Muça, and I hope he will believe—
That I thought of him at morning, and thought of him at eve;
That, musing on my lover, when down the sun was gone,
His ear-rings in my hand I held, by the fountain all alone;
And that my mind was o'er the sea, when from my hand they
    fell,
And that deep his love lies in my heart, as they lie in the well."

THE LAMENTATION FOR CELIN

At the gate of old Granada, when all its bolts are barred,
At twilight at the Vega gate there is a trampling heard;
There is a trampling heard, as of horses treading slow,
And a weeping voice of women, and a heavy sound of woe.
" What tower is fallen, what star is set, what chief come these
    bewailing ? "
" A tower is fallen, a star is set. Alas! alas for Celin! "

Three times they knock, three times they cry, and wide the
    doors they throw;
Dejectedly they enter, and mournfully they go;
In gloomy lines they mustering stand beneath the hollow porch,
Each horseman grasping in his hand a black and flaming torch;
Wet is each eye as they go by, and all around is wailing,
For all have heard the misery. " Alas! alas for Celin! "—

Him yesterday a Moor did slay, of Bencerraje's blood,
'Twas at the solemn jousting, around the nobles stood;
The nobles of the land were by, and ladies bright and fair
Looked from their latticed windows, the haughty sight to share;
But now the nobles all lament, the ladies are bewailing,
For he was Granada's darling knight. " Alas! alas for Celin! "

Before him ride his vassals, in order two by two,
With ashes on their turbans spread, most pitiful to view;
Behind him his four sisters, each wrapped in sable veil,
Between the tambour's dismal strokes take up their doleful
    tale;
When stops the muffled drum, ye hear their brotherless be-
    wailing,
And all the people, far and near, cry—" Alas! alas for Celin! "

Oh! lovely lies he on the bier, above the purple pall,
The flower of all Granada's youth, the loveliest of them all;
His dark, dark eyes are closed, his rosy lip is pale,
The crust of blood lies black and dim upon his burnished mail,
And evermore the hoarse tambour breaks in upon their wailing,
Its sound is like no earthly sound—" Alas! alas for Celin! "

The Moorish maid at the lattice stands, the Moor stands at his
    door,
One maid is wringing of her hands, and one is weeping sore—
Down to the dust men bow their heads, and ashes black they
    strew
Upon their broidered garments of crimson, green, and blue—
Before each gate the bier stands still, then bursts the loud be-
    wailing,
From door and lattice, high and low—" Alas! alas for Celin! "

An old, old woman cometh forth, when she hears the people
    cry;
Her hair is white as silver, like horn her glazèd eye.
'Twas she that nursed him at her breast, that nursed him long
    ago;
She knows not whom they all lament, but soon she well shall
    know.
With one deep shriek she thro' doth break, when her ears receive
    their wailing—
" Let me kiss my Celin ere I die—Alas! alas for Celin! "

THE STORY OF SIDI BRAHIM
OF MASSAT

—

[Translated by Réne Basset and Chauncey C. Starkweather]

THE STORY OF SIDI BRAHIM OF MASSAT

I

THE Taleb Sidi Brahim, son of Amhammed of Massat, in the province of Sous, tells the following story about himself: When he was still a child at his father's house he went to the mosque to read with a taleb. He studied with him for twelve and a half years. His father gave him bread and kouskous, and he ate eight deniers' worth a day. I will make known the country of Massat. It contains seventeen towns. In the middle of these is a market. The Jews have a refuge in the village of the chief named Mobarek-ben-Mahomet. He lives with a sheik called Brahim-Mahomet-Abon-Djemaa. These two chiefs levy a tax on the Jews. They receive from them four ounces per family at the beginning of each month. If the festival of the Mussulmans coincides with the Sabbath of the Jews, the latter pay to each of the chiefs one ounce for a Jew or a Jewess, boy or girl, little or big. The following are the details of the population of Massat. It includes 1,700 men. As to the women, little boys or girls, only the Lord knows their number. There are 1,250 houses. The horses amount to 180. They ride them and make them work like oxen and mules. They also fight on horseback. The country has trees, vines, figs, cacti, dates, oranges, lemons, apples, apricots, melons, and olives. There is a river which flows from there to the sea. The commerce is considerable. There are Jews and Mussulmans. The number of books in the mosque is unknown, unless it be by God. The teachers are numerous as well as the pilgrims, the descendants of Mahomet, and the saints. May God aid us with his blessing!

We will now speak of the tribute which the people of Massat pay yearly to Prince Mouley-Abd-Er-Rahman. Up to our days they had, for fifty-one years, given him 5,000 livres of silver. The prince said to them, "You must pay 1,000 livres

more." They answered, " By the Lord, we will only give you
as before, 5,000 livres, a slave, a servant, and a horse." The
kaid Abd-el-Cadik, who was caliph of the King of Taroundant,
hastened to send against them forty-five horsemen, and said
to them: " You must give me six thousand livres of silver,
and a slave, a servant, and a horse in addition." They refused and drove away the cavalry, saying, " Return to the kaid
who sent you against us, and say to him that we will not increase our tribute as he demands." The horsemen returned
and arrived at Taroundant. The kaid asked him, " Tell me
what happened to you with the people of Massat." They
answered him, " They read in their assembly the letter that
you sent them, and told us to go back, and that they would
pay no larger sum." The kaid called a council and asked what
had better be done with the people of Massat. The sheiks of
the Achtouks answered, " Make complaints to the Sultan at
Morocco." He wrote to the Sultan, asking him to send an
army to destroy the rebels of Massat. The Sultan sent a force
of 3,500 horsemen, to whom he gave for chief, Ettaib Eddin,
who rejoined them near the khalifah of the King at Taroundant.
When the royal troops arrived, the fourth night, he started
and led them to the taleb Mahomet of the Aggars, in the midst
of the country of the Achtouks. The taleb said to him:
" Return to Taroundant. Let your lieutenant go with them
and we will talk about it." The kaid answered, " Very well."
The chiefs of the Achtouks mounted their horses and led the
army toward the country of Hama, in the mountain which is
between the Achtouks and Ida-Oultit. The troops hastened
toward the foot of the mountain, near the river Alras, in the
country of Takourt. The mountaineers marched against them
and fought for three days until the holy men and the sherifs
arrived and quieted them. The mountaineers came down
toward the army. The kaid betrayed them. He seized fourteen of their leaders and sent them to the kaid at Taroundant.
He cut off their heads and hung them up at the gate. As to
the army that was above the river Alras, it attacked the people
of Massat on account of the tribute demanded by the kaid. It
made the onset with cavalry, and destroyed the country. The
natives received them with powder, and they fought half a
day. The natives gained the advantage in the fight. The

enemy abandoned their cannons. The natives slew them until the Sultan's troops retreated. They captured 700 horses. The troops of the Sultan abandoned their baggage except six chests of silver. Many guns were broken on that day, until the flying invaders reached the country of the Achtouks. The people of Massat had for allies the tribes of Aglou and Tizpit, who equalled them in number. As for the cannons abandoned the day of the battle, the conquerors took two of them to their country. They kept them until they were repaid the 6,500 livres of silver, which had been taken from them. Then they gave back the cannons. Such is the complete story of that which happened between the tribe of Massat, the Khalifah of the King, and the neighboring tribes.

II

Information about the country of Tazroualt. The Taleb Sidi Brahim, son of Mahomet, of Massat in Sous, tells the following: He started for the zaouiah of Tazroualt, to study there during seven months with the taleb Sidi Mahomet Adjeli, one of the greatest lights. The number of students was seventy-four. Forty-two of these studied the law. The others read the Koran. None of the students paid for his living. It was furnished by the chief of the country, Hecham. He gave to the zaouiah mentioned, six servants and six slaves to cook the food of the students. The number of the villages of this country is nine. The Kashlah of Hecham is situated in the middle of the country. The Jewish quarter is at the left. The market is held every day at the entrance to the fort. This latter is built of stone, lime, and pine planks and beams. Riches abound. Caravans go from there to Timbuctoo, the Soudan, Sahara, and Agadir-Ndouma. They go to these countries to buy ivory, ostrich feathers, slaves, gold and silver. If it hurries, a caravan consumes a whole year in visiting these places. The people of the different countries buy from them and give in exchange other merchandise, such as linen, cotton, silks, iron, steel, incense, corals, cloves, spikenard, haberdashery, pottery, glass, and everything that comes, as they say, from the country of Christians. When these goods enumerated above have arrived, the merchants, both Jews and Mussulmans, come forward and buy them according to the needs of their business. I will add here, with more details, some words about Hecham. He has twelve sons, all horsemen, who have thirty-six horses. As for oxen, sheep, and camels, God alone could tell the figure. The number of the wives that Hecham has married is four white and six slaves—the latter black. His only son has as many white wives as his father, but more black ones. The men of Tizeroualt are of the number of 1,400. But for the women, boys, and girls, God alone knows the figure. They possess 200 horses, beside those of Hecham. There are 750 houses; the number of books in the mosque is 130—in the Chelha language.

III

The sheik Sidi Hammad, son of Mahomet Mouley Ben-Nacer, has written his book in Amazir. It is entitled the "Kitab-amazir." This work treats of obligations and traditions of things permitted and forbidden.

IV

There are 3,500 men in the Aglou country. They have 2,200 houses and 960 horses. This district is on the sea-coast and possesses a stone-harbor. There are barks which are used in fishing. The inhabitants were living in tranquillity when one day, as they were starting out to fish, a ship arrived off shore. They fled in fear and left it in the sea. The ship waited till midnight. Then it entered the port and ran up a red flag. It remained at anchor for fifteen days. The people of Aglou assembled day and night, big and little, even the horsemen before it. No one was missing. The chiefs of the town wrote letters which they sent to all the villages. They sent one to Sidi Hecham couched in these words: " Come at once. The Christians have made an expedition against us, and have taken this port." Sidi Hecham sent messengers to all the provinces over which he ruled and said in his letters: " You must accompany me to the country of Aglou, for the Christians have made an expedition against us." All the neighboring tribes assembled to march against the Christians. When Sidi

Hecham had joined them he said, " You must raise a red flag like theirs."

They raised it. When it was seen by those on the ship, a sailor came ashore in a small boat and approached the Mussulmans there assembled.

" Let no one insult the Christian," said Sidi Hecham, " until we learn his purpose in landing here."

They asked him, " What do you want? "

The Christian replied, " We wish to receive, in the name of God, pledges of security."

All who were present said, " God grants to you security with us."

The Christian then continued, " My object is to trade with you."

" That is quite agreeable to us," answered Hecham. Then Hecham asked the Christian what he wanted to purchase."

" Oil, butter, wheat, oxen, sheep, and chickens," said he.

When the Mussulmans heard this they gathered together wheat, oil, oxen, and everything he had mentioned. He made his purchases, and was well supplied. The master of the ship then said:

" Our business is finished. We must go back home. But we shall return to you." Hecham answered:

" That which I have done for you is not pleasing to the people of Aglou. It is only on account of the pledge of security that I have been able to restrain them. I have given you all you asked. Next time you come, bring us fifty cannons and ten howitzers."

" Very well," answered the Christian, " I shall return this time next year."

" Do as you promise," replied Hecham, " and I will give you whatever you want in the country of the Mussulmans."

V

A Story about the Country of Ait-Bamouran

There arrived in this country at the beginning of the year another ship which stopped at a place called Ifni, in the tribe of Ait-Bamouran, and stayed there three days. Then one of the sailors got into a small boat, came ashore, and said to the inhabitants, " I will buy bread, meat, and water from you."

The Mussulmans brought him bread, figs, and water, saying: " You must send two of your men ashore while we go on board the ship with you."

" It is well," replied the Christian. Then he went to get two of his men whom he brought ashore and said to the Mussulmans: " You must give me one of your men."

They gave him a hostage to remain on board the Christian ship. Then they filled a boat, and boarded the ship themselves to deliver what they had sold. They ran all over the ship looking at everything. Then they said, " Come with us to the spring and we will draw water." The Christians accompanied them to the fountain to fill their water-casks. The other natives, to the number of fifteen, got into a boat and went to the ship. With the water-party and the hostages ashore there were only four Christians on the ship when the Mussulmans boarded it.

" Don't come aboard till our men have come back," said the Christians.

" We will come aboard by force," he was answered, and the attack began. One of the Christians killed a native with a gun. Then they fought until the Christians were overcome. Two Christians were killed and the rest captured and taken ashore and imprisoned with the others of the water-party. The ship was sold for 180 mithkals. The Christians were all sold and dispersed among the tribes. The news of this spread to Taccourt. The merchants there sent to Ait-Bamouran and bought all the Christians at any price. They secured seven. Three were missing, of whom two were in the country of Ait-bou-Bekr with the chief of that tribe named Abd-Allah, son of Bou-Bekr. The third, who was a boy, was with the sheik of Aglou, who said:

"I will not sell this one, for he has become as dear to me as a son." Then addressing the young boy he said, "I wish to convert you; be a Mussulman." The boy acquiesced and embraced Islamism. The day of his abjuration the sheik killed in his honor an ox for a festival, and gave to the convert the name of Mahomet. Then he sent to say to all his tribe: "Come to my house. I have prepared a repast." The Mussulmans came and diverted themselves with their horses and gunpowder. The chief told them, " I have given a fourth of my possessions, a slave, and a servant to this young man." He added, " He shall live with my son." They both occupied the same room, and the master taught the young convert the whole Koran. The Mussulmans called him Sidi Mahomet, son of Ali. Seven Christians were ransomed and sent back to their own country.

VI

Information about the country Tiznit: This place is a kind of a city surrounded on all sides by a wall, and having only two gates. The water is in the centre, in a fountain. The fortress is built above the fountain, in the middle of the city. It is entirely constructed of mortar, cut stone, marble, and beams, all from Christian countries. It was the residence of the khalifah of the King in the time of Mouley-Soliman. When this prince died, the people of Tiznit revolted, drove away the lieutenant, and made a concerted attack upon the citadel, which they completely destroyed. They took the stones and beams and built a mosque on the spot, near the fountain of which we have spoken. But when Mouley-Abd-Er-Rahman came to the throne he sent a caliph to Tiznit. He gave him 300 horsemen. When the caliph arrived near the town he waited three days and they gave him food and barley. At the end of this time he made a proclamation summoning all the people to him. When they came he read them the royal edict and said:

"I must enter your city to occupy the fortress of the King!"

They said: "No; go back whence you came and say to your master: 'You shall not rule over us. Your fortress is totally destroyed, and with the material we have built a big mosque in the middle of our city.'"

Prince Mouley-Abd-Er-Rahman sent at once against them his son Sidi-Mahomet with the khalifah and 6,000 horsemen. The people of Tiznit were informed of the approach of the army under the Sultan's son, and that the advancing guard was near. The soldiers arrived in the middle of the country of the Achtouks and camped in the city of Tebouhonaikt near the river Alras. There was a day's march between them and Tiznit. The inhabitants, frightened, sent deputies to the other districts, saying:

"Come and help us, for the Sultan's son has come and ordered us to build him a fort in the space of one month or he will fall upon us, cut a passage, and destroy our city." The tribes around Tiznit assembled and marched against the royal army. The Sultan's son stayed twenty-two days at Tebouhonaikt, then he crossed the river Alras and marched against the rebels. He surrounded Tiznit on all sides. The inhabitants made a sortie, engaged in battle, and fought till the morning star. At the fall of day the battle recommenced. The royal army was defeated and driven across the river Alras. The son of the Sultan killed eight rebels and thirty-five horses, but many of his soldiers fell. He retreated to Morocco.

VII

Information about the country of Taragoust: This is a unique district situated near the source of the Ourd-Sous. It is distant from Taroundant about a day and a half's march. When a young man becomes of age his father buys him a gun and a sabre. The market is in the middle of the country. But no man goes there without his weapons. The sheiks judge each one in the market for four months in the year in turn and during their period of office. They decided who was guilty and demanded price of blood for those killed in the market. One of them said:

"I will give nothing. Find the murderer. He will give you the price of blood."

The sheik replied: "Pay attention. Give us part of your goods."

"I will give you nothing," he answered.

In this way they quarrelled, until they began fighting with

guns. Each tried to steal the other's horses and oxen in the night and kill the owner. They kept acting this way toward each other until Ben-Nacer came to examine the villages where so many crimes were committed, and he reëstablished peace and order.

VIII

Concerning guns and sabres: They were all brought into the city of Adjadir in the government of Sidi Mahomet-ben-Abd-Alla. They introduced guns, poniards, sabres, English powder, and everything one can mention from the country of the Christians. Sidi Mahomet-ben-Abd-Allah sent there his khalifah, called Ettaleb Calih. He busied himself during his administration in amassing a great fortune. The guns imported into the provinces were called merchandise of the taleb Calih. This officer revolted against the Sultan, sent him no more money, and consulted him no longer in the administration of affairs. When the prince ordered him to do such and such a thing with the Christians, Mussulmans, or others, he replied:

"I shall do as I please, for all the people of Sous are under my hand. I leave the rest to you." The Sultan sent much money to Sidi Mahomet-ben-Abd-Allah, and ordered him with troops against the rebel. The latter fought against the divan until he was captured and put in fetters and chains. The partisans of the Emperor said to him:

"We have captured your khalifah Ettaleb Calih and his accomplices."

The prince responded: "Make him a bonnet of iron and a shirt of iron, and give him but a loaf of bread a day." In a letter that he sent he said also:

"Collect all the goods you can find and let the Christian ships take them all to Taccourt, leaving nothing whatever." Guns, sabres, powder, sulphur, linens, cottons, everything was transported.

During the reign of Sidi Mouley Soliman he built the city as it is at present. He increased it, and said to the Christians:

"You must bring me cannons, mortars, and powder, and I

will give you in exchange wheat, oil, wool, and whatever you desire."

The Christians answered: "Most willingly, we shall return with our products." They brought him cannons, mortars, and powder. In return he supplied them with woollens, wheat, oil, and whatever they desired.

The Ulmas reproached him, saying: "You are not fulfilling the law in giving to the Christians wheat, oil, and woollens. You are weakening the Mussulmans."

He answered them: "We must make sacrifices of these goods for two or three years, until the Christians have stocked us with cannons, powder, and so forth. These I will place in the coast towns to drive off the infidels when they arrive."

IX

More words about guns: They only make them in three cities in the interior of Sous. The workmen are very numerous. They make also gun-barrels, pistols, gun-locks, and all such things. As for sabres and poniards, they are made by Arab armorers. They make powder in every province, but only in small quantities.

FIVE BERBER STORIES

—

[Translated by G. Mercier and Chauncey C. Starkweather]

FIVE BERBER STORIES

DJOKHRANE AND THE JAYS

THE ancestor of the grandfather of Mahomet Amokrane was named Djokhrane. He was a Roman of old times, who lived at T'kout at the period of the Romans. One of his countrymen rose against them, and they fought. This Roman had the advantage, until a bird of the kind called jays came to the assistance of Djokhrane, and pecked the Roman in the eyes until he saved his adversary. From that time forth he remained a friend to Djokhrane. The latter said to his children:

"As long as you live, never eat this bird. If you meet anyone who brings one of these birds to eat, buy it and set it free." To this day when anyone brings a jay to one of his descendants, he buys it for silver and gives it liberty. This story is true, and is not a lie.

THE OGRE AND THE BEAUTIFUL WOMAN

Some hunters set out with their camels. When they came to the hunting-ground they loosed their camels to let them graze, and hunted until the setting of the sun, and then came back to their camp. One day while one of them was going along he saw the marks of an ogre, each one three feet wide, and began to follow them. He proceeded and found the place where the ogre had lately made his lair. He returned and said to his companions:

"I've found the traces of an ogre. Come, let us seek him."

"No," they answered, "we will not go to seek him, because we are not stronger than he is."

"Grant me fourteen days," said the huntsman. "If I return, you shall see. If not, take back my camel with the game."

The next day he set out and began to follow the traces of the ogre. He walked for four days, when he discovered a cave, into which he entered. Within he found a beautiful woman, who said to him:

"What brings thee here, where thou wilt be devoured by this ogre?"

"But thou," answered the hunter, "what is thy story and how did the ogre bring thee here?"

"Three days ago he stole me," she replied. "I was betrothed to the son of my uncle, then the ogre took me. I have stayed in the cavern. He often brings me food. I stay here, and he does not kill me."

"Where does he enter," asked the hunter, "when he comes back here?"

"This is the way," she answered. The hunter went in to the middle of the cave, loaded his gun, and waited. At sunset the ogre arrived. The hunter took aim and fired, hitting the ogre between the eyes as he was sitting down. Approaching him he saw that he had brought with him two men to cook and eat them. In the morning he employed the day in collecting the hidden silver, took what he could, and set out on the return. On the fourteenth day he arrived at the place where he had left his comrades, and found them there.

"Leave the game you have secured and return with me to the cave," he said to them. When they arrived they took all the arms and clothing, loaded it upon their camels, and set out to return to their village. Half way home they fought to see which one should marry the woman. The powder spoke between them. Our man killed four, and took the woman home and married her.

THE FALSE VEZIR

A king had a wife who said to him: "I would like to go and visit my father."

"Very well," said he; "wait to-day, and to-morrow thou shalt go with my vezir." The next day they set out, taking the children with them, and an escort lest they should be attacked on the way. They stopped at sunset, and passed the night on the road. The vezir said to the guards, " Watch that we be not taken, if the robbers should come to seize us." They guarded the tent. The vezir asked the King's wife to marry him, and killed one of her sons because she refused. The next day they set out again. The next night he again asked the King's wife to marry him, threatening to kill a second child should she refuse. She did refuse, so he killed the second son. The next morning they set out, and when they stopped at night again he asked the King's wife to marry him.

" I'll kill you if you refuse."

She asked for delay, time to say her prayers. She prayed to God, the Master of all worlds, and said: " O God, save me from the vezir." The Master of the worlds heard her prayer. He gave her the wings of a bird, and she flew up in the sky.

At dawn she alighted in a great city, and met a man upon the roadside. She said: " By the face of God, give me your raiment and I'll give thee mine."

" Take it, and may God honor you," he said. Then she was handsome. This city had no king. The members of the council said:

" This creature is handsome; we'll make him our king." The cannon spoke in his honor and the drums beat.

When she flew up into the sky, the vezir said to the guards: " You will be my witnesses that she has gone to the sky, so that when I shall see the King he cannot say, ' Where is she? ' " But when the vezir told this story, the King said:

" I shall go to seek my wife. Thou hast lied. Thou shalt accompany me." They set out, and went from village to village. They inquired, and said: " Has a woman been found here recently? We have lost her." And the village people said, " We have not found her." They went then to another village and inquired. At this village the Sultan's wife recognized them, called her servant, and said to him, " Go, bring to me this man." She said to the King, " From what motive hast thou come hither? "

He said, " I have lost my wife."

She answered: " Stay here, and pass the night. We will give thee a dinner and will question thee."

When the sun had set she said to the servant, "Go, bring the dinner, that the guests may eat." When they had eaten she said to the King, "Tell me your story."

He answered: "My story is long. My wife went away in the company of a trusted vezir. He returned and said: 'By God, your wife has gone to heaven.'

"I replied: 'No, you have lied. I'll go and look for her.'" She said to him, "I am your wife."

"How came you here?" he asked.

She replied: "After having started, your vezir came to me and asked me to marry him or he would kill my son. 'Kill him,' I said, and he killed them both."

Addressing the vezir, she said: "And your story? Let us hear it."

"I will return in a moment," said the vezir, for he feared her. But the King cut off his head.

The next day he assembled the council of the village, and his wife said, "Forgive me and let me go, for I am a woman."

THE SOUFI AND THE TARGUI

Two Souafa were brothers. Separating one day one said to the other: "O my brother, let us marry thy son with my daughter." So the young cousins were married, and the young man's father gave them a separate house. It happened that a man among the Touareg heard tell of her as a remarkable woman. He mounted his swiftest camel, ten years old, and went to her house. Arrived near her residence, he found some shepherds.

"Who are you?" he said.

"We are Souafa."

He confided in one of them, and said to him: "By the face of the Master of the worlds, O favorite of fair women, man of remarkable appearance, tell me if the lady so and so, daughter of so and so, is here."

"She is here."

"Well, if you have the sentiments of most men, I desire you to bring her here, I want to see her."

"I will do what you ask. If she'll come, I'll bring her. If not, I will return and tell you."

He set out, and, arriving at the house of the lady, he saw some people, and said "Good-evening" to them.

"Come dine with us," they said to him.

"I have but just now eaten and am not hungry." He pretended to amuse himself with them to shorten the night, in reality to put to sleep their vigilance. These people went away to amuse themselves while he met the lady.

"A man sends me to you," he said, "a Targui, who wants to marry you. He is as handsome as you are, his eyes are fine, his nose is fine, his mouth is fine."

"Well, I will marry him." She went to him and married him, and they set out on a camel together. When the first husband returned, he found that she had gone. He said to himself: "She is at my father's or perhaps my uncle's." When day dawned he said to his sister, "Go see if she is in thy father's house or thy uncle's." She went, and did not find her there. He went out to look for her, and perceived the camel's traces. Then he saddled his own camel.

The women came out and said: "Stay! Do not go; we will give thee our own daughters to marry."

"No," he replied, "I want to find my wife." He goes out, he follows the tracks of the camel, here, here, here, until the sun goes down. He spends the night upon the trail. His camel is a runner of five years. When the sun rises he starts and follows the trail again.

About four o'clock he arrives at an encampment of the Touareg, and finds some shepherds with their flocks. He confides in one of these men, and says to him: "A word, brave man, brother of beautiful women, I would say a word to thee which thou wilt not repeat."

"Speak."

"Did a woman arrive at this place night before last?"

"She did."

"Hast thou the sentiments of a man of heart?"

"Truly."

"I desire to talk to her."

"I will take thee to her. Go, hide thy camel; tie him up. Change thy clothing. Thou wilt not then be recognized among the sheep. Bring thy sabre and come. Thou shalt walk as the sheep walk."

"I will walk toward you, taking the appearance of a sheep, so as not to be perceived."

"The wedding-festival is set for to-night, and everybody will be out of their houses. When I arrive at the tent of this lady I will strike a stake with my stick. Where I shall strike, that is where she lives."

He waits and conceals himself among the flocks, and the women come out to milk. He looks among the groups of tents. He finds his wife and bids her come with him.

"I will not go with thee, but if thou art hungry, I will give thee food."

"Thou'lt come with me or I will kill thee!"

She goes with him. He finds his camel, unfastens him, dons his ordinary clothing, takes his wife upon the camel's back with him, and departs. The day dawns. She says:

"O thou who art the son of my paternal uncle, I am thirsty." Now she planned a treachery.

He said to her: "Is there any water here?"

"The day the Targui took me off we found some in that pass." They arrived at the well.

"Go down into the well," said the Soufi.

"I'm only a woman. I'm afraid. Go down thyself." He goes down. He draws the water. She drinks. He draws more water for the camel, which is drinking, when she pours the water on the ground.

"Why dost thou turn out the water?"

"I did not turn it out; thy camel drank it." And nevertheless she casts her glances and sees a dust in the distance. The Targui is coming. The woman says:

"Now I have trapped him for thee."

"Brava!" he cries, and addressing the Soufi: "Draw me some water that I may drink." He draws the water, and the Targui drinks. The woman says to him: "Kill him in the well. He is a good shot. Thou art not stronger than he is."

"No," he answered, "I do not want to soil a well of the tribes. I'll make him come up." The Soufi comes up till his shoulders appear. They seize him, hoist and bind him, and tie his feet together. Then they seize and kill his camel.

"Bring wood," says the Targui to the woman; "we'll roast some meat." She brings him some wood. He cooked the meat and ate it, while she roasted pieces of fat till they dripped upon her cousin.

"Don't do that," says the Targui.

She says, "He drew his sword on me, crying, 'Come with me or I will kill thee.'"

"In that case do as you like." She dropped the grease upon his breast, face, and neck until his skin was burnt. While she was doing this, the Targui felt sleep coming upon him, and said to the woman, "Watch over him, lest he should slip out of our hands."

While he slept the Soufi speaks: "Word of goodness, O excellent woman, bend over me that I may kiss thy mouth or else thy cheek. She says: "God make thy tent empty. Thou'lt die soon, and thou thinkest of kisses?"

"Truly I am going to die, and I die for thee. I love thee more than the whole world. Let me kiss thee once. I'll have a moment of joy, and then I'll die." She bends over him, and he kisses her.

She says, "What dost thou want?"

"That thou shalt untie me." She unties him. He says to her: "Keep silent. Do not speak a word." Then he unfastens the shackles that bind his feet, puts on his cloak, takes his gun, draws out the old charge and loads it anew, examines the flint-lock and sees that it works well. Then he says to the woman, "Lift up the Targui." The latter awakes.

"Why," says he, "didst thou not kill me in my sleep?"

"Because thou didst not kill me when I was in the well. Get up. Stand down there, while I stand here."

The Targui obeys, and says to the Soufi: "Fire first."

"No, I'll let thee fire first."

The woman speaks: "Strike, strike, O Targui, thou art not as strong as the Soufi."

The Targui rises, fires, and now the woman gives voice to a long "you—you." It strikes the *chechias* that fly above his head. At his turn the Soufi prepares himself and says:

"Stand up straight now, as I did for thee." He fires, and hits him on the forehead. His enemy dead, he flies at him and cuts his throat.

He then goes to the camel, cuts some meat, and says to the woman: "Go, find me some wood, I want to cook and eat."

"I will not go," she says. He approaches, threatening her, and strikes her. She gets up then and brings him some wood. He cooks the meat and eats his fill. He thinks then of killing the woman, but he fears that the people of his tribe will say, "Thou didst not bring her back." So he takes her on the camel and starts homeward. His cousins are pasturing their flocks on a hill. When he had nearly arrived a dust arose. He draws near, and they see that it is he. His brother speaks, "What have they done to thee?"

He answers, "The daughter of my uncle did all this."

Then they killed the woman and cut her flesh in strips and threw it on a jujube-tree. And the jackals and birds of prey came and passed the whole day eating it, until there was none left.

AHMED EL HILALIEU AND EL REDAH

Ahmed el Hilalieu was not loved by people in general. His enemies went and found an old sorceress, and spoke to her as follows: "O sorceress, we want you to drive this man out of our country. Ask what you will, we will give it to you!"

She said to them: "May God gladden your faces. Call aloud. Our man will come out and I will see him." They obeyed her, crying out that a camel had escaped. Straightway Ahmed goes to find his father, and tells him his intention of going to join in the search. He starts forth mounted on his courser, and on the way meets some people, who tell him, "It is nothing." He makes a half turn, not forgetting to water his horse, and meets at the fountain the sorceress, who was drawing water.

"Let me pass," he said to her, "and take your buckskin out of my way."

"You may pass," she answered. He started his horse, which stepped on the buckskin and tore it.

"You who are so brave with a poor woman," she said, "would you be able to bring back Redah Oum Zaid?"

"By the religion of Him whom I adore, you shall show me where this Redah lives or I'll cut off your head."

"Know, then, that she lives far from here, and that there is between her and you no less than forty days' journey."

Ahmed went home, and took as provisions for the journey forty dates of the deglet-nour variety, putting them into his pocket. He mounted his steed and departed.

He goes and goes without stopping, until he comes to the country of the sand. The charger throws his feet forward and buries himself in the sand up to his breast, but soon stops, conquered and worn out by fatigue. Ahmed el Hilalieu then addresses him:

> " My good gray horse, of noble mien, the sand,
> The cruel sand would eat your very eyes.
> The air no longer thy loud whinnies bears,
> No strength is left thee in thy head or heart.
> The prairies of Khafour I'll give to thee,
> With Nouna's eyes I'll quench thy thirst, by God.
> A mule's whole pack of barley shalt thou have
> That Ben Haddjouna shall bring here for thee."

In his turn the steed spoke and said: " Dismount, unfasten the breast-strap, tighten the girth, for some women are coming to show themselves to us in this country." Ahmed unfastened the breast-strap, then remounts and departs. While he proceeds he sees before him the encampment of a tribe, and perceives a horseman coming, mounted on a white mare, engaged in herding camels.

"Blessings upon you!" cried Ahmed; "you behind the camels!" The horseman kept silence, and would not return his salutations.

"Greetings to you," cried Ahmed again, "you who are in the middle of the camels." The same obstinate silence.

"Greetings to you, you who are before the camels." The horseman still was silent. Ahmed then said: "Greetings to you, you who own the white mare."

"Greetings to you!" replied the horseman.

"How comes it that you would not answer my greetings for so long?"

The horseman answered: "You cried to me, 'Greetings to you, you who are behind the camels.' Now, behind them are their tails. Then you said, 'Greetings to you, you who are in the middle of the camels.' In the middle of them are their bellies. You said, again, 'Greetings to you, you who are be-

fore the camels.' Before them are their heads. You said,
' Greetings to you, O master of the white mare.' And then I
answered to you, ' Greetings to you also.' "

Ahmed el Hilalieu asked of the shepherd, " What is your
name? "

" I am called Chira."

" Well, Chira, tell me where Redah lives. Is it at the city
of the stones or in the garden of the palms? "

" Redah dwells in the city. Her father is the Sultan. Seven
kings have fought for her, and one of them has refreshed his
heart. He is named Chalau. Go, seek the large house. You
will be with Redah when I see you again."

Ahmed sets out, and soon meets the wife of the shepherd,
who comes before him and says, " Enter, be welcome, and
may good luck attend you! " She ties his horse, gives him to
drink, and goes to find dates for Ahmed. She takes care to
count them before serving him with them. He takes out a
pit, closes the date again, puts them all together, and puts
down the pit. He ate nothing, and he said to the woman:
" Take away these dates, for I have eaten my fill." She looks,
takes up the tray, counts the dates again, and perceives that
none of them has been eaten. Nevertheless, there is a pit, and
not a date missing. She cries out:

> " Alas! my heart for love of this young man
> Is void of life as is this date of pit."

Then she heaved a sigh and her soul flew away.

Ahmed remained there as if in a dream until the shepherd
came back. " Your wife is dead," he said to him, " and if you
wish, I'll give you her weight in gold and silver."

But the shepherd answers: " I, too, am the son of a sultan.
I have come to pay this woman a visit and desire to see her.
Calm yourself. I will take neither your gold nor silver. This
is the road to follow; go, till you arrive at the castle where
she is."

Ahmed starts, and when he arrives at the castle, he stands
up in his stirrups and throws the shadow of his spear upon the
window.

Redah, addressing her negress, said to her: "See now what casts that shadow. Is it a cloud, or an Arab's spear?"

The negress goes to see, comes back to her mistress, and says to her, "It is a horseman, such as I have never seen the like of before in all my life."

"Return," said Redah, "and ask him who he is." Redah goes to see, and says:

> "O horseman, who dost come before our eyes,
> Why seekest thou thy death? Tell me upon
> Thine honor true, what is thine origin?

He answers:

> "Oh, I am Ahmed el Hilalieu called. Well known
> 'Mongst all the tribes of daughters of Hilal.
> I bear in hand a spear that loves to kill,
> Who'er attacks me counts on flight and dies."

She says to him:

> "Thou'rt Ahmed el Hilalieu? Never prowls
> A noble bird about the Zeriba;
> The generous falcon turns not near the nests,
> O madman! Why take so much care
> About a tree that bears not any dates?"

He answers:

> "I will demand of our great Lord of all
> To give us rain to cover all the land
> With pasturage and flowers. And we shall eat
> Of every sort of fruit that grows on earth."

Redah:

> "We women are like silk. And only those
> Who are true merchants know to handle us."

Ahmed el Hilalieu then says:

> "I've those worth more than thou amid the girls
> Of Hilal, clad in daintiest of silk
> Of richest dye, O Redah, O fifth rite."

And, turning his horse's head, he goes away. But she recalls him:

> " I am an orange, thou the gardener;
> I am a palm and thou dost cut my fruit;
> I am a beast and thou dost slaughter me.
> I am—upon thine honor—O gray steed,
> Turn back thy head. For we are friends henceforth."

She says to the negress, " Go open wide the door that he may come."

The negress admits him, and ties up his horse. On the third day he sees the negress laughing.

" Why do you laugh, negress?"

" You have not said your prayers for three days."

POEMS OF THE MAGHREB

—

[Translated by M. C. Sonneck and Chauncey C. Starkweather]

POEMS OF THE MAGHREB

ALI'S ANSWER

[ARGUMENT.—It is related that a young man named Aly ben Bou Fayd, falling in love with a young woman, begged his father to ask her in marriage for him. His father refused. Angered, Aly procured a gun, engraved his name upon it, and betook himself to the chase. His father having claimed this gun he answered :]

YOU ask the gun I have that bears my name.
   I will not give it, save against my will.

How comes it, father, that you treat me thus?
You say, " Bring back the gun to put in pledge."
Now, may God pardon you for acting thus!
I leave you in your land, and, all for you,
I swear by God I never shall return.

Your conduct is unwise. Our enemies
Insult me, O my father. And I think
That you will give up your ancestral home
And garden too. And can I after that
Recover my good gun?

           ·I shall not be
Enfeebled that I am no more with you.
No longer are you father unto me,
And I shall be no more your cherished son.
I think, my sire, that you are growing old.
Your teeth are falling out from day to day.
They whom you visit will not serve you more.

Your friends won't serve you longer, and your sire,
He who begot you, will not help you now.
In your adversity no help will come

From all your kindred's high nobility.
May God make easy all the paths you tread!

His uncle having threatened him with death, he answered:

Keep far away from him who has not come
To thee in his misfortune. Leave him free.
My uncle writes to me this very day
That if he held in his own hands the leaf
Of my life's destiny he'd blot it out.
If he had in his hands this leaf, O say to him:

Let him efface it openly, nor hide
You'll not be able, save with God's own help
To bear the separation. As for those
Who are so evil, we will spare them now.
The barrel of this gun is rusted red.
The lock is forceless, 'twill no longer act.
Misfortune overtake the man who leaves
His child to perish! For the least of things
He says to me, " Come, give me up this gun."

I go to seek the desert. I will go
Among the tribe they call Oulad Azyz,
And live by force. But, pray you say to her,
The fair one with the deftly braided hair,
I leave the tribe, but shall return for her.

I disappear, but shall come back for her.
And while I live, I never shall forget.
I swear it by the head of that sweet one
Who for the sake of Ali was accused.
The cup of passion which I offered her
O'ercame her lovely spirit's tenderness.

The cup of love intoxicated her.
O God, Creator of us all, give her
The strength to bear my absence! Sad for me
The hour I dream of her I love so well.
Her love is in my heart and burns it up.

My heart is sad. 'Tis love that crushes it.
It leaves my heart reduced to naught but dust.
So that I am consumed by vigils long,
And never taste refreshing sleep at all.
So that I'm like a bird with broken wings,

Just like a bird who tries to lift its wings!
And so my spirit is not healed. There comes
To me no comfort nor relief. The eyes
Of my beloved are as bright as day.
One word from her would send the friends to death.

IN HONOR OF LALLA AYCHA-EL-MANNOUBYYA

A fire burns at the bottom of my heart,
For love has conquered me, and I am now
His hostage and his prisoner. My soul
Is torn out from my body, and sweet sleep
Keeps far aloof from my tired eyelids' need.
'Tis Aycha causes this, the pretty one.
With blackest eyes, Aycha the pure, from whom
I'm parted now, whose name is finest gold.
Why? why? Oh, tell me, El Mannoubyya.

Why all this coldness, O my best beloved?
For thy dear love I have drunk deep of scorn.
For thy love, maiden with the darksome looks,
I wither while thou bear'st a port of oak.
The fire that burns me eats my very soul.
My spirit is distracted by these proofs.
O thou, rebellious to my warm desires,
My black-eyed beauty, if thou'rt vexed with me
I'll make apology before the world,
I'll bring an offering to thee at once,
The symbol of my homage. May it please!

Instruct me, sympathetic with my pain
Have you not said: " I'll bring thee soon good news "?
O come! That in my sleep my eyes may see
Thee coming toward me, my black-pupilled one!

Awaiting thy fair image I'm consumed,
I am exhausted. Why, El Mannoubyya?

I long have hoped to see thee, O my sweet.
And ever farther off appears the end
Of my awaiting. All my nights are passed
In cries for thee, as some poor mariner
Cries to the angry floods that dash aloft.
For thee I'm mad with love, my pretty one,
Struck with thy mien so full of nobleness.
And I alone must wither, 'mongst my friends.
O unpersuadable, with teasing eyes,
I am in a most pitiable state.
Since thou repell'st me and declin'st to keep
Thy promise to me, I'll not hesitate
To call thee before God.

              Unless thou deign'st
To cast thy looks on me the coming day,
I shall, all clad in vestments rich, make plaint
Unto the envoy of our God, the last
Of all the prophets. For thou said'st to me,
" I'll draw thee from the sea of thy despair."
I worship at thy sanctuary, sweet,
My beauty, with large eyes of darkest night.
Why? why? El Mannoubyya, tell me why.

Let thyself bend and call thy servitor,
Inhabitant of Tunis—city green.
I will apologize and come to thee,
O cruel one, with heavy frontlets dark.
We've heard the story of thy deeds so fine.
From common brass whene'er thou walk'st abroad,
Thou drawest silver pure, queen of thy time,
'Mongst men illumined by thy piety.
The wretch, led on by love, accosted thee.
Receiving grace, despite his base design
He was, nathless, forgiven and saved from sin;
So was it from eternity decreed.
They all consulted thee, queen of thy day,

'And thou didst answer: " This man truly loved.
Pour him a cup of wine." By thee he came
Unto perfection's acme, step by step.
Our Lord, all-powerful, gave to thee this power.

These are thy merits, fairest citizen!
To whom God gave strength irresistible.
O beauty with enchanting eyes, Aycha,
Our queen.

   Si Alimed Khoudja, greatest bard
Of all that time, has said: " I wrote these words
The year one thousand one hundred just,
But thou who read'st these lines, where'er it be,
Add to these numbers, after ninety-eight."
Now I salute all those united here
And him who hates me here I steep in scorn.
Why? why? El Mannoubyya! Why?

SAYD AND HYZYYA

Give me your consolation, noble friends;
The queen of beauties sleeps within the tomb.
A burning fire consumes my aching breast;
I am undone. Alas! O cruel fate!
My heart's with slim Hyzyya in the grave.

Alas! we were so happy a short while
Ago, just like the prairie flow'rs in spring;
How sweet to us was life in those dear days!
Now like a phantom's shadow she has gone,
That young gazelle, of utter loveliness.
Removed by stern, inevitable fate.

When she walked forth, not looking right or left,
My beauteous loved one rendered fools the wise.
Impressed thus was the great bey of the camp.
A gleaming poniard rested in his belt.
He went hemmed in by soldiers and a horde
Of horsemen, glad to follow where he led.

All haste to bring him costly gifts. He bore
A sabre of the Ind, and with one stroke
He cleaved a bar of iron, split a rock.
How many rebels fell beneath his blow!
Haughty and proud, he challenged all who came.
Enough now we have glorified the bey.
Speak, singer, in a song that's sweet and new,
The praises of the dainty girl I loved,
The daughter of good Ahmed ben el Bey.

Give me your consolation, noble friends;
The queen of beauties sleeps within the tomb.
A burning fire consumes my aching breast;
I am undone! Alas! O cruel fate!

She lets her tresses flow in all the breeze,
Exhaling sweet perfume. Thy brows are arched
In beauty's curve. Thy glance is like a ball
Shot from a Christian's gun, which hits the mark.
Thy cheek is lovely as the morning rose
Or bright carnation, and thy ruby blood
Gives it the shining brightness of the sun.
Thy teeth are ivory-white, and thy warm kiss
Is sweet as milk or honey loved by all.
Oh, see that neck, more white than palm-tree's heart,
That sheath of crystal, bound with bands of gold.
Thy chest is marble, and thy tender breasts
Are apples whose sweet scent makes well the ill.
Thy body is, like paper, shining, white,
Or cotton or fine linen, or, again,
Just like the snow that falls in a dark night.
Hyzyya lets her sash hang gracefully,
Down-falling to the earth, in fold on fold.
Her fine limbs jingle with gems she wears.
Her slippers clink with coupled rings of gold.

We were encamped at Bazer. Every day
At dawn I saw the beauty, and we were
So glad together! Every dawn I brought
My wishes to my love and followed fate
More happy than if I alone possessed

All riches and all treasures of the earth.
Wealth equals not the tinkle of her gems.
When I had crossed the mountain there I met
Hyzyya, and she walked amid the fields
With every grace, and made her bracelets ring.
My reason wandered, heart and head were vexed.

After a happy summer passed at Tell,
We came, my dearest one and I, Sahara-ward.

The litters now are closed, the powder sounds.
My gray horse to Hyzyya bears me swift.
The palanquin of my coquette's on route.
At Azal when night comes we pitch our tents.
Sydy-l-Ahsen is before us now;
Ez-Zerga, too. Then faring on we go
To Sydy Sayd, and Elmetkeouk,
And Medoukal-of-palms, where we arrive
At eventide. We saddle up at dawn,
Just when the breeze begins. Our halting-place,
Sydy Mehammed, decks this peaceful earth.
From there the litters seek El Mekheraf.
My charger gray straight as an eagle goes.
I wend to Ben Serÿer with my love,
Of tattooed arms. When we had crossed Djedy
We passed the wide plain, and we spent the night
At Rous-et-toual, near the gleaming sands.
Ben Djellal was our next day's resting-place;
And, leaving there, I camped at El Besbas,
And last at El-Herymek, with my love.

How many festivals beheld us then!
In the arena my good steed of gray
Fled like a ghost. And sweet Hyzyya there,
Tall as a flagstaff, bent her gaze on me,
Her smile disclosing teeth of purest pearl.
She spoke but in allusions, causing thus
That I should understand whate'er she meant.
Hamyda's daughter then might be compared
Unto the morning-star or a tall palm,
Alone, erect among the other trees.

The wind uprooted it, and dashed it down.
I did not look to see it fall, this tree
I hoped forever to protect. I thought
That God, divinely good, would let it live.
But God, the Master, dashed it to the earth.

I take up now my song. We made but one
Encampment, at Oned Itel. 'Twas there
My friend, the queen of damsels, said farewell.
'Twas in the night she paid the debt of death.
'Twas there my dark-eyed beauty passed away.
She pressed her heart to mine and, sighing, died.
My cheeks were flooded with a sea of tears.
I thought to lose my reason. I went forth
And wandered through the fields, ravines, and hills.
She bore my soul away, my black-eyed love.
The daughter of a noble race. Alas!
She still increased the burnings of my heart.

They wrapped her in a shroud, my noble love.
The fever took me, burning up my brain.
They placed her on a bier, all decked with gems.
And I was in a stupor, dull to see
All that was passing on that dreadful day.
They bore my beauty in a palanquin—
Her pretty palanquin—this lovely girl,
Cause of my sorrows, tall as a straight staff.
Her litter is adorned with odd designs,
Shining as brilliant as the morning-star,
And like the rainbow glowing 'midst the clouds,
All hung with silk and figured damask-cloth.
And I, like any child, was in despair,
Mourning Hyzyya. Oh, what pangs I felt
For her whose profile was so pure! She nevermore
Will reappear upon this earth again.
She died the death of martyrs, my sweet love,
My fair'st one, with Koheul-tinted lids!

They took her to a country that is called
Sydy Kaled, and buried her at night,
My tattooed beauty. And her lovely eyes,

Like a gazelle's, have never left my sight.
O sexton, care now for my sweet gazelle,
And let no stones fall on Hyzyya's grave.
I do adjure thee by the Holy Book
And by the letters which make up the name
Of God, the Giver of all good, let no
Earth fall upon the dame with mirror decked.

Were it to claim her from a rival's arms
I would attack three troops of warriors.
I'd take her from a hostile tribe by force.
Could I but swear by her dear head, my love,
My black-eyed beauty—I would never count
My enemies, 'though they a hundred were.
Were she unto the strongest to belong
I swear she never would be swept from me.

In the sweet name Hyzyya I'd attack
And fight with cavaliers innumerable.
Were she to be the spoil of conqueror,
You'd hear abroad the tale of my exploits.
I'd take her by main strength from all who vied.
Were she the meed of furious encounters
I'd fight for years for her, and win at last!
For I am brave. But since it is the will
Of God, the mighty and compassionate,
I cannot ward away from me this blow.
I'll wait in patience for the happy day
When I shall join thee. For I only think
Of thee, my dearest love, of thee alone!

My gray steed fell dead as he leaped. O friends,
After my love, he's gone and left me, too.
My charger, 'mid these hills, was of all steeds
The fleetest, and in fiercest war's attack
All saw him at the head of the platoon.
What prodigies he wrought in war's red field!
He showed himself ahead of all his peers.
A blood-mare was his mother. He excelled
In all the contests 'twixt the wandering camps;
I tourneyed with him careless of my fate.

When just a month had passed I lost the steed.
Hyzyya first, and then this noble horse.
He did not long survive my well-beloved.
They both are gone, leaving their last farewells.
O grief! my charger's reins have fallen down.
God made my life a death, in leaving me
Behind. For them I die. Oh, cruel hurt!
I weep for this just as a lover weeps.
Each day my heart burns fiercer, and my joy
Has fled away. Now tell me, O my eyes,
Why shed so many tears? Beyond a doubt
The pleasures of the world will capture you.
And will you grant no mercy? My sad soul
But sees its torments grow. My pretty one,
With lashes black, who was my heart's delight,
Now sleeps beneath the sod. I do but weep
And my head whitens for the beauteous one,
With pearly teeth. My eyes no longer can
Endure the separation from their friend.

The sun that lights us to the zenith climbs,
Then gains the west. It disappears from sight
When it has gained the summit of the vault
Celestial. And the moon, which comes and shines
At Ramadan, beholds the hour approach
Of sleep, and says farewell to all the world.
To these would I compare the lovely queen
Of all this age, the daughter of Ahmed,
Descendant of a race illustrious,
The daughter of Donaonda.

                              Such is
The will of God, all-powerful Lord of men.
The Lord hath shown his will and borne away
Hyzyya. Grant me patience, O my Lord!
My heart dies of its hurt. Hyzyya's love
Did tear it from me when she left the earth.

She's worth a hundred steeds of noble race,
A thousand camels, and a grove of palms

In Zyban. Yes, all Djryd is she worth,
From near to far. The country of the blacks,
Haoussa and its people is she worth,
Arabians of Tell and dry Sahara,
And the encampments of the tribes, as far
As caravans can reach by all the ways,
All nomads and all travellers, she's worth,
And those who settle down as citizens.
The treasurer of all riches is she worth,
My black-eyed beauty. And if thou dost think
This all too small, add all the cities' folk.
She's worth all flocks and nicely chisel'd gold,
She's worth the palms of Dra and Chaouyya;
All that the sea contains, my love is worth,
The fields and cities from beyond Djebel
Amour, as far as Ghardaya. She is worth
All Mzab, the plains of Zab. She pleases, too,
The people of the Goubba, holy folk,
And friends of God. She's worth all noble steeds
However richly housed—or evening's star
When twilight comes. Too small—'tis all too small
For my sweet love, sole cure of all my woes.
O God majestic, pardon this poor wretch!
Pardon, O Lord and Master, him who grieves!

Just three-and-twenty years! That was the age
Of her who wore the silken sash. My love
Has followed her, ne'er to revive within
My widowed heart. Console me, Mussulmans,
My brothers, for the loss of my sweet one,
Gazelle of all gazelles, who dwelleth now
In her cold, dark, eternal home.
Console me, O young friends, for having lost
Her whom you'd call a falcon on its nest.
Naught but a name she left behind which I
Gave to the camp wherein she passed away.
Console me, men, for I have lost my fair,
Dear one, that silver *khelkals* wore.
Now is she covered with a veil of stone,
On strong foundation laid. Console me, friends,

For all this loss, for she loved none but me.
With my own hands my love's chest I tattooed,
Likewise her wrists, with checkered patterns odd,
Blue as the collar of the gentle dove.
Their outlines did not clash, so deftly drawn,
Although without *galam*—my handiwork.
I drew them 'twixt her breasts, and on her wrists
I marked my name. Such is the sport of fate!

Now Sa'yd, always deep in love with thee,
Shall never see thee more! The memory
Of thy dear name fills all his heart, my sweet.

Oh, pardon, God compassionate, forgive
Us all. Sa'yd is sad, he weeps for one
Dear as his soul. Forgive this love, Lord!
Hyzyya—join them in his sleep, O God most high.
Forgive the author of these verses here!
It is Mahomet that recites this tale.

O Thou who hast the future in thy hand,
Give resignation to one mad with love!
Like one exiled from home, I weep and mourn.
My enemies might give me pity now.
All food is tasteless, and I cannot sleep.
I write this with my love but three days dead.
She left me, said farewell, and came not back.

This song, O ye who listen, was composed
Within the year twelve hundred finished now,
The date by adding ninety-five years more. [1295.]

This song of Ould-es-Serge we have sung
In Ayd-el-Rebye, in the singing month,
At Sydy-Khaled-ben Sinan. A man,
Mahomet ben Guytoun, this song has sung
Of her you'll never see again alive.
My heart lies there in slim Hyzyya's tomb.

THE AÏSSAOUA IN PARIS*

Come, see what's happened in this evil year.
The earthquake tumbled all the houses down,
Locusts and crickets have left naught behind.

Hear what has happened to those negro scamps,
Musicians—rogues, and Aïssaoua.
They spoke of nothing but their project great.
Bad luck to him who lacks sincerity!

On learning of the tour of Rayyato
They all began to cry and run about,
Half with bare feet, although the rest were shod.
The Lord afflicts them much in this our world.
'Twas only negroes, poor house-colorers,
Who did not follow them about in crowds.

The Christian Salvador put them on ship.
One felt his breast turn and exclaimed, " I'm sick."
A wench poured aromatics on the fire,
And thus perfumed the air. For Paris now
They're off, to see the great Abd-el-Azyz.

The Christians packed them like a cricket-swarm,
Between the sea and church, upon the wharf
He drew them, wonders promising, and led
Them but to beggary.

                    He takes them to
His land to show them to the chief of all
His masters, to the Emperor. He hopes
To get a present and thus pay them back,
Retaining all the money he advanced.

* Former student of the Medersa of Algiers, bookbinder, lutemaker, and copier of manuscripts, Qaddour ben Omar ben Beuyna, best known among his coreligionists as Qaddour el Hadby (the hunchback), who died during the winter of 1897–1898, has sung for thirty years about all the notables of his city. This lively poem was composed by him on the occasion of the departure for Paris of a band of musicians, singers, and Aïssaoua, who figured at the Exposition of 1867, under the direction of a professor of music named Salvador Daniel. The original is in couplets of six hemistichs.

Perhaps they'll show themselves upon some stage
Or elsewhere as his fancy leads. The blacks
Begin to dance to sound of castanets.
The Christians bet on what will happen next.

They say a letter has arrived which says
That they've suppressed ablutions and their prayers.
One has been very ill—" I do not know
What is the matter with me "—but the cause
Of all his illness was because he fell
On the perfuming-pans that they had brought.

For Imam they have ta'en the dancing-girl
Who leads the dances. With her boxes small
In basket made of grass, a picture fine!
Come, see it now; you'd think it was a ghost.

The Christian works them all, and most are seized
With folly. Would you know the first of all?
Well, sirs, 'tis Et-Try, and he is the son
Of one Et-Germezlyya. Never has
He thought of doing well, he lives for crime.

The shrewd " Merkanty " made a profit on them.
Et-Try served them as an interpreter.
The Christian ought to make them this year gain
A thousand d'oros. But I pray to God
To send those two men to the fires of hell.

Now Aly Et-Try is their manager;
He runs about all day, with naught achieved.
The Christian kept them in a stable shut,
And like a squad of soldiers took them out.
He herded them like oxen there, and naught
Was lacking but the drover's lusty cries.

Consider now the plight of Ould Sayyd,
The big-jawed one. He gained ten thousand francs,
And lost them all at gambling. Naught remains
Except the benches and some coffee-grounds.

The leader of musicians, wholly daft,
Whose beard is whiter than the whitest wool,
Has gone to Paris gay to see the sights.
(I hope he'll bring up in the fires of hell!)
If he comes back deceived, at least he'll say
He's been abroad, and dazzle all his friends.

The oboe-player, Sydy Ali, was
Barber and cafékeeper, eager for
A change, and crazy to get gold. " This trip,"
He told his friends, " is but a pilgrimage."
There's nothing lacking but the telbyya.

" I've taken trips before and with good luck.
I was the master, with my art acclaimed.
I was director of the Nouba, at
The court, when Turkey held the reins of power.
I was a court buffoon and broke my heart.
O Lord, why send'st thou not thy servant death?

" I left a workman in my shop so that
I might not lose my trade. I went to show
My oboe, for someone might ask for it.
I used to travel with musicians once."

God bless him!—what a workman. He conversed
With all the customers who passed that way.
He took them in the shop and told his case—
" I'm here for a short while." Then he began
To praise his patron, who, he said, would have
A gift for him.

                And his lieutenant, named
Oulyd-el-Hadj Oualy, is a fool
Who thinks his word superior to all,
And that there's no one like him in this world.
When he has gone there and come back again,
He will be perfect. All he contradicts
Who speak to him, and will not let them lift
A finger. Little love he hath for those

Who speak with candor, but he's very fond
Of liars, and always bids them come to him.

"My childhood was so pampered!" he remarks,
And flies into a passion if one doubts.
He only lives on semolina coarse,
And empty is his paunch, all slack and limp.
Yet every day he tells you how he's dined.

"I have discovered," he is wont to say
"A certain semolina lately brought
By a Maltese, who lives some distance off.
You never saw the like. I'm going to have
Some fine cakes made of it, and some *meqrout*."

And El-Hadj Mostefa was dragged along
By all these lies and by the love of gain.
If God had not abandoned him, he'd be
Still making lasts. But 'twas the crowd that led
Him on, and that is how it came to pass.

With them is donkey-faced Hamȳda, who
Sold flowers in the market-place. He left
His family no coins to live upon,
But told them only: "Moderate your pace.
I'll buy a house for you when I get back,
And we shall live in plenty evermore."

Sydy Ahmed et Tsoqba timbals had
As big as goat-skin bottles. He desired
To play in unison, but the musicians all
Abhorred him, for he could not keep in time.

The heart of Sydy Ahmed glows with love
For Ayn-bou-Sellouf, who is very fair.
I hope that cares and fainting-fits may swell
Him out, and yellow he will straight become
As yellow as a carrot in a field.

I love Sydy-t-Tayyeb when he sings
And plays the tambourine. Such ugliness

My eyes have never seen. You'd think he was
A clown. He says: " No one could vanquish me
Were I not just a trifle ill to-day."

Qaddour, the little cock, the drummer-boy,
Who hangs on walls and colors houses here
Or tars roofs with his mates, exclaims: " I took
This voyage just to get a bit of air."

Koutchouk stayed here, he did not go away.
Fresh apricots he sells down in the square.
" Repose," he murmurs, " is the best of foods,
And here my little heart shall stay in peace."

When Abd-el-Quader, undertaker's son,
Falls in his fits of folly, he binds round
His figure with a cord and does not lie
Inert and stiff. But still they scorpions see
In Allal's hand, Chaouch of Aïssaoua.

Faradjy—fop—eats fire and fig-leaves now;
The while Hasan the Rat excites him on
To doughty deeds with his loud tambourine,
Playing with all his might and all his soul.
They dragged the hedge-rows green of El Qettár
To pay this tribute to the Emperor.

That fop, Ben Zerfa, who chopped hashish seeds
Among us here, said: " We have had good luck
This summer, and I'm going to pay my debts.
I'll execute my drill with stick and sword
And serve my sheik the very best I can."

If you had seen Ben Zerfa as he ran,
So lightly, bearing on his sturdy back
A basket filled with, heaven alone knows what!
It looked like cactus-pears, the basket closed.

El Hadj Batâta—see his silly trance!
With shirt unbuttoned and with collar off,
And cap on eyes, at beating of the drums,
He shows his tuft denuded all of hair.

Even Móstafa ben el Meddâh desired
To go to Paris and his fortune make.
" On my return," he said, " I'll buy a lamp,
A coffee-tray, and goodly sugar-bowl;
A big and little mattress, too, I'll buy,
A carpet and a rug so soft and fine."
Es Snybla, bellows-faced, who used to work
For our good mayor, off to Paris went
To make the soldiers' coffee.   When he comes
Back home again, so much he will have earned.
He will be richer than a merchant great.

Oh, welcome, Sydy Omar!   All of Paris
Is charmed to see you, O my Snybla dear!
If he would only go to Mexico,
And stay there it would be a riddance good.

He is a cafékeeper, and his son
A baker.   For associate he has
Sydy Aly Mehraz, who does his work
Astride a thorn; he surely doth deserve
Our compliments.   All three you see are dressed
In duck, in fashion of the Christian men.
There's de Merzong; the people say he's good,
But still they fear him, he is so uncouth.
Good God!   When he begins aloud to cry
In Soudanese, it is enough to make
You fly to the antipodes away.

Oulyd ben Zamoum saw his cares increase—
Since he is a musician, as he thinks,
The world is rid of him.   And when he starts
To play the first string of the violin,
The while the Jewess doth begin to sing!

With him two Jews departed, and the like
You never saw on earth.   A porcupine
The first resembled, and the other one
Was one-eyed.   You should hear them play the lute!

Some persons heard my story from afar,
Oulyd Sydy Sáŷd, among them, and

Brymat, who laughed abundantly. And with
Them was the chief of Miliana. All
Were seated on an iron bench, within
The right-hand shop. They called me to their booth
Where I had coffee and some sweets. But when
They said, " Come take a smoke," I was confused.
" Impossible," I answered, " for I have
With Sydy Hasan Sydy Khelyl studied,
And the Senousyya. So I cannot."

Ben Aysa came to me, with angry air,
" The Antichrist," he said, " shall spring from thee.
I saw within that book you have at home
His story truly told." " You're right," said I,
" Much thanks ! " And then I laughed to see
Him turn his eyes in wrath.

                              He said to me
'Tis not an action worthy of a man ;
He glared at me with eyes as big as cups
And face an egg-plant blue. He wanted to
Get at me, in his rage, and do me harm.

With him my uncle was, Mahomet-ben-
El-Haffaf, who remains at prayer all day.
He heard this prelude and he said to them,
" It is not an affair." " Fear not," they said,
" For they will put you also in the song."

He's tickled by the urchins' eulogies,
Who praise him as the master of chicane.
" 'Tis finished now for thee to climb up masts."
They add : " You're but a laughing-stock for all.
You've stayed here long enough. You'd better go
And teach Sahary oxen how to read ! "

When I recited all these lines to Sy
Mahomet Oulyd el-Isnam, who has
To the supreme degree the gift of being
A bore he said to me, " Now this is song
Most flat." The mice in droves within his shop
Have eaten an ounce of wool.

He is installed
Within the chamber of El Boukhary.
In posture of a student, in his hands
Some sky-blue wool. " It is," he says, " to make
Some socks for little children, for I have
But little wool."

When I had finished quite
This dittyramb, and El-Hadj-ben-er-Rebha
Became acquainted with it, he began
To laugh, telling his beads the while, and then
His decoration from his wallet took,
Which had been there enclosed.

My song spread wide.
They found it savory. Respected sirs,
It is the latest Friday in the month
Of El Mouloud and in the year we call
Twelve hundred ninety-four, that I complete
This tale fantastic.

Would you know my name?
I am Qaddour, well known to all the world,
Binder to Sydy Boû Gdour, and attired
In gechchabyya-blouse. And if my back
Were not deformed, none could compete with me.

They told me, " When those folk come back again
Thou'd better hide thyself for fear of harm.
They'll break thy hump and send thee home to heaven."
" Oh, I'll protect myself," I said, " or else complain
To the police."

If I were not so busy
I'd still have many other things to say.
Those who have heard my prattle say it's good;
So say the singers and musicians, too,
Ez Zohra ben-el-Foul among them, who
Pays compliments to me, from window-seat.

He who hath nothing found that's useful here
Will find in this my song what suits him best.

But if he wants to see here something more,
Then stretch him 'neath the stick and give him straight
A thousand blows upon the belly; then
Take him away to the physician, who
Will bleed him well.

                                    And now may hearts not be
Made sad by what I have so lightly said.
I've placed myself among you, so that I
May not incur your blame, O brothers mine.
I've told you my deformity, and all
My miseries unveiled before your gaze.

SONG OF FATIMA *

My spirit is in pain, for it cannot
Forget my sweet gazelle, with eyes so black.
A fire burns in my heart, and all my frame
But wastes and withers.   Where's thy cure, O Taleb?

I find no medicine that cureth love,
In vain I search.   Sweet Fatima's the cause
Of all my woes, with *khelkal* tinted blue.
My heart endureth passion's pangs, my grief
Continues.   Where's thy remedy, O Taleb?
Thy remedy is lost, my good Lord Taleb.

Pray God for me, O Taleb, I implore.
But how to cure the malady of love?
There is no remedy, and all is lost.
I die for lack of strength to bear my trials.
It is to thee that I intrust myself,
The healer who must bring rest to my heart;
For now a living brand burns in my breast.
If thou art skilful, find a cure for me.

---

* This elegy is the work of a celebrated sheik of Tlemcen, Mahomet-
Ben-Sahla, whose period was the first
half of the eighteenth century. He left
a son, Ben Medien, a poet, too, and his
descendants still live, near Tlemcen, in
a village called Feddan-es-Seba.

Look in thy book and calculate for me
If thou canst quench the burning brand within.
I will become thy slave, and thou may'st keep
Me or at auction sell. Where is thy cure!
Thy remedy is lost, my good Lord Taleb.

The Taleb looked at me and said: " Take heart,
O lover, courage! Thou hast sipped, I see,
The cup of death already, and thou hast
Not long to live. But hear my counsel now.
Have patience! 'Tis the only thing that will
Sustain thee. Thou shalt thus obtain the gifts
Of Him who only knows thy future days.
Thy fate shall be unrolled according to
The will of God, the sovereign Lord most high.

" Turn to thy God. Beseech him constantly.
He hears with mercy and he knows all souls.
He turns away no one who comes to him.
He sees the bottom of their hearts, and lists.
Bear his decrees with patience camels show.
They walk from land to land and hope to lose
At last their burdens." Where's thy cure, O Taleb?
Thy remedy is lost, my good Lord Taleb.

O Taleb, search within thy book and find
The letters that give birth to friendship sweet.
Write them for me, and skilful be, I pray,
So God may give me happiness by them,
And cause my dear gazelle to pardon me,
And drive my bitter sorrows all away.
My punishment too long has lasted. I
Am tired of waiting. Never was adventure
More strange than mine.

                              My cares continue, and
I am fatigued with efforts obstinate.
The trouble that I've taken to deserve
That pretty one, has been for me like that
Of daring merchant who doth undertake
A venture and gets nothing back but loss

And weariness. Where is thy cure, O Taleb?
Thy remedy is lost, my good Lord Taleb.

The Taleb answered unto me and said:
" Support her rigors. Listen now to me,
And I will give thee counsel sound and good.
Turn thy true heart aside from memory.
Forget thy love as she's forgotten thee.
Courage! Her loss now wastes and makes thee pale.
For her thou hast neglected everything,
And sacrificed a good part of thy days.

" My counsels heed and turn me not aside.
Hear what sages in their proverbs say:
' That which is bitter never can turn sweet.'
' Leave him whose intercourse is troublesome,
And cleave to one who hath an easy way.'
' Endure the pangs of love until they pass,' "
Where is thy cure, O Taleb? Tell me where.
Thy remedy is lost, O good Lord Taleb.

If thou art powerful, Taleb, my excuse
Accept, and give assistance to my cause.
Thy words are all in vain, they but increase
My woes. For ne'er can I forget my love,
My dear accomplished beauty. While I live,
I love her, queen of beauties, and she is
Soul of my soul, light of my eyes, my sweet.

And, oh, how grows my love! A slave I'd be,
Obedient to a man despised. Perhaps
That which is far removed, the nearest comes.
And if the moment comes, thou know'st it well
Who knoweth all the proverbs! He that's well
Shall perish, and the invalid be cured.
Where is thy cure, O Taleb? Tell me where.
Thy remedy is lost, my good Lord Taleb.

And then the Taleb answered him and said:
" Thou'rt taken in the snares of Qeys—thou know'st.
He laid strong siege to Leyla's heart and then

Awaited trembling at the trysting-place.
Thou now hast wooed thy love for two long years
And she will not relent, nor speak to thee.
God bless us both!"

                          The Lord is generous.
He sees. If trouble comes, he'll make it pass.
My lot is sad and I am full of fear.
The mountains tall would melt and turn to sand
If I to them my sorrows should relate.
Where is thy cure, O Taleb? Tell me where.
Thy remedy is lost, O good Lord Taleb.

O Taleb, should I tell my tale of grief
Unto a sabre of the Ind, 'twould melt
On hearing my laments. My heart cannot
Endure these tortures, and my breast's on fire.

My tale is finished, here I end my song,
And publish forth my name along with it;
It is Ben Sahla. I do not conceal
How I am called, and in my black despair
I do not cease my lamentations loud.

O ye who have experienced the stings
Of love, excuse me now and blame me not
In this affair. I know that I shall die,
O'ercome by woe. The doctor of my heart
Protracts my suffering. He cures me not,
Nor yet cuts short the thread of my sad life.
Where is thy cure, O Taleb? Tell me where.
Thy remedy is lost, O good Lord Taleb.

THE CITY GIRL AND THE COUNTRY GIRL

O thou who hearest me, I will recite
One of these stories I am master of—
A tale that's true. By these I move the hearts
Of lovers like to thee, and I divert
Their minds with pleasant stories. As I hear,
So I relate them, and they please my friends,
By flow of wit and eloquence of thought.
I tell of beauties' battle. And my song
Is written in perfection, straight and clear.

Thinking of naught I walked along one day
When I had gone to see some beauties fair
Whose like I ne'er have seen in city nor
In country yet. I should have said
That they were sun and moon, and that the girls
Of that time were bright stars surpassing far
The Pleiades. The stars are envious
In their far firmaments, each of
The other. That's the reason why we see
Eclipses of the sun and moon.

My tale

Is true. The women, like unto the stars,
Are jealous also. Two young virgins met
The day I saw them, a sad day for them,
For one was jealous of the other one.

The citizeness said to the Bedouine:
" Look at thy similars and thou shalt see
In them but rustics, true dogs of the camp.
Now what art thou beside a city girl?
Thou art a Bedouine. Dost thou not dream
Of goat-skin bottles to be filled at dawn?
And loads of wood that thou must daily cut?
And how thou'rt doomed to turn the mill all night,
Fatigued, harassed? Thy feet, unshod, are chapped
And full of cracks. Thy head can never feel
The solace of uncovering, and thou,

All broken with fatigue, must go to sleep
Upon the ground, in soot and dust to lie,
Just like a serpent coiled upon himself.
Thy covering is the tatters of old tents,
Thy pillow is the stones upon the hearth.
All clad in rags thou hast a heavy sleep
Awaking to another stupid day.
Such is the life of all you country folk.
What art thou then compared to those who live
In shade of walls, who have their mosques for prayer
Where questions are discussed and deeds are drawn?"

The Arab woman to the city girl
Replied: "Get out! Thou'rt like a caverned owl.
And who art thou beside the Arab girls,
The daughters of those tribes whose standards wave
Above brave bands of horsemen as they speed?
Look at thy similars. The doctor ne'er
Can leave their side. Without an illness known
They're faded, pale, and sallow. The harsh lime
Hath filled thy blood with poison. Thou art dead,
Although thou seem'st alive. Thou ne'er hast seen
Our noble Arabs and their feats of strength,
Who to the deserts bring prosperity
By their sharp swords! If thou could'st see our tribe
When all the horsemen charge a hostile band,
Armed with bright lances and with shields to break
The enemy's strong blow! Those who are like
To them are famed afar and glorified.
They're generous hosts and men of nature free.
Within the mosques they've built and lodgings made
For *tolba* and for guests. All those who come
To visit them, bear gifts away, and give
Them praises. Why should they reside in town
Where everything's with price of silver bought?

The city girl replied: "Oh, Bedouine,
Thou dost forget all that thou hast to do.
Thou go'st from house to house, with artichokes
And mallows, oyster-plants, and such,

Thy garments soaked all through and through with grease.
This is thy daily life. I do not speak
Of what is hid from view. Thy slanders cease!
What canst thou say of me? Better than thee
I follow all the precepts of the Sonna
And note more faithfully the sacred hours.
Hid by my veil no eye hath seen my face:
I'm not like thee, forever in the field.
I've streets to go on when I walk abroad.
What art thou, then, beside me? I heard not
The cows and follow them about all day.
Thou eatest sorrel wild and heart of dwarf
Palm-tree. Thy feet are tired with walking far,
And thy rough hands with digging in the earth."

" Now what impels you, and what leads you on,"
The country girl of city girl inquired,
" To outrage us like this and say such words
Against us, you who are the very worst
Of creatures, in whom all the vices are
Assembled? You are wicked sinners all,
And Satan would not dare to tell your deeds.
You are all witches. And you would betray
Your brother, not to speak of husbands. You
Walk all unguarded in the street alone,
Against your husband's will. And you deny
Your holy faith. The curse of heav'n will weigh
Upon you when you go to meet your God.
Not one of you is honest. O ye blind
Who do not wish to see, whence comes your blindness?
You violate the law divine, and few
Among you fear the Lord. 'Tis in the country,
Amid the fields, that women worship God.
Why say'st thou that the city women sole
Are pious? Canst thou say my prayers for me?"

" What pleasure have the country girls?" replied
The city girl. " They've no amusements there.
There's nothing to divert the eyes. Their hands
They do not stain with henna, setting off

A rounded arm. Rich costumes they wear not,
Which cost some hundred silver pieces each,
Nor numerous garments decked with precious stones.
They are not coifed with kerchiefs of foulard
With flowers brocaded. Neither have they veils
Nor handkerchiefs of silk and broidered gold.
They never have a negress nurse to bring
Their children up and run on services
Throughout the house. And yet they boast as loud
As any braggart. Why bring'st thou the charge
That I a blameful life do lead, whilst thine
Deserves reproof? Dirt in the country holds
Supreme control. The water's scarce enough
To drink, with none left for the bath. The ground
Serves you as bed, and millet is your food,
Or rotten wheat and barley."

                    Then took up
The word, and spoke the Arab woman dark:
"Who are thy ancestors? Which is thy tribe
Among all those that fill the mighty world?
You're only Beny Leqyt, and the scum
Of people of all sorts. Thou call'st thyself
A city woman. What are city men?
Thy lords don't slander folk. 'Tis only those
Who come whence no one knows who have so rude
A tongue. Thou wouldst insult me, thou, of stock
Like thine, with such a name abroad! And thou
Wouldst taunt a Qorechyte, a Hachemite
Of glorious ancestors who earned their fame.
'Tis proper for a woman born of such
A stock illustrious to vaunt herself
Upon her origin. But thou, a vile
Descendant of a conquered race!

                      " Thou call'st
Thyself a Sunnite, yet thou knowest not
The three great things their Author gave to us:
(He knows all secrets.) First is Paradise,
Then the Koran, and then our Prophet great,

Destroyer of false faiths and for all men
The interceder. Whosoe'er loves him
Doth love the Arabs, too, and cleaves to them.
And whosoe'er hates them hates, too, in truth,
The chosen one of God. Thou hatest him,
For thou revil'st my ancestors, and seek'st
To lower their rank and vilify their fame.
Think on thine evil deeds, against the day
When in thy grave thou'lt lie, and that one, too,
When thou shalt rise again, insulter of
The Arabs, king of peoples on the earth."

" The Arabs I do not at all despise,"
The city woman said, " nor yet decry
Their honor, and 'tis only on account
Of thee I spoke against them. But 'tis thou
Who hast insulted all my family, and placed
Thy race above. He who begins is e'er
At fault, and not the one who follows. Thou
The quarrel didst commence. Pray God, our Lord,
To pardon me, as I will pray him, too,
And I the Arabs will no more attack.
If they offend me I will pardon them
And like them for our holy prophet's sake.
I shall awake in Paradise some day.
From them 'tis given, far beyond all price.
Frankly, I love them more than I do love
Myself. I love them from my very heart.
He who a people loveth shall arise
With them. And here's an end to all our words
Of bickering and mutual abuse."

I told them that it was my duty plain
To reconcile them. I accorded both
Of them most pure intentions. Then I sent
Them home, and made agreeable the way.
Their cares I drove away with honeyed words.
I have composed the verses of this piece,
With sense more delicate than rare perfume
Of orange-flower or than sugar sweet,

For those kind hearts who know how to forgive.
As for the evil-minded, they should feel
The *zeqqoum*. With the flowers of rhetoric
My song is ornamented: like the breast
Of some fair virgin all bedeckéd with stones
Which shine like bright stars in the firmament.
Some of its words will seem severe to those
Who criticise. I culled them like unto
A nosegay in the garden of allusions.
May men of lion hearts and spirit keen—
Beloved by God and objects of his care—
Receive my salutations while they live,
My countless salutations.

                I should let
My name be known to him who's subject to
The Cherfa and obeys their mighty power.
The *mym* precedes, then comes the written *ha*.
The *mym* and *dal* complete the round and make
It comprehensible to him who reads
Mahomet. May God pardon me this work
So frivolous, and also all my faults
And errors. I place confidence in him,
Creator of all men, with pardon free
For all our sins, and in his mercy trust,
Because he giveth it to him who seeks.

The country girl and city girl appeared
Before the judge, demanding sentence just.
In fierce invectives for a while they joined,
But after all I left them reconciled.

POPULAR TALES OF THE BERBERS

—

[Translated by René Basset and Chauncey C. Starkweather]

POPULAR TALES OF THE BERBERS

STORIES OF ANIMALS

The Turtle, the Frog, and the Serpent

ONCE upon a time the turtle married a frog. One day they quarrelled. The frog escaped and withdrew into a hole. The turtle was troubled and stood in front of his door very much worried. In those days the animals spoke. The griffin came by that way and said: "What is the matter with you? You look worried this morning."

"Nothing ails me," answered the turtle, "except that the frog has left me."

The griffin replied, "I'll bring him back."

"You will do me a great favor."

The griffin took up his journey and arrived at the hole of the frog. He scratched at the door.

The frog heard him and asked, "Who dares to rap at the door of a king's daughter?"

"It is I, the griffin, son of a griffin, who lets no carrion escape him."

"Get out of here, among your corpses. I, a daughter of the King, will not go with you."

He departed immediately.

The next day the vulture came along by the turtle and found it worrying before its door, and asked what was the trouble. It answered: "The frog has gone away."

"I'll bring her back," said the vulture.

"You will do me a great favor."

The vulture started, and reaching the frog's house began to beat its wings.

The frog said: "Who comes to the east to make a noise at the house of the daughter of kings, and will not let her sleep at her ease?"

"It is I, the vulture, son of a vulture, who steals chicks from under her mother."

The frog replied: "Get away from here, father of the dunghill. You are not the one to conduct the daughter of a king."

The vulture was angry and went away much disturbed. He returned to the turtle and said: "The frog refuses to come back with me. Seek someone else who can enter her hole and make her come out. Then I will bring her back even if she won't walk."

The turtle went to seek the serpent, and when he had found him he began to weep. "I'm the one to make her come out," said the serpent. He quickly went before the hole of the frog and scratched at the door.

"What is the name of this other one?" asked the frog.

"It is I, the serpent, son of the serpent. Come out or I'll enter."

"Wait awhile until I put on my best clothes, gird my girdle, rub my lips with nut-shells, put some *koheul* in my eyes; then I will go with you."

"Hurry up," said the serpent. Then he waited a little while. Finally he got angry, entered her house, and swallowed her. Ever since that time the serpent has been at war with the frog. Whenever he sees one he chases her and eats her.

THE HEDGEHOG, THE JACKAL, AND THE LION

Once upon a time the jackal went in search of the hedgehog and said to it: "Come along. I know a garden of onions. We will fill our bellies."

"How many tricks have you?" asked the hedgehog.

"I have a hundred and one."

"And I," said the other, "have one and a half."

They entered the garden and ate a good deal. The hedgehog ate a little and then went to see if he could get out of the entrance or not. When he had eaten enough so that he could just barely slip out, he stopped eating. As for the jackal, he never stopped eating until he was swollen very much.

As these things were going on, the owner of the garden arrived. The hedgehog saw him and said to his companion:

"Escape! the master is coming." He himself took flight. But in spite of his exhortations the jackal couldn't get through the opening. "It is impossible," he said.

"Where are those one hundred and one tricks? They don't serve you now."

"May God have mercy on your parents, my uncle, lend me your half a trick." "Lie down on the ground," answered the hedgehog. "Play dead, shut your mouth, stretch out your paws as if you were dead, until the master of the garden shall see it and cast you into the street, and then you can run away."

On that the hedgehog departed. The jackal lay down as he had told him until the owner of the garden came with his son and saw him lying as if dead. The child said to his father:

"Here is a dead jackal. He filled his belly with onions until he died."

Said the man, "Go, drag him outside."

"Yes," said the child, and he took him and stuck a thorn into him.

"Hold on, enough!" said the jackal. "They play with reeds, but this is not sport."

The child ran to his father and said, "The jackal cried out, 'A reed! a reed!'"

The father went and looked at the animal, which feigned death. "Why do you tell me that it still lives?"

"It surely does."

"Come away and leave that carrion." The child stuck another thorn into the jackal, which cried, "What, again?" The child went to his father. "He has just said, 'What, again?'"

"Come now," said the man, and he sent away his son. The latter took the jackal by the motionless tail and cast him into the street. Immediately the animal jumped up and started to run away. The child threw after him his slippers. The jackal took them, put them on, and departed.

On the way he met the lion, who said, "What is that footwear, my dear?"

"You don't know, my uncle? I am a shoemaker. My father, my uncle, my mother, my brother, my sister, and the little girl who was born at our house last night are all shoemakers."

"Won't you make me a pair of shoes?" replied the lion.

"I will make you a pair. Bring me two fat camels. I will skin them and make you some good shoes."

The lion went away and brought the two fat camels. "They are thin," said the jackal. "Go change them for others."

He brought two thin ones.

"They are fat," said the jackal. He skinned them, cut some thorns from a palm-tree, rolled the leather around the lion's paws and fastened it there with the thorns.

"Ouch!" screamed the lion.

"He who wants to look finely ought not to say, 'Ouch.'"

"Enough, my dear."

"My uncle, I will give you the rest of the slippers and boots." He covered the lion's skin with the leather and stuck in the thorns. When he reached the knees, "Enough, my dear," said the lion. "What kind of shoes are those?"

"Keep still, my uncle, these are slippers, boots, breeches, and clothes."

When he came to the girdle the lion said, "What kind of shoes are those?"

"My uncle, they are slippers, boots, breeches, and clothing." In this way he reached the lion's neck. "Stay here," he said, "until the leather dries. When the sun rises look it in the face. When the moon rises, too, look it in the face."

"It is good," said the lion, and the jackal went away.

The lion remained and did as his companion had told him. But his feet began to swell, the leather became hard, and he could not get up. When the jackal came back he asked him, "How are you, my uncle?"

"How am I? Wretch, son of a wretch, you have deceived me. Go, go; I will recommend you to my children."

The jackal came near and the lion seized him by the tail. The jackal fled, leaving his tail in the lion's mouth.

"Now," said the lion, "you have no tail. When my feet get well I will catch you and eat you up."

The jackal called his cousins and said to them, "Let us go and fill our bellies with onions in a garden that I know." They went with him. Arriving he tied their tails to the branches of a young palm-tree, and twisted them well. "Who has tied our tails like this?" they asked. "No one will come before you have filled your bellies. If you see the master of the garden approach, struggle and fly. You see that I, too, am bound as you are." But he had tied an onion-stalk on himself. When the owner of the garden arrived, the jackal saw him coming. They struggled, their tails were all torn out, and stayed behind with the branches to which they were fastened. When the jackal saw the man, he cut the onion stem and escaped the first of all.

As for the lion, when his feet were cured, he went to take a walk and met his friend the jackal. He seized him and said, " Now I've got you, son of a wretch."

The other answered, " What have I done, my uncle?"

" You stuck thorns in my flesh. You said to me, 'I will make you some shoes.' Now what shall I do to you?"

" It was not I," said the jackal.

" It was you, and the proof is that you have your tail cut off."

" But all my cousins are without tails, like me."

" You lie, joker."

" Let me call them and you will see."

" Call them."

At his call the jackals ran up, all without tails.

" Which of you is a shoemaker?" asked the lion.

" All of us," they answered.

He said to them: " I am going to bring you some red pepper. You shall eat of it, and the one who says, ' Ouch! ' that will be the one I'm looking for."

" Go and get it."

He brought them some red pepper, and they were going to eat it when the first jackal made a noise with his shoes, but he said to the lion, " My uncle, I did not say, ' Ouch! ' " The lion sent them away, and they went about their business.

The Stolen Woman

It is related that a man of the Onlad Draabad married his cousin, whom he loved greatly. He possessed a single slave and some camels. Fearing lest someone should carry off his wife on account of her beauty, he resolved to take her to a place where no one should see her. He started, therefore, with his slave, his camels, and his wife, and proceeded night and day until he arrived at the shore of the great salt sea, knowing that nobody would come there.

One day when he had gone out to see his camels and his slave, leaving his wife alone in the tent, she saw a ship that had just then arrived. It had been sent by a sultan of a far country, to seek in the islands of the salt sea a more beautiful wife for him than the women of his land. The woman in the tent, seeing that the ship would not come first to her, went out first in front. The people said to her, " Come on board in order to see the whole ship." She went aboard. Finding her to be just the one for whom they were seeking, they seized her and took her to their Sultan. On his return, the husband, not finding his wife, realized that she had been stolen. He started to find the son of Keij, the Christian. Between them there existed a friendship. The son of Keij said to him: " Bring a ship and seven men, whose guide I will be on the sea. They need not go astray nor be frightened. The city is three or four months' journey from here." They set sail in a ship to find the city, and were on the way the time that he had said.

Arriving they cast their anchor near the city, which was at the top of a high mountain. Their chief went ashore and saw a fire lighted by someone. He went in that direction. It was an old woman, to whom he told his story. She gave him news of his wife. They agreed to keep silence between themselves. Then the old woman added: " In this place there are two birds that devour people. At their side are two lions like to them, and two men. All of these keep guard over your wife."

He bought a sheep, which he killed; then he went to the two birds and threw them a part of it. While they were quarrelling over it he passed by them and came near to the two lions, to which he did the same. Approaching the two men, he found them asleep. He went as far as the place where his wife was in prison, and attracted her attention by scratching her foot. He was disguised and said to her, " I have sought you to tell you something." He took her by the hand. They both went out, and he swore that if she made the slightest noise he would kill her. He also asked her which was the swiftest boat for the journey. She pointed out the best boat there, and they embarked in it. There were some stones on board, and when he threw one at a ship it was crushed from stem to stern, and all on board perished.

He started to find the son of Keij. While they were at sea a marine monster swallowed them and the ship on which they were sailing. The chief took some pitch and had it boiled in a kettle. The monster cast up the ship on the shore of the sea. They continued their journey, proceeding by the seaside.

Behold one day they came to a deserted city. They desired to take what it contained of riches, silver, and gold. All of a sudden the image of an armed man appeared to them. They could not resist or kill him at first, but finally they destroyed him and took all the riches of the houses. When they arrived near the son of Keij he said to them: " I want only the ship." So the other man took the treasures and returned home with his wife.

The King, the Arab, and the Monster

In former times there was a king of the At Taberchant (the son of a negress), whose city was situated at the foot of a mountain. An enormous beast came against them, entered the city, and devoured all the people. The beast established itself in the city and stayed there a century. One day it was hungry. It came out into the plain, found some Arabs with their tents, their sheep, their oxen, their mares, and their camels. The beast fell upon them in the night and ate them all up, leaving the earth all white with their bones; then it went back to the city.

A single man escaped, thanks to his good mare. He arrived at a city of the At Taberchant and, starving, began to beg. The King of the Jews said to him: "Whence do you come into our country—you who invoke the lord of men [Mahomet]? You don't know where you are. We are Jews. If you will embrace our religion, we will give you food."

"Give me some food," said the Arab, "and I will give you some good advice."

The King took him to his house and gave him some supper, and then asked him what he had to say.

"An enormous monster has fallen upon us," said the Arab. "It ate up everybody. I will show you its city. It has two gates, one at the north and the other at the south."

"To-morrow," said the King.

When he awoke the next day, they mounted horses and followed the way to the gate of the monster's city. They looked at it and went away.

"What shall we do?" said the King.

"Let us make a great trap of the size of the entrance to the city, at the southern gate. At the northern gate we will place a forty-mule load of yellow sulphur. We will set it on fire, and then escape and see what will happen."

"Your advice is good," said the King.

They returned to the city of the Jews, ordered the smiths to make a big trap and commanded the citizens to furnish the sulphur. When all was ready, they loaded the mules, went to the monster's city, set the trap at the southern gate, and at the northern they placed the sulphur, which they set on fire, and then fled. The monster came out by the southern gate. Half of his body was caught in the trap that the two men had set. He was cut in two, filling the river with blood. The King and the Arab entered the city and found a considerable treasure, which they removed in eighty loads to the city of the Jews. When they had got back to the palace the King said to his companion: "Be my caliph. My fortune and thine shall be the same."

They sat down and had supper. The prince put in the stew some poison and turned it to the Arab. The latter observed what he had done and said, "Where did that bird come from?" When the King of the Jews raised his head to look, the Arab turned the dish around, placing the poison side of it in front of the King. He did not perceive the trick, and died on the spot. The Arab went to the gate of the city and said to the inhabitants: " I am your King. You are in my power. He who will not accept my religion, I will cut off his head." They all embraced Islamism and practised fasting and prayer.

THE LION, THE JACKAL, AND THE MAN

In times past, when the animals spoke, there existed, they say, a laborer who owned a pair of oxen, with which he worked. It was his custom to start out with them early in the morning, and in the evening he returned with one ox. The next day he bought another and went to the fallow land, but the lion came and took one ox from him and left him only one. He was in despair, seeking someone to advise him, when he met the jackal and told him what had taken place between him and the lion. The jackal demanded:
" What will you give me if I deliver you from the lion? "
" Whatever you wish I will give it to you."
" Give me a fat lamb," answered the jackal. " You will follow my advice. To-morrow when the lion comes, I will be there. I will arrive on that hill on the other side. You will bring your axe very well sharpened and when I say to you, ' What is that which I see with you now? ' you must answer, ' It is an ass which I have taken with me to carry barley.' I will say to you, ' I am looking for the lion, and not for an ass.' Then he will ask you, ' Who is speaking to you? ' Answer him, ' It is the nems! ' He will say to you, ' Hide me, for I am afraid of him.' When I ask you, ' Who is that stretched there before you? ' answer, ' It is a beaver.' I will say, ' Take your axe and strike, to know if it be not the lion.' You will take your axe and you will strike the lion hard between the eyes. Then I will continue: ' I have not heard very well. Strike him again once more until he shall really be dead.' " The next day he came to him as before to eat an ox. When the jackal saw him he called his friend and said, " Who is that with you? "
" It is a beaver which is before me."
The jackal answered: " Where is the lion? I am looking for him."

" Who is talking to you? " asked the lion, of the laborer.
" The ' nems.' "

" Hide me," cried the lion, " for I fear him."

The laborer said to him, " Stretch yourself out before me, shut your eyes, and don't move." The lion stretched out before him, shut his eyes, and held his breath.

The peasant said to the jackal, " I have not seen the lion pass to-day."

" What is that stretched before you? "

" It is a beaver."

" Take your axe," said the jackal, " and strike that beaver." The laborer obeyed and struck the lion violently between the eyes.

" Strike hard," said the jackal again; " I did not hear very well."

He struck him three or four times more, until he had killed him. Then he called the jackal: " See, I have killed him. Come, let me embrace you for your good advice. To-morrow you must come here to get the lamb which I will give you." They separated and each went his way. As for the peasant, the next day, as soon as dawn, he took a lamb, put it into a sack, tied it up, went into the court-yard and hung it up. Then while he went to get his oxen to till his fields, at that moment, his wife opened the sack, set the lamb free, and replaced it by a dog. The peasant took the sack and went to his work. He attached his oxen and set to work, till the arrival of the jackal. The jackal said to him, " Where is that promise you made me? "

" It is in the sack. Open it and you'll find the lamb which I give you."

He followed his advice, opened the sack, and saw two eyes which shone more brightly than those of a lamb, and said to the laborer, " My friend, you have deceived me."

" How have I deceived you? " asked the other. " As for the lamb, I put him in the sack. Open it well; I do not lie."

The jackal followed his advice, he opened the sack, a dog jumped fiercely out. When the jackal saw the dog he ran away, but the dog caught him and ate him up.

SALOMON AND THE GRIFFIN

Our Lord Salomon was talking one day with the genii. He said to them: "There is born a girl at Dabersa and a boy at Djaberka. This boy and this girl shall meet," he added. The griffin said to the genii: "In spite of the will of the divine power, I shall never let them meet each other." The son of the King of Djaberka came to Salomon's house, but hardly had he arrived when he fell ill; then the griffin carried away the daughter of the King of Djaberka and put her upon a big tree at the shore of the sea. The wind impelled the prince, who had embarked. He said to his companions, "Put me ashore." He went under the big tree and fell asleep. The young girl threw leaves at him. He opened his eyes, and she said to him: "Beside the griffin, I am alone here with my mother. Where do you come from?"

"From Djaberka."

"Why," she continued, "has God created any human beings except myself, my mother, and our Lord Salomon?"

He answered her, "God has created all kinds of human beings and countries."

"Go," she said, "bring a horse and kill it. Bring also some camphor to dry the skin, which you will hang on the top of the mast." The griffin came, and she began to cry, saying, "Why don't you conduct me to the house of our Lord Salomon?"

"To-morrow I will take you."

She said to the son of the King, "Go hide inside the horse." He hid there.

The next day the griffin took away the carcass of the horse, and the young girl departed also. When they arrived at the house of our Lord Salomon, the latter said to the griffin, "I told you that the young girl and the young man should be united."

Full of shame the griffin immediately fled and took refuge in an island.

Adventure of Sidi Mahomet

One day Mouley Mahomet summoned Sidi Adjille to come to Morocco, or he would put him in prison. The saint refused to go to the city until the prince had sent him his chaplit and his "dalil" as pledges of safety. Then he started on the way and arrived at Morocco, where he neither ate nor drank until three days had passed. The Sultan said to him:

"What do you want at my palace? I will give it to you, whatever it may be."

Sidi Adjille answered, "I ask of you only one thing, that is, to fill with wheat the feed-bag of my mule."

The prince called the guardian, and said to him, "Fill the feed-bag of his mule." The guardian went and opened the door of the first granary and put wheat in the feed-bag until the first granary was entirely empty. He opened another granary, which was soon equally exhausted, then a third, and so on in this fashion until all the granaries of the King were emptied. Then he wanted to open the silos, but their guardian went and spoke to the Sultan, together with the guardian of the granaries.

"Lord," they said, "the royal granaries are all empty, and yet we have not been able to fill the feed-bag of the saint's mule."

The donkey-drivers came from Fas and from all countries, bringing wheat on mules and camels. The people asked them,

"Why do you bring this wheat?"

"It is the wheat of Sidi Mahomet Adjille that we are taking." The news came to the King, who said to the saint, "Why do you act so, now that the royal granaries are empty?" Then he called together the members of his council and wanted to have Sidi Mahomet's head cut off. "Go out," he said to him.

"Wait till I make my ablutions" [for prayer], answered the saint.

The people of the makhzen who surrounded him watched him among them, waiting until he had finished his ablutions, to take him to the council of the King and cut off his head. When Sidi Mahomet had finished washing, he lifted his eyes to heaven, got into the tub where was washing, and vanished completely from sight. When the guardians saw that he was no longer there, they went vainly to continue the search at his house at Tagountaft.

THE HAUNTED GARDEN

A man who possessed much money had two daughters. The son of the caliph of the King asked for one of them, and the son of the cadi asked for the other, but their father would not let them marry, although they desired it. He had a garden near his house. When it was night, the young girls went there, the young men came to meet them, and they passed the night in conversation. One night their father saw them. The next morning he killed his daughters, buried them in his garden, and went on a pilgrimage.

That lasted so until one night the son of the cadi and the son of the caliph went to a young man who knew how to play on the flute and the rebab. "Come with us," they said to him, "into the garden of the man who will not give us his daughters in marriage. You shall play for us on your instruments." They agreed to meet there that night. The musician went to the garden, but the two young men did not go. The musician remained and played his music alone. In the middle of the night two lamps appeared, and the two young girls came out of the ground under the lamps. They said to the musician: "We are two sisters, daughters of the owner of the garden. Our father killed us and buried us here. You, you are our brother for this night. We will give you the money which our father has hidden in three pots. Dig here," they added. He obeyed, found the three pots, took them away, and became rich, while the two girls returned to their graves.

THE WOMAN AND THE FAIRY

A woman who was named Omm Halima went one day to the stream to wash at the old spring. Alone, in the middle of the day, she began her work, when a woman appeared to her and said: "Let us be friends, you and I, and let us make a promise. When you come to this spring, bring me some herma and perfumes. Cast them into the fountain which faces the qsar. I will come forth and I will give you money." And so the wife of Ben Sernghown returned every day and found the other woman, who gave her pieces of money. Omm Khalifah was poor. When she "became friends" with the fairy she grew rich all of a sudden. The people were curious to know how she had so quickly acquired a fortune. There was a rich man, the possessor of much property. He was called Mouley Ismail. They said to Omm Khalifah:

" You are the mistress of Mouley Ismail, and he gives you pieces of money."

She answered, " Never have I been his mistress." One day, when she went to the spring to bathe, the people followed her until she arrived. The fairy came to meet her as usual, and gave her money. The people surprised them together. But the fairy never came out of the fountain again.

HAMED-BEN-CEGGAD

There was in a city a man named Hamed-ben-Ceggad. He lived alone with his mother. He lived upon nothing but the chase. One day the inhabitants of the city said to the King:

" Hamed-ben-Ceggad is getting the better of you."

He said to them, " Tell me why you talk thus to me, or I will cut off your heads."

" As he only eats the flesh of birds, he takes advantage of you for his food."

The King summoned Hamed and said to him, " You shall hunt for me, and I will supply your food and your mother's, too." Every day Hamed brought game to the prince, and the prince grew very proud of him.

The inhabitants of the city were jealous of him, and went to the Sultan and said: " Hamed-ben-Ceggad is brave. He could bring you the tree of coral-wood and the palm-tree of the wild beasts."

The King said to him, " If you are not afraid, bring me the tree of coral-wood and the palm-tree of the wild beasts."

" It is well," said Hamed. And the next day he took away all the people of the city. When he came to the tree, he killed all the wild beasts, cut down the palm-tree, loaded it upon the shoulders of the people, and the Sultan built a house of coral-wood.

Seeing how he succeeded in everything, they said to the King, "Since he achieves all that he attempts, tell him to bring you the woman with the set of silver ornaments."

The prince repeated these words to Hamed, who said:

"The task you give me is harsh, nevertheless I will bring her to you." He set out on the way, and came to a place where he found a man pasturing a flock of sheep, carrying a millstone hanging to his neck and playing the flute. Hamed said to him: "By the Lord, I cannot lift a small rock, and this man hangs a millstone to his neck." The shepherd said: "You are Hamed-ben-Ceggad, who built the house of coral-wood?"

"Who told you?"

"A bird that flew into the sky." He added, "I will go with you."

"Come," said Hamed. The shepherd took the millstone from his neck, and the sheep were changed into stones.

On the way they met a naked man, who was rolling in the snow. They said [to themselves], "The cold stings us, and yet that man rolls in the snow without the cold killing him."

The man said to them, "You are Hamed-ben-Ceggad, who built the house of coral-wood?"

"Who told you that?"

"A bird that passed flying in the sky told me. I will accompany you."

"Come," said Hamed. After they had pursued their way some time, they met a man with long ears.

"By the Lord," they said, "we have only small ears, and this man has immense ones."

"It is the Lord who created them thus, but if it pleases God I will accompany you, for you are Hamed-ben-Ceggad."

They arrived at the house of the woman with the silver ornaments, and Hamed said to the inhabitants, "Give us this woman, that we may take her away."

"Very well," said her brother, the ogre. They killed an ox, placed it upon a hurdle, which they lifted up and put down with the aid of ninety-nine men.

" Give us one of your men who can lift this hurdle."

He who wore millstones hanging from his neck said, " I can lift it." When he had placed it on the ground, they served a *couscous* with this ox. The ogre said, " Eat all that we give you." They ate a little, and the man with the long ears hid the rest of the food. The brother continued: " You give us one of you who will go to gather a branch of a tree that stands all alone on the top of a mountain two days' march in the snow." The one who had rolled in the snow departed, and brought back the branch.

" There remains one more proof," said the ogre. " A partridge is flying in the sky; let one of you strike it." Hamed-ben-Ceggad killed it.

They gave him the woman, but before her departure her brother gave her a feather and said to her, " When anyone shall try to do anything to you against your will, cast this feather on the hearth and we will come to you."

People told the woman, " The old Sultan is going to marry you."

She replied, " An old man shall never marry me," and cast the feather into the fire. Her brother appeared, and killed all the inhabitants of the city, as well as the King, and gave the woman to Hamed-ben-Ceggad.

THE MAGIC NAPKIN

A taleb made a proclamation in these terms: " Is there anyone who will sell himself for 100 mitquals?" A man agreed to sell himself. The stranger took him to the cadi, who wrote out the bill of sale. He took the 100 mitquals and gave them to his mother and departed with the taleb. They went to a place where the latter began to repeat certain formulas. The earth opened and the man entered it. The other said to him, " Bring me the candlestick of reed and the box." He took this and came out keeping it in his pocket.

" Where is the box?" asked the taleb.

" I did not find it."

" By the Lord, let us go." He took him to the mountains, cast a stone at him, and went away. He lay on the ground for three days. Then he came to himself, went back to his own country, and rented a house. He opened the box, found inside a silk napkin, which he opened, and in which he found seven folds. He unfolded one. Genii came around the chamber, and a young girl danced until the day dawned. The man stayed there all that day until night. The King•came out that night, and, hearing the noise of the dance, he knocked at the door, with his·vezir. They received him with a red *h'aik.* He amused himself until the day dawned. ' Then he went home with his vezir. The latter sent for the man and said, "Give me the box which you have at home." He brought it to the King, who said to him : " Give 'me the box which you have so that I may amuse myself with it, and I will marry you to my daughter." The man obeyed and married the Sultan's daughter. The Sultan amused himself with the box, and after his death his son-in-law succeeded him.

The Child and the King of the Genii

There was a sheik who gave instruction to two talebs. One day they brought to one of them a dish of *couscous* with meat. The genius stole him and bore him away. When they had arrived down there he taught him. One day the child was crying. The King of the genii asked him, " Why do you cry ? "

" I am crying for my father and my mother. I don't want to stay here any longer."

The King asked his sons, " Who will take him back ? "

" I," said one of them ; " but how shall I take him back ? "

" Carry him back after you have stuffed his ears with wool so that he shall not hear the angels worshipping the Lord."

They had arrived at a certain place, the child heard the angels worshipping the Lord, and did as they did. His guide released him and he remained three days without awaking. When he came to himself, he took up his journey and found a mother-dog which slept while her little ones barked, although yet unborn. He proceeded and met next an ass attacked by a swarm of flies. Further on he saw two trees, on one perched a blue bird. Afterward it flew upon the other tree and began to sing. He found next a fountain of which the bottom was of silver, the vault of gold, and the waters white. He went on and met a man who had been standing for three days without saying a word. Finally he arrived at a village protected by God, but which no one entered. He met a wise man and said to him:

" I want to ask you some questions."

" What do you wish to ask me? "

" I found a mother-dog which was asleep while her little ones were barking, although yet unborn."

The sage answered, " It is the good of the world that the old man should keep silence because he is ashamed to speak."

" I saw an ass attacked by a swarm of flies."

" It is Pjoudj and Madjoudj of God (Gog and Magog) and the Antichrist."

" I met two trees, a blue bird perched on one, then flew upon the other and began to sing."

" It is the picture of the man who has two wives. When he speaks to one the other gets angry."

" I saw a fountain of which the bottom was of silver, the vault of gold, and the waters white."

" It is the fountain of life; he who drinks of it shall not die."

" I found a man who was praying. I stayed three days and he did not speak."

" It is he who never prayed upon the earth and is now making amends."

" Send me to my parents," concluded the child.

The old man saw a light cloud and said to it, " Take this human creature to Egypt." And the cloud bore him to his parents.

THE SEVEN BROTHERS

Here is a story that happened once upon a time. A man had seven sons who owned seven horses, seven guns, and seven pistols for hunting. Their mother was about to increase the family. They said to their father: " If we have a little sister we shall remain. If we have a little brother we shall go." The woman had a little boy. They asked, " Which is it? "

" A boy."

They mounted their horses and departed, taking provisions with them. They arrived at a tree, divided their bread, and ate it. The next day they started and travelled as far as a place where they found a well, from which they drew water. The older one said, "Come, let us put the young one in the well." They united against him, put him in, and departed, leaving him there. They came to a city.

The young man remained some time in the well where they had put him, until one day a caravan passing that way stopped to draw water. While the people were drinking they heard something moving at the bottom of the well. "Wait a moment," they said; they let down a rope, the young man caught it and climbed up. He was as black as a negro. The people took him away and sold him to a man who conducted him to his house. He stayed there a month and became white as snow. The wife of the man said:

"Come, let us go away together."

"Never!" he answered.

At evening the man returned and asked, "What is the negro doing?"

"Sell him," said the woman.

He said, "You are free. Go where you please."

The young man went away and came to a city where there was a fountain inhabited by a serpent. They couldn't draw water from this fountain without his eating a woman. This day it was the turn of the King's daughter to be eaten. The young man asked her:

"Why do you weep?"

"Because it is my turn to be devoured to-day."

The stranger answered, "Courage, I will kill the serpent, if it please God."

The young girl entered the fountain. The serpent darted toward her, but as soon as he showed his head the young man struck it with his stick and made it fly away. He did the same to the next head until the serpent was dead. All the people of the city came to draw water. The King said:

"Who has done this?"

"It is he," they cried, "the stranger who arrived yesterday." The King gave him his daughter and named him his lieutenant. The wedding-feast lasted seven days. My story is finished before my resources are exhausted.

HALF-A-COCK

In times past there was a man who had two wives, and one was wise and one was foolish. They owned a cock in common. One day they quarrelled about the cock, cut it in two, and each took half. The foolish wife cooked her part. The wise one let her part live, and it walked on one foot and had only one wing. Some days passed thus. Then the half-a-cock got up early, and started on his pilgrimage. At the middle of the day he was tired and went toward a brook to rest. A jackal came there to drink. Half-a-Cock jumped on his back, stole one of his hairs, which it put under its wing and resumed its journey. It proceeded until evening and stopped under a tree to pass the night there. It had not rested long when it saw a lion pass near the tree where it was lying. As soon as it perceived the lion it jumped on its back and stole one of its hairs, which it put with that of the jackal. The next morning it got up early and took up its journey again. Arrived at the middle of a forest, it met a boar and said:

"Give me a hair from your back, as the king of the animals and the trickiest of them have done—the jackal and the lion."

The boar answered, "As these two personages so important among the animals have done this, I will also give you what you request." He plucked a hair from his back and gave it to Half-a-Cock. The latter went on his way and arrived at the palace of a king. It began to crow and to say:

"To-morrow the King will die, and I will take his wife."

Hearing these words the King gave to his negroes the command to seize Half-a-Cock, and cast him into the middle of the sheep and goat-pen to be trampled upon and killed by them, so that the King might get rid of his crowing. The negroes seized him and cast him into the pen to perish. When he got there Half-a-Cock took from under his wing the jackal's hair and burnt it in the fire. As soon as it was near the fire the jackal came and said:

"Why are you burning my hair? As soon as I smelled it, I came running."

Half-a-Cock replied, "You see what situation I am in. Get me out of it."

"That is an easy thing," said the jackal, and immediately

blowed in order to summon his brothers. They gathered around him, and he gave them this command: "My brothers, save me from Half-a-Cock, for it has a hair from my back which it has put in the fire. I don't want to burn. Take Half-a-Cock out of the sheep-pen, and you will be able to take my hair from its hands." At once the jackals rushed to the pen, strangled everything that was there, and rescued Half-a-Cock. The next day the King found his stables deserted and his animals killed. He sought for Half-a-Cock, but in vain. The latter, the next day at the supper hour, began to crow as it did the first time. The prince called his negroes and said to them:

"Seize Half-a-Cock and cast him into the cattle-yard so that it may be crushed under their feet."

The negroes caught Half-a-Cock and threw him into the middle of the cow-pen. As soon as it reached there, it took the lion's hair and put it into the fire. The lion came, roaring, and said:

"Why do you burn my hair? I smelled from my cave the odor of burning hair, and came running to learn the motive of your action."

Half-a-Cock answered: "You see my situation. Help me out of it."

The lion went out and roared to call his brothers. They came in great haste and said to him, "Why do you call us now?"

"Take the Half-a-Cock from the ox-yard, for it has one of my hairs, which it can put into the fire. If you don't rescue Half-a-Cock, it will burn the hair, and I don't want to smell the odor of burning hair while I am alive."

His brothers obeyed. They at once killed all the cattle in the pen. The King saw that his animals were all dead, and he fell into such a rage that he nearly strangled. He looked for Half-a-Cock to kill it with his own hands. He searched a long time without finding it, and finally went home to rest. At sunset Half-a-Cock came to his usual place and crowed as on the former occasions. The King called his negroes and said to them:

"This time when you have caught Half-a-Cock, put it in a house and shut all the doors till morning. I will kill it myself."

The negroes seized him immediately and put him in the treasure-room. When it got there, it saw money under its feet. It waited till it had nothing to fear from the masters of the house, who were all sound asleep, took from under its wing the hair of the boar, started a fire, and placed the hair in it. At once the boar came running and shaking the earth. It thrust its head against the wall. The wall shook and half of it fell down, and going to Half-a-Cock the boar said:

" Why are you burning my hair at this moment? "

" Pardon me, you see the situation in which I am, without counting what awaits me in the morning, for the King is going to kill me with his own hands if you don't get me out of this prison."

The boar replied: " The thing is easy; fear not, I will open the door so that you may go out.   In fact, you have stayed here long enough.   Get up, go and take money enough for you and your children."

Half-a-Cock obeyed.   It rolled in the gold, took all that stuck to its wing and its foot, and swallowed as much as it could hold.   It took the road it had followed the first day and when it had arrived near the house it called the mistress and said: " Strike now, be not afraid to kill me."   His mistress began to strike until Half-a-Cock called from beneath the mat: " Enough now.   Roll the mat."

She obeyed and saw the earth all shining with gold.

At the time when Half-a-Cock returned from his pilgrimage the two women owned a dog in common.   The foolish one seeing that her companion had received much money said to her:

" We will divide the dog between us."

The wise woman answered: "We can't do anything with it.   Let it live, I will give you my half.   Keep it for yourself. I have no need of it."

The foolish one said to the dog, " Go on a pilgrimage as Half-a-Cock did and bring me some gold."

The dog started to carry out the commands of his mistress. She began her journey in the morning and came to a fountain. As she was thirsty she started to drink.   As she stopped she saw in the middle of the fountain a yellow stone.   She took it in her mouth and ran back home. When she reached the house she called her mistress and said to her:

" Get ready the mats and the rods, you see that I have come back from the pilgrimage."

The foolish one prepared the mats under which the dog ran as soon as she heard the voice of her mistress and said, " Strike gently." The woman seized the rods and struck with all the force possible. The dog cried out to her a long while for her to stop the blows. Her mistress refused to stop until the animal was cold. She lighted up the mats and found the dog dead with the yellow stone in its mouth.

Strange Meetings

Once upon a time a man was on a journey and he met a mare who grazed in the meadow. She was thin, lean, and had only skin and bone. He went on until he came to a place where he found a mare which was fat, although she did not eat. He went on further until he met a sheep which kicked against a rock till evening to pass the night there. Advancing he met a serpent which hung in a hole from which it could not get out. Farther on, he saw a man who played with a ball, and his children were old men. He came to an old man who said to him:

" I will explain all that to you. The lean mare which you saw represents the rich man whose brothers are poor. The fat mare represents the poor man whose brothers are rich. The serpent which swings unable to enter nor to leave the hole is the picture of the word which once spoken and heard can never go back. The sheep which kicks against the rock to pass the night there, is the man who has an evil house. The one whose children you saw aged while he was playing ball, what does he represent? That is the man who has taken a pretty wife and does not grow old. His children have taken bad ones.

The King and His Family

In times gone by a king reigned over Maghreb. He had four sons. He started, he, his wife, and his children, for the Orient. They set sail, but their ship sank with them. The waves bore them all in separated directions. One wave took the wife; another bore the father alone to the middle of the sea on an island where he found a mine of silver. He dug out enough silver until he had a great quantity and he established himself in the country. His people after heard tell of him and learned that he dwelt in the midst of the sea. They built houses until there was a great city. He was king of that country. Whoever came poor to him he gave him pieces of money. A poor man married his wife. As for his sons, they applied themselves to a study, each in a different country. They all became learned men and feared God. The King had a search made for *tolbas* who should worship God. The first of the brothers was recommended to him. He sent for him. He sought also a *khodja*. The second brother was designated. He summoned him to the court. The prince also especially wanted an *adel*. Another brother was pointed to him. He made him come to him as, indeed, he also did the *imam*, who was none other than the fourth brother. They arrived at their father's without knowing him or being known by him. The wife and the man who had espoused her also came to the King to make complaint. When they arrived the wife went alone that night to the palace. The prince sent for the four *tolba* to pass the night with him until morning. During the night he spied upon them to see who they were. One of them said to the others, " Since sleep comes not upon us, let each one make known who he is."

One said: " My father was a king. He had much money and four sons whose names were like yours."

Another said: " My father was a king. My case is like yours."

Another said: " My father was a king. My case is like yours."

The fourth said in his turn: " My father, too, was a king. My case is like that of your three. You are my brothers."

Their mother overheard them and took to weeping until day.

They took her to the prince, who said, " Why do you weep? "

She answered: " I was formerly the wife of a king and we had four sons. We set sail, he, our children, and I. The ship which bore us was wrecked. Each one was borne away alone, until yesterday when they spoke before me during the night and showed me what had happened to them, to their father, and to their mother."

The King said, " Let me know your adventure."

They told him all that had happened. Then the prince arose, weeping, and said, " You are my children," and to the woman, " You are my wife." God reunited them.

BEDDOU

Two men, one of whom was named Beddou and the other Amkammel, went to market bearing a basket of figs. They met a man who was working, and said to him:

" God assist you! "

" Amen! " he answered. One of them wanted to wash himself, but there was no water. The laborer, him who was with him (*sic*), said, " What is your name? "

" Beddou."

" By the Lord, Beddou, watch my oxen while I go to drink."

" Go! "

When he had gone, he took away one of the oxen. On his return the laborer saw that one was missing. He went to the other traveller and asked him:

" By my father, what is your name? "

" Amkammel Ouennidhui " (" The Finisher "), he answered.

" By the Lord, Amkammel Ouennidhui, watch this ox for me while I go look for the one that is gone."

" Go! "

He stole the other one. When the laborer returned he didn't even find the second.

The two thieves went away, taking the oxen. They killed them to roast them. One drank all the water of the sea, the

other all the fresh water, to wash it down. When they had
finished, one stayed there to sleep, the other covered him with
ashes. The former got up to get a drink and the ashes fell
on the road. When he came back, the second covered himself with the ox-head. His brother, who had gone to get a
drink, was afraid, and ran away. They divided the other ox
to eat it. The one who had drunk the sea-water now drank
fresh water, and the one who had drunk fresh water now
drank sea-water. When they had finished their repast they
took up their journey. They found an old woman who had
some money, upon which she was sitting. When they arrived
they fought. She arose to separate them. One of them took
her place to pass the night, and pretended that he was dead.
The old woman said to him:

"Get up, my son."

He refused. In the evening one of them stole the money,
and said to his brother:

"Arise! Let us go!"

They went away to a place where was sleeping the one who
had taken the money. The other took away the *dirkhems* and
departed, leaving the first asleep. When he awaked he found
nothing. He started in pursuit of the other, and when he
arrived he found him dying of illness. The latter had said to
his wife, "Bury me." She buried him. He who had first stolen
the money went away. He said, "It is an ox."

"It is I, my friend," he cried. "Praise be to God, my
friend! May your days pass in happiness!" Beddou said to
him: "Let us go for a hunt."

They went away alone. Beddou added: "I will shave you."

He shaved him, and when he came to the throat he killed
him and buried his head. A pomegranate-tree sprang up at
this place. One day Beddou found a fruit, which he took to
the King. When he arrived he felt that it was heavy. It was
a head. The King asked him:

"What is that?"

"A pomegranate."

"We know what you have been doing," said the King, and
had his head cut off. My story is finished.

The Language of the Beasts

Once upon a time there was a man who had much goods. One day he went to market. There came a greyhound, which ate some meat. The butcher gave it a blow, which made it yelp. Seeing this, the heart of the man was touched with compassion. He bought of the butcher half a piece of meat and flung it to the greyhound. The dog took it and went away. It was the son of a king of the nether world.

Fortune changed with the man. He lost all his possessions, and began to wash for people. One day, he had gone to wash something, he stretched it on the sand to dry. A jerboa appeared with a ring in its ear. The man ran after it, killed it, hid the ring, made a fire, cooked the jerboa and ate it. A woman came out of the earth, seized him, and demanded, " Haven't you seen my son, with an ear-ring? "

" I haven't seen anybody," he answered; " but I saw a jerboa which had a ring in its ear."

" It is my son." She drew him under the earth and told him: " You have eaten my son, you have separated me from him. Now I will separate you from your children, and you shall work in the place of my son." He who was changed into a greyhound saw this man that day, and said to him: " It is you who bought some meat for a greyhound and threw it to him? "

" It is I."

" I am that greyhound. Who brought you here? "

" A woman," answered the man, and he recounted all his adventure.

" Go and make a complaint to the King," answered the other. " I am his son. I'll tell him: ' This man did me a good service.' When he asks you to go to the treasure and take as much money as you wish, answer him: ' I don't want any. I only want you to spit a benediction into my mouth.' If he asks you, ' Who told you that? ' answer, ' Nobody.' "

The man went and found the King and complained of the woman. The King called her and asked her: " Why have you taken this man captive? "

" He ate my son."

" Why was your son metamorphosed into a jerboa? When

men see one of those they kill him and eat him." Then addressing the man: "Give her back the ear-ring." He gave it to her.

"'Go," said the King, "take this man to the place from which you brought him."

The son of the King then said to his father: "This man did me a favor; you ought to reward him."

The King said to him: "Go to the treasure, take as much money as you can."

"I don't want money," he answered; "I want you to spit into my mouth a benediction."

"Who told you that?"

"Nobody."

"You will not be able to bear it."

"I will be able."

"When I have spat into your mouth, you will understand the language of beasts and birds; you will know what they say when they speak; but if you reveal it to the people you will die."

"I will not reveal it." So the King spat into his mouth and sent him away, saying to the woman, "Go and take him back where you found him." She departed, and took him back there.

He mounted his ass and came back to his house. He arranged the load and took back to the people the linen he had washed. Then he remounted the beast to go and seek some earth. He was going to dig when he heard a crow say in the air:

"Dig beneath; you will sing when God has made you rich."

He understood what the crow said, dug beneath, and found a treasure. He filled a basket with it. On the top he put a little earth and went home, but often returned to the spot. On one of these occasions his ass met a mule, which said:

"Are you working still?"

The ass replied: "My master has found a treasure and he is taking it away."

The mule answered: "When you are in a crowd balk and throw the basket to the ground. People will see it, all will be discovered, and your master will leave you in peace."

The man had heard every word of this. He filled his basket

with earth only. When they arrived at a crowd of people the ass kicked and threw the load to the ground. Her master beat her till she had enough. He applied himself to gathering the treasure, and became a rich merchant.

He had at home some chickens and a dog. One day he went into the granary, and a hen followed him and ate the grain. A cock said to her:

"Bring me a little."

She answered, "Eat for yourself."

The master began to laugh. His wife asked him:

"What are you laughing at?"

"Nothing."

"You are laughing at me."

"Not at all."

"You must tell me what you are laughing at."

"If I tell you I shall die."

"You shall tell me, and you shall die."

"To-night." He brought out some grain and said to his wife, "Give alms." He invited the people, bade them to eat, and when they had gone he brought food to the dog, but he would not eat. The neighbor's dog came, as it did every day, to eat with his dog. To-day it found the food intact.

"Come and eat," it said.

"No," the dog answered.

"Why not?"

Then the dog told the other: "My master, hearing the chickens talk, began to laugh. His wife asked him: 'Why are you laughing?' 'If I tell you, I shall die.' 'Tell me and die.' That is why," continued the dog, "he has given alms, for when he reveals his secret he will die, and I shall never find anyone to act as he has."

The other dog replied: "As he knows our language, let him take a stick and give it to his wife until she has had enough. As he beats her let him say: 'This is what I was laughing at. This is what I was laughing at. This is what I was laughing at,' until she says to him, 'Reveal to me nothing.'"

The man heard the conversation of the dogs, and went and got a stick. When his wife and he went to bed she said to him, "Tell me that now."

Then he took the stick and beat her, saying: "This is what I was laughing at. This is what I was laughing at. This is what I was laughing at," until she cried out:

"Don't tell it to me. Don't tell it to me. Don't tell it to me."

He left her alone. When the dogs heard that, they rejoiced, ran out on the terrace, played, and ate their food. From that day the wife never again said to her husband, "Tell me that!" They lived happy ever after. If I have omitted anything, may God forgive me for it.

THE APPLE OF YOUTH

There once lived a king who had five daughters and no sons. They grew up. He wanted them to marry, but they would not have any of the young men of the city. A youth came from a far country and stood under the castle, beneath the window of the youngest daughter. She saw him, and told her father she would marry him.

"Bring him in," said the King.

"He will come to-morrow."

"God be praised," said the King, "that you are pleased with us."

The young man answered, "Give me your daughter for a wife."

"Advise me," said the King.

The stranger said, "Go and wait till to-morrow."

The next day the young man said to the King: "Make all the inhabitants of the city come out. You will stand with the clerks at the entrance to the gate. Dress your daughters and let them choose their husbands themselves."

The people began to come out. The eldest daughter struck one of them on the chest with an apple, and they said: "That daughter has chosen a husband. Bravo!" Each one of the daughters thus selected a husband, and the youngest kept hers. A little while afterward, the King received a visit from one of his sons-in-law, who said to him, "What do you want us to give you?"

"I'll see what my daughters want," he answered. "Come back in six days."

When they went to see their wives the King said to them, " I will ask of you a thing about which they have spoken to me."

" What is it? We are anxious to know."

" It is an apple, the odor of which gives to the one who breathes it youth, no matter what his age may be."

" It is difficult," they answered. " We know not where it can be found."

" If you do not bring it to me, you cannot marry my daughter."

They kept silent, and then consulted with each other. The youngest said to them, " Seek the means to satisfy the King."

" Give us your advice——"

" Father-in-law, to-morrow we shall bring you the apple." His brothers-in-law added: " Go out. To-morrow we will meet you outside the city."

The next day they all five met together. Four of them said to the other, " Advise us or we will kill you."

" Cut off your fingers," he said.

The first one began, and the three others did the same. The youngest one took them and put them into his game-bag, and then he added, " Wait near the city till I come back."

He went out into the desert and came to the city of the ogress. He entered, and found her ready to grind some wheat. He said to the ogress, " Show me the apple whose color gives eternal youth to the old man who smells it."

" You are in the family of ogres," she said. " Cut a hair from the horse of their King. When you go into the garden cast this hair into the fire. You will find a tree, from which you must pick five fruits. When plucking them do not speak a word, and keep silence on your return. It is the smallest fruit that possesses the magic power."

He took the apple and went back to the city, where he found his companions. He concealed in his breast the wonderful fruit, and gave the others to his brothers-in-law, one to each. They entered the palace of the King, who was overjoyed to see them, gave them seats, and asked them, " Have you brought it or not?"

" We have brought it," they answered.

He said to the eldest, " Give me your apple first."

He took a mirror in his left hand, and the fruit in the right hand, bent down, and inhaled the odor of the apple, but without results. He threw it down upon the ground. The others gave him their apples, with no more success.

"You have deceived me," he said to them. "The apples do not produce the effect that I sought."

Addressing, then, the stranger, he said, "Give me your apple."

The other son-in-law replied: "I am not of this country. I will not give you my fruit."

"Give it to me to look at," said the King. The young man gave it to him, saying, "Take a mirror in your right hand and the apple in your left hand."

The King put the apple to his nose, and, looking at his beard, saw that it became black. His teeth became white. He grew young again. "You are my son," he said to the young man. And he made a proclamation to his subjects, "When I am dead he shall succeed me on the throne." His son-in-law stayed some time with him, and after the death of the King he reigned in his place and did not marry the other daughters of the King to his companions.

POPULAR TALES OF THE KABYLES

—

[*Translated by J. Rivière and Chauncey C. Starkweather*]

POPULAR TALES OF THE KABYLES

ALI AND OU ALI

ALI and Ou Ali were two friends. One day they met at the market. One of them bore ashes and the other carried dust. The first one had covered his goods with a little flour. The other had concealed his merchandise under some black figs. " Come, I will sell you some flour," said Ali.

" Come, I will sell you some black figs," answered Ou Ali.

Each regained his own horse. Ali, who thought he was carrying flour, found, on opening his sack, that it was only ashes. Ou Ali, who thought he was bearing black figs, found on opening his sack that it was nothing but dust. Another day they again greeted each other in the market. Ali smiled. Ou Ali smiled, and said to his friend:

" For the love of God, what is your name? "

" Ali; and yours? "

" Ou Ali."

Another time they were walking together, and said to each other:

" Let us go and steal."

One of them stole a mule and the other stole a rug. They passed the night in the forest. Now, as the snow was falling, Ali said to Ou Ali:

" Give me a little of your rug to cover me."

Ou Ali refused. " You remember," he added, " that I asked you to put my rug on your mule, and you would not do it." An instant afterward Ali cut off a piece of the rug, for he was dying of cold. Ou Ali got up and cut the lips of the mule. The next morning, when they awaked, Ou Ali said to Ali:

" O my dear friend, your mule is grinning."

" O my dear friend," replied Ali, " the rats have gnawed your rug."

And they separated. Some time afterward they met anew. Ali said to Ou Ali:

"Let us go and steal."

They saw a peasant, who was working. One of them went to the brook to wash his cloak there, and found it dry. He laid the blade of his sabre so that it would reflect the rays of the sun, and began to beat his cloak with his hands as if to wash it. The laborer came to the brook also, and found the man who was washing his cloak without water.

"May God exterminate you," said he, "who wash without water."

"May God exterminate you," answered the washer, "who work without a single ox."

The other robber watched the laborer, and had already stolen one of his oxen. The laborer went back to his plough, and said to the washer, "Keep this ox for me while I go and hunt for the other." As soon as he was out of sight the robber took away the ox left in his charge. The laborer returned, and seizing the goad by one end he gave a great blow on the plough-handle, crying:

"Break, now. It matters little."

The robbers met in a wood and killed the oxen. As they lacked salt, they went to purchase it. They salted the meat, roasted it, and ate it. Ali discovered a spring. Ou Ali not being able to find water, was dying of thirst.

"Show me your spring," he said to Ali, "and I will drink."

"Eat some salt, my dear friend," answered Ali. What could he do? Some days afterward Ou Ali put ashes on the shoes of Ali. The next day he followed the traces of the ashes, found the spring, and discovered thus the water that his friend was drinking. He took the skin of one of the oxen and carried it to the fountain. He planted two sticks above the water, hung the skin on the sticks, and placed the horns of the ox opposite the road. During the night his friend went to the spring. At the sight of the skin thus stretched out, fear seized him, and he fled.

"I am thirsty," said Ou Ali.

"Eat some salt, my dear friend," answered Ali, "for salt removes thirst."

Ali retired, and, after having eaten, ran to examine the skin that he had stretched out. Ou Ali ate the salt, and was dying of thirst.

"For the love of God," he said finally, "show me where you drink."

Ali was avenged. "Come, Jew-face, and I will show you the water." He made him drink at the spring, and said to him: "See what you were afraid of." The meat being finished, they started away. Ou Ali went to the house of Ali, and said to him:

"Come, we will marry you to the daughter of an old woman."

Now, the old woman had a herd of oxen. She said to Ali: "Take this drove to the fields and mount one of the animals." Ali mounted one of the oxen. He fell to the ground; the oxen began to run and trample on him. Ou Ali, who was at the house, said to the old woman:

"O my old woman, give me your daughter in marriage."

She called her daughter. "Take a club," she said to her, "and we will give it to him until he cries for mercy."

The daughter brought a club and gave Ou Ali a good beating. Ali, who was watching the herd, came at nightfall and met his friend.

"Did the old woman accept you?" he asked him.

"She accepted me," answered Ali. "And is the herd easy to watch?"

"From morning till night I have nothing to do but to repose. Take my place to-morrow, and mount one of the oxen."

The next day Ou Ali said to the old woman, "To-day I will take care of the herd." And, on starting, he recommended Ali to ask the old woman for her daughter's hand.

"It is well," answered Ali. Ou Ali arrived in the fields; one of the oxen seized him with his horns and tossed him into the air. All the others did the same thing. He regained the horse half dead. Ali, who had remained at the house, asked the old woman for her daughter's hand. "You ask me again?" said she. She took a club and gave it to him till he had had enough. Ou Ali said to Ali: "You have played me a trick." Ali answered him: "Without doubt they gave me the stick so hard that I did not hear the last blow."

"It is well, my dear friend. Ali owes nothing to Ou Ali."
They went away. The old woman possessed a treasure.
Ou Ali therefore said to Ali: "I will put you in a basket, for
you know that we saw that treasure in a hole." They returned to the old woman's house. Ali goes down into the
hole, takes the treasure, and puts it into the basket. Ou Ali
draws up the basket, takes it, abandons his friend, now a prisoner, and runs to hide the treasure in the forest. Ali was in
trouble, for he knew not how to get out. What could he do?
He climbed up the sides of the hole. When he found himself
in the house, he opened the door and fled. Arriving at the
edge of the forest he began to bleat. Ou Ali, thinking it was
a ewe, ran up. It was his friend.

"O my dear," cried Ali, "I have found you at last."

"God be praised. Now, let us carry our treasure."

They started on the way. Ou Ali, who had a sister, said to
Ali: "Let us go to my sister's house." They arrived at night-
fall. She received them with joy. Her brother said to her:
"Prepare some pancakes and some eggs for us."

She prepared the pancakes and the eggs and served them
with the food."

"O my sister," cried Ou Ali, "my friend does not like
eggs; bring us some water." She went to get the water. As
soon as she had gone, Ali took an egg and put it into his
mouth. When the woman returned, he made such efforts to
give it up that he was all out of breath. The repast was
finished, and Ali had not eaten anything. Ou Ali said to his
sister: "O my sister, my friend is ill; bring me a skewer."
She brought him a skewer, which he put into the fire. When
the skewer was red with the heat, Ou Ali seized it and applied
it to the cheek of Ali. The latter uttered a cry, and rejected
the egg. "Truly," said the woman, "you do not like eggs."

The two friends started and arrived at a village.

"Let us go to my sister's house," said Ali to his friend. She
received them with open arms.

Ali said to her: "O my sister, prepare a good stew for us."

They placed themselves at the table at nightfall, and she
served them with food.

"O my sister," cried Ali, "my friend does not like stew."

Ali ate alone. When he was satisfied, the two friends

started, without forgetting the treasure. On the way Ali said to Ou Ali: "Give it to me to-day and I will deposit it in my house." He took it and gave it to his wife. "Bury me," he said to her. "And if Ou Ali comes tell him that his old friend is dead, and receive him with tears." Ou Ali arrived, and asked the woman in tears to see the tomb of his dead friend. He took an ox-horn and began to dig in the earth that covered the body.

"Behind! behind!" cried the pretended dead man.

"Get up, there, you liar," answered Ali.

They went away together. "Give me the treasure," asked Ou Ali; "to-day I will take it to my house." He took it to his house, and said to his wife: "Take this treasure. I am going to stretch myself out as if I were dead. When Ali comes receive him weeping, and say to him: 'Your friend is dead. He is stretched out in the bedroom.'"

Ali went and said to the woman: "Get me some boiling water, for your husband told me to wash him when he should die." When the water was ready the woman brought it. Ali seized the kettle and poured it on the stomach of Ou Ali, who sprang up with a bound. Thus he got even for the trick of his friend. The two friends divided the treasure then, and Ali went home.

THE INFIDEL JEW

A man went on a journey. At the moment of departure he placed with a Jew, his friend, a jar filled with gold. He covered the gold with butter and said to the Jew: "I trust to your care this jar of butter, as I am going on a journey." On his return he hastened to the house of his friend. "Give me the jar of butter that I left with you," he said. The Jew gave it to him. But the poor traveller found nothing but butter, for the Jew had taken the gold. Nevertheless, he did not tell anybody of the misfortune that had happened to him. But his countenance bore traces of a secret sorrow. His brother perceived it, and said to him:

"What is the matter with you?"

"I intrusted a jar filled with gold to a Jew," he answered,

"and he only returned a jar of butter to me. I don't know what to do to recover my property."

His brother replied: "The thing is easy. Prepare a feast and invite your friend the Jew."

The next day the traveller prepared a feast and invited the Jew. During this time the brother of the traveller ran to a neighboring mountain, where he captured a monkey. During the night he entered the house of the Jew and found a child in the cradle. He took the child away and put the monkey in its place. When day had come the mother perceived the monkey tied in the cradle. She called her husband with loud cries, and said to him:

"See how God has punished us for having stolen your friend's gold. Our child is changed into a monkey. Give back the stolen property."

They immediately had the traveller summoned, and returned his gold to him. The next night the child was taken back to the cradle and the monkey was set free. As I can go no further, may God exterminate the jackal and pardon all our sins!

THE SHEIK'S HEAD

A man died, leaving a son. The child spent day and night with his mother. The sheik chanted a prayer every morning and waked him up. The child went to find the sheik, and said:

"Ali Sheik, do not sing so loudly, you wake us up every morning—my mother and me."

But the sheik kept on singing. The child went to the mosque armed with a club. At the moment when the sheik bowed to pray he struck him a blow and killed him. He ran to his mother, and said to her:

"I have killed that sheik; come, let us bury him."

They cut off his head and buried his body. The child went to the Thadjeinath, where the men of the village were assembled. In his absence his mother killed a sheep. She took the head and buried it in place of the sheik's head. The child arrived at the Thadjeinath and said to those present:

"I have killed the sheik who waked us up every morning."

"It is a lie," said they.

"Come to my mother's house and we will show you where we buried his head." They went to the house, and the mother said to them:

"Ali Sidi, this child is mad. It is a sheep that we have killed. Come and see where we buried its head." They went to the spot, dug, and found a sheep's head.

THE WAGTAIL AND THE JACKAL

At the time when all the animals spoke, a wagtail laid her eggs on the ground. The little ones grew up. A jackal and a fox came to them. The jackal said to the fox:

"Swear to me that the wagtail owes me a pound of butter." The fox swore to it. The bird began to weep. A greyhound came to her and asked her what was the matter. She answered him:

"The fox has calumniated me."

"Well," said the hound, "put me in this sack of skin."

She put him in the sack. "Tie up the top well," said the hound. When the jackal returned she said to him:

"Come and measure out the butter."

The jackal advanced and unfastened the sack. He saw the hound, who stretched out his paws and said to the fox:

"I am ill; come and measure, fox."

The fox approached. The hound seized him. The jackal said, "Remember your false testimony."

THE FLUTE-PLAYER

A servant tended the sheep of his master. Arrived in the meadow, he played the flute. The sheep heard him, and would not browse. One day the master perceived that his sheep did not graze. He followed the servant to the fields and hid himself in the bush. The shepherd took his flute and began to play. His master began to dance so that the bushes brought blood upon him. He returned home.

"Who scratched you so?" asked his wife.

"The servant played on the flute, and I began to dance."

" That is a lie," said she; " people don't dance against their will."

" Well," answered the husband, " tie me to this post and make the servant play."

She tied him to the post and the servant took the flute. Our man began to dance. He struck his head against a nail in the post and died. The son of the dead man said to the servant:

" Pay me for the loss of my father."

They went before the cadi. On the way they met a laborer, who asked them where they were going.

" Before the cadi."

" Could you tell me why? "

" This man killed my father," answered the son of the dead man.

" It was not I that killed him," answered the shepherd; " I played on the flute, he danced and died."

" That is a lie! " cried the laborer. " I will not dance against my will. Take your flute and we shall see if I dance."

The shepherd took his flute. He began to play, and the laborer started dancing with such activity that his oxen left to themselves fell into the ravine.

" Pay me for my oxen," he cried to the shepherd.

" Come before the cadi," he answered. They presented themselves before the cadi, who received them on the second floor of the house. They all sat down. Then the cadi said to the servant:

" Take your flute and play before me. I will see how you play." The servant took his flute and all began to dance. The cadi danced with the others, and they all fell down to the ground floor and were killed. The servant stayed in the house of the cadi and inherited the property of all.

THE CHILD

A child had a thorn in his foot. He went to an old woman and said to her:

"Take out this thorn for me."

The old woman took out the thorn and threw it away.

"Give me my thorn," and he began to cry.

"Take an egg."

He went to another old woman, "Hide me this egg."

"Put it in the hen's nest."

In the night he took his egg and ate it. The next day he said to the old woman: "Give me my egg."

"Take the hen," she answered.

He went to another old woman, "Hide my hen for me."

"Put her on the stake to which I tie my he-goat."

At night he took away the hen. The next morning he demanded his hen.

"Look for her where you hid her."

"Give me my hen."

"Take the he-goat."

He went to another old woman, "O old woman, hide this goat for me."

"Tie him to the sheep's crib."

During the night he took away the buck. The next day he claimed the buck.

"Take the sheep."

He went to another old woman, "O old woman, keep my sheep for me."

"Tie him to the foot of the calf."

During the night he took away the sheep. Next morning he demanded his sheep.

"Take the calf."

He went to another old woman, "Keep my calf for me."

"Tie him to the cow's manger."

In the night he took away the calf. The next morning he asked for his calf.

"Take the cow."

He went to another old woman, "Keep my cow for me."

"Tie her to the foot of the old woman's bed."

In the night he took away the cow. The next morning he demanded his cow.

"Take the old woman."

He went to another old woman and left the old dame, whom he killed during the night. The next morning he demanded his old woman.

"There she is by the young girl."

He found her dead.

"Give me my old woman."

"Take the young girl."

He said to her: "From the thorn to the egg, from the egg to the hen, from the hen to the buck, from the buck to the sheep, from the sheep to the calf, from the calf to the cow, from the cow to the old woman, from the old woman to the young girl, and now come and marry me."

THE MONKEY AND THE FISHERMAN

A fisherman went one day to the sea to catch some fish. In the evening he sold his catch, and bought a little loaf of bread, on which he made his supper. The next day he returned to his fishing and found a chest. He took it to his house and opened it. Out jumped a monkey and said to him: "Bad luck to you. I am not the only one to conquer. You may bewail your sad lot."

"My lot is unbearable," he answered. The next day he returned to his fishing. The monkey climbed to the roof of the house and sat there. A moment afterward he cut all the roses of the garden. The daughter of the King saw him, and said to him:

"O Sidi Mahomet, what are you doing there? Come here, I need you."

He took a rose and approached.

"Where do you live?" asked the princess.

"With the son of the Sultan of India," answered the monkey.

"Tell him to buy me."

"I will tell him, provided he will accept."

The next day he stayed in the house and tore his face. The princess called him again. The monkey brought her a rose.

" Who put you in that condition ? " she cried.

" It was the son of the Sultan of India," answered the monkey. " When I told him to buy you he gave me a blow."

The princess gave him 100 ecus, and he went away. The next day he scratched his face worse and climbed on the house. The daughter of the King called him:

" Sidi Mahomet! "

" Well? "

" Come here. What did you say to him? "

" I told him to buy you, and he gave me another blow."

" Since this is so, come and find me to-morrow."

The next day the monkey took the fisherman to a shop and bought him some clothes. He took him to the baths and made him bathe. Then he went along the road and cried:

" Flee, flee, here is the son of the Sultan of India! "

They went into a coffee-house, and Si Mahomet ordered two coffees. They drank their coffees, gave an ecu to the proprietor, and went out. While going toward the palace Si Mahomet said to the fisherman:

" Here we are at the house of your father-in-law. When he serves us to eat, eat little. When he offers us coffee, drink only a little of it. You will find silken rugs stretched on the floor; keep on your sandals."

When they arrived the fisherman took off his sandals. The King offered them something to eat; the fisherman ate a great deal. He offered them some coffee, and the fisherman did not leave a drop of it. They went out. When they were outside the palace Si Mahomet said to the fisherman:

" Jew of a fisherman, you are lucky that I do not scratch your face."

They returned to their house. Si Mahomet climbed upon the roof. The daughter of the King perceived him, and said:

" Come here."

The monkey approached.

" Truly you have lied. Why did you tell me that the son of the Sultan of India was a distinguished person? "

" Is he a worthless fellow? "

" We furnished the room with silken rugs, he took off his sandals. We gave him food, and he ate like a servant. We offered him some coffee, and he licked his fingers."

The monkey answered: "We had just come out of the coffee-house. He had taken too much wine and was drunken, and not master of himself. That is why he ate so much."

"Well," replied the princess, "come to the palace again to-morrow, but do not take him to the coffee-house first."

The next day they set out. On the way the monkey said to the fisherman: "Jew of a fisherman, if to-day you take off your sandals or eat too much or drink all your coffee, look out for yourself. Drink a little only, or I will scratch your eyes out."

They arrived at the palace. The fisherman walked on the silken rugs with his sandals. They gave him something to eat, and he ate little. They brought him some coffee, and he hardly tasted it. The King gave him his daughter. Si Mahomet said to the King:

"The son of the Sultan of India has quarrelled with his father, so he only brought one chest of silver."

In the evening the monkey and the fisherman went out for a walk. The fisherman said to Si Mahomet:

"Is it here that we are going to find the son of the Sultan of India?"

"I can show him to you easily," answered the monkey. "To-morrow I will find you seated. I will approach, weeping, with a paper in my hands; I will give you the paper, and you must read it and burst into tears. Your father-in-law will ask you why you weep so. Answer him: 'My father is dead. Here is the letter I have just received. If you have finally determined to give me your daughter, I will take her away and we will go to pay the last duties to my father.'"

"Take her," said the King. He gave him an escort of horsemen and soldiers. Arriving at the place, Si Mahomet said to the soldiers:

"You may return to the palace, for our country is far from here."

The escort went back to the palace, and the travellers continued on their journey. Soon Si Mahomet said to the fisherman: "Stay here till I go and look at the country of your father." He started, and arrived at the gates of a city he found closed he mounted upon the ramparts. An ogress perceived him, "I salute you, Si Mahomet."

"May God curse you, sorceress! Come, I am going to your house."

"What do you want of me, Si Mahomet?"

"They are seeking to kill you."

"Where can I hide?" He put her in the powder-house of the city, shut the door on her, and set the powder on fire. The ogress died. He came back to the fisherman.

"Forward," he said. They entered the city and established themselves there. One day Si Mahomet fell ill and died. The two spouses put him in a coffin lined with silk and buried him. My story is told.

THE TWO FRIENDS

Sidi El-Marouf and Sidi Abd-el-Tadu were travelling in company. Toward evening they separated to find a resting-place. Sidi Abd-el-Tadu said to his friend:

"Let us say a prayer, that God may preserve us from the evil which we have never committed."

Sidi El-Marouf answered, "Yes, may God preserve us from the evil that we have not done!"

They went toward the houses, each his own way. Sidi El-Marouf presented himself at a door. "Can you entertain a traveller?"

"You are welcome," said a woman to him. "Enter, you may remain for the night."

Night came. He took his supper. The woman spread a mat on the floor and he went to sleep. The woman and her husband slept also. When all was quiet, the woman got up, took a knife, and killed her husband. The next day at dawn she began to cry:

"He has killed my husband!"

The whole village ran up to the house and seized the stranger. They bound him, and everyone brought wood to burn the guilty man.

Sidi Abd-el-Tadu came also, and saw his friend in tears. "What have you done?" he asked.

"I have done no evil," answered Sidi El-Marouf.

"Did I not tell you yesterday," said Sidi Abd-el-Tadu,

"that we would say the prayer that God should preserve us from the evil we had never committed? And now you will be burned for a crime of which you are innocent!"

Sidi El-Marouf answered him, "Bring the woman here."

"Did he really kill your husband?" asked Sidi Abd-el-Tadu.

"He killed him," she replied.

There was a bird on a tree nearby. Sidi Abd-el-Tadu asked the bird. The bird answered:

"It was the woman who killed her husband. Feel in her hair and you will find the knife she used."

They searched her hair and found the knife still covered with blood, which gave evidence of the crime. The truth was known and innocence was defended. God avenged the injustice.

THE ROBBER AND THE TWO PILGRIMS

Two robbers spent their time in robbing. One of them got married, and the other continued his trade. They were a long time without seeing each other. Finally the one who was not married went to visit his friend, and said to him:

"If your wife has a daughter, you must give her to me."

"I will give her to you seven days after her birth."

The daughter was born, and the robber took her to bring up in the country. He built a house, bought flocks, and tended them himself. One day some pilgrims came to the house. He killed a cow for them and entertained them. The next day he accompanied them on their pilgrimage. The pilgrims said to him:

"If you come with us, two birds will remain with your wife."

The woman stayed in the country. One day the son of the Sultan came that way to hunt. One of the birds saw him and said to the woman, "Don't open the door." The prince heard the bird speak, and returned to the palace without saying a word. An old woman was called to cast spells over him, and said to the King:

"He could not see a woman he has never seen."

The prince spoke and said to her: " If you will come with me, I will bring her here." They arrived.

The old dame called the young woman, " Come out, that we may see you."

She said to the bird, " I am going to open the door."

The bird answered: " If you open the door you will meet the same fate as Si El-Ahcen. He was reading with many others in the mosque. One day he found an amulet. His betrothed went no longer to school, and as she was old enough he married her. Some days after he said to his father, ' Watch over my wife.' ' Fear nothing,' answered the father.

" He started, and came back. ' Watch over my wife,' he said to his father again. ' Fear nothing,' repeated his father. The latter went to the market. On his return he said to his daughter-in-law, ' There were very beautiful women in the market.' ' I surpass them all in beauty,' said the woman; ' take me to the market.'

" A man offered 1,000 francs for her. The father-in-law refused, and said to her: ' Sit down on the mat. The one that covers you with silver may have you.' A man advanced. ' If you want to marry her,' said her father-in-law, ' cover her with silver, and she will be your wife.'

" Soon Si El-Ahcen returned from his journey and asked if his wife were still living. ' Your wife is dead,' said his father; ' she fell from her mule.' Si El-Ahcen threw himself on the ground. They tried to lift him up. It was useless trouble. He remained stretched on the earth.

" One day a merchant came to the village and said to him, ' The Sultan married your wife.' She had said to the merchant, ' The day that you leave I will give you a message.' She wrote a letter to her husband, and promised the bearer a flock of sheep if he would deliver it.

" Si El-Ahcen received the letter, read it, was cured, ran to the house, and said to his father: ' My wife has married again in my absence; she is not dead. I brought home much money. I will take it again.'

" He took his money and went to the city where his wife lived. He stopped at the gates. To the first passer-by he gave five francs, to the second five more.

" ' What do you want, O stranger?' they asked. ' If you

want to see the Sultan we will take you to him.' They presented him to the Sultan.

"'Render justice to this man.' 'What does he want?' 'My lord,' answered Sidi El-Ahcen, 'the woman you married is my wife.' 'Kill him!' cried the Sultan. 'No,' said the witnesses, 'let him have justice.'

"'Let him tell me if she carries an object.' Si El-Ahcen answered: 'This woman was betrothed to me before her birth. An amulet is hidden in her hair.' He took away his wife, returned to the village, and gave a feast.

"If you open the door," continued the bird, "you will have the same fate as Fatima-ou-Lmelh. Hamed-ou-Lmelh married her. Fatima said to her father-in-law, 'Take me to my uncle's house.' Arriving there she married another husband. Hamed-ou-Lmelh was told of this, and ran to find her. At the moment he arrived he found the wedding over and the bride about to depart for the house of her new husband. Then Hamed burst into the room and cast himself out of the window. Fatima did the same, and they were both killed.

"The intended father-in-law and his family returned to their house, and were asked the cause of the misfortune. 'The woman was the cause,' they answered.

"Nevertheless, the father of Hamed-ou-Lmelh went to the parents of Fatima and said: 'Pay us for the loss of our son. Pay us for the loss of Fatima.'

"They could not agree, and went before the justice. Passing by the village where the two spouses had died they met an old man, and said, 'Settle our dispute.' 'I cannot,' answered the old man. Farther on they met a sheep, which was butting a rock. 'Settle our dispute,' they said to the sheep. 'I cannot,' answered the sheep. Farther on they met a serpent. 'Settle our dispute,' they said to him. 'I cannot,' answered the serpent. They met a river. 'Settle our dispute,' they said to it. 'I cannot,' answered the river. They met a jackal. 'Settle our dispute,' they said to him. 'Go to the village where your children died,' answered the jackal. They went back to the village, and applied to the Sultan, who had them all killed."

The bird stopped speaking, the pilgrims returned. The old woman saw them and fled. The robber prepared a feast for the pilgrims.

THE LITTLE CHILD

" Come, little child, eat your dinner."
" I won't eat it."
" Come, stick, beat the child."
" I won't beat him."
" Come, fire, burn the stick."
" I won't burn it."
" Come, water, quench the fire."
" I won't quench it."
" Come, ox, drink the water."
" I won't drink it."
" Come, knife, kill the ox."
" I won't kill him."
" Come, blacksmith, break the knife."
" I won't break it."
" Come, strap, bind the blacksmith."
" I won't bind him."
" Come, rat, gnaw the strap."
" I won't gnaw it."
" Come, cat, eat the rat."
" Bring it here."

" Why eat me? " said the rat; " bring the strap and I'll gnaw it."

" Why gnaw me? " said the strap; " bring the blacksmith and I'll bind him."

" Why bind me? " said the blacksmith; " bring the knife and I'll break it."

" Why break me? " said the knife; " bring the ox and I'll kill him."

" Why kill me? " said the ox; " bring the water and I'll drink it."

" Why drink me? " said the water; " bring the fire and I'll quench it."

" Why quench me? " said the fire; " bring the stick and I'll burn it."

" Why burn me? " said the stick; " bring the child and I'll strike him."

" Why strike me? " said the child; " bring me my dinner and I'll eat it."

THE WREN

A wren had built its nest on the side of a road. When the eggs were hatched, a camel passed that way. The little wrens saw it, and said to their father when he returned from the fields:

" O papa, a gigantic animal passed by."

The wren stretched out his foot. " As big as this, my children? "

" O papa, much bigger."

He stretched out his foot and his wing. " As big as this? "

"O papa, much bigger."

Finally he stretched out fully his feet and legs. " As big as this, then? "

" Much bigger."

" That is a lie; there is no animal bigger than I am."

" Well, wait," said the little ones, " and you will see." The camel came back while browsing the grass of the roadside. The wren stretched himself out near the nest. The camel seized the bird, which passed through its teeth safe and sound.

" Truly," he said to them, " the camel is a gigantic animal, but I am not ashamed of myself."

On the earth it generally happens that the vain are as if they did not exist. But sooner or later a rock falls and crushes them.

THE MULE, THE JACKAL, AND THE LION

The mule, the jackal, and the lion went in company. " We will eat the one whose race is bad," they said to each other.

" Lion, who is your father? "

" My father is a lion and my mother is a lioness."

" And you, jackal, what is your father? "

" My father is a jackal and my mother, too."

" And you, mule, what is your father? "

" My father is an ass, and my mother is a mare."

" Your race is bad; we will eat you."

He answered them: " I will consult an old man. If he says that my race is bad, you may devour me."

He went to a farrier, and said to him, " Shoe my hind feet, and make the nails stick out well."

He went back home. He called the camel and showed him his feet, saying: " See what is written on this tablet."

" The writing is difficult to decipher," answered the camel. " I do not understand it, for I only know three words—*outini, ouzatini, ouazakin.*" He called a lion, and said to him: " I do not understand these letters; I only know three words—*outini, ouzatini, ouazakin.*"

" Show it to me," said the lion. He approached. The mule struck him between the eyes and stretched him out stiff.

He who goes with a knave is betrayed by him.

THADHELLALA

A woman had seven daughters and no son. She went to the city, and there saw a rich shop. A little farther on she perceived at the door of a house a young girl of great beauty. She called her parents, and said:

" I have my son to marry; let me have your daughter for him."

They let her take the girl away. She came back to the shop and said to the man in charge of it:

" I will gladly give you my daughter; but go first and consult your father."

The young man left a servant in his place and departed. Thadhellala (that was her name) sent the servant to buy some bread in another part of the city. Along came a caravan of mules. Thadhellala packed all the contents of the shop on their backs and said to the muleteer:

" I will go on ahead; my son will come in a moment. Wait for him—he will pay you."

She went off with the mules and the treasures which she had packed upon them. The servant came back soon.

" Where is your mother?" cried the muleteer; " hurry and pay me."

" You tell me where she is and I will make her give me back what she has stolen." And they went before the justice.

Thadhellala pursued her way, and met seven young students. She said to one of them, " A hundred francs and I will marry you." The student gave them to her. She made the same offer to the others, and each one took her word.

Arriving at a fork in the road, the first one said, " I will take you," the second one said, " I will take you," and so on to the last.

Thadhellala answered: " You shall have a race as far as that ridge over there, and the one that gets there first shall marry me."

The young men started. Just then a horseman came passing by. " Lend me your horse," she said to him. The horseman jumped off. Thadhellala mounted the horse and said:

" You see that ridge? I will rejoin you there."

The scholars perceived the man. " Have you not seen a woman?" they asked him. " She has stolen 700 francs from us."

" Haven't you others seen her? She has stolen my horse?"

They went to complain to the Sultan, who gave the command to arrest Thadhellala. A man promised to seize her. He secured a comrade, and they both pursued Thadhellala, who had taken flight. Nearly overtaken by the man, she met a negro who pulled teeth, and said to him:

" You see my son coming down there; pull out his teeth." When the other passed the negro pulled out his teeth. The poor toothless one seized the negro and led him before the Sultan to have him punished. The negro said to the Sultan: " It was his mother that told me to pull them out for hm."

" Sidi," said the accuser, " I was pursuing Thadhellala."

The Sultan then sent soldiers in pursuit of the woman, who seized her and hung her up at the gates of the city. Seeing herself arrested, she sent a messenger to her relatives.

Then there came by a man who led a mule. Seeing her he said, " How has this woman deserved to be hanged in this way?"

" Take pity on me," said Thadhellala; " give me your mule and I will show you a treasure." She sent him to a certain place where the pretended treasure was supposed to be hidden. At this the brother-in-law of Thadhellala had arrived.

" Take away this mule," she said to him. The searcher for

treasures dug in the earth at many places and found nothing. He came back to Thadhellala and demanded his mule.

She began to weep and cry. The sentinel ran up, and Thadhellala brought complaint against this man. She was released, and he was hanged in her place.

She fled to a far city, of which the Sultan had just then died. Now, according to the custom of that country, they took as king the person who happened to be at the gates of the city when the King died. Fate took Thadhellala there at the right time. They conducted her to the palace, and she was proclaimed Queen.

THE GOOD MAN AND THE BAD ONE

Two men, one good and the other bad, started out together to do business, and took provisions with them. Soon the bad one said to the good one: " I am hungry; give me some of your food." He gave him some, and they both ate.

They went on again till they were hungry. " Give me some of your food," said the bad one. He gave him some of it, and they ate.

They went on until they were hungry. " Give me some of your food," said the bad one. He gave him some, and they ate.

They went on until they were hungry. The good man said to his companion: " Give me some of your food."

" Oh, no, my dear," said the bad one.

" I beg you to give me some of your food," said the good one.

" Let me pluck out one of your eyes," answered the bad one. He consented. The bad one took his pincers and took out one of his eyes.

They went on until they came to a certain place. Hunger pressed them. " Give me some of your food," said the good man.

" Let me pluck out your other eye," answered his companion.

" O my dear," replied the good man, " leave it to me, I beg of you."

"No!" responded the bad one; "no eye, no food."

But finally he said, "Pluck it out."

They proceeded until they came to a certain place. When hunger pressed them anew the bad one abandoned his companion.

A bird came passing by, and said to him: "Take a leaf of this tree and apply it to your eyes." He took a leaf of the tree, applied it to his eyes, and was healed. He arose, continued on his way, and arrived at a city where he found the one who had plucked out his eyes.

"Who cured you?"

"A bird passed near me," said the good man. "He said to me, 'Take a leaf of this tree.' I took it, applied it to my eyes, and was cured.

The good man found the King of the city blind.

"Give me back my sight and I will give you my daughter."

He restored his sight to him, and the King gave him his daughter. The good man took his wife to his house. Every morning he went to present his respects to the King, and kissed his head. One day he fell ill. He met the bad one, who said to him:

"Eat an onion and you will be cured; but when you kiss the King's head, turn your head aside or the King will notice your breath and will kill you."

After these words he ran to the King and said: "O King, your son-in-law disdains you."

"O my dear," answered the King, "my son-in-law does not disdain me."

"Watch him," answered the bad one; "when he comes to kiss your head he will turn away from you."

The King remarked that his son-in-law did turn away on kissing his head.

"Wait a moment," he said to him. Immediately he wrote a letter to the Sultan, and gave it to his son-in-law, commanding him to carry it to the Sultan. Going out of the house he met the bad one, who wanted to carry the letter himself. The good man gave it to him. The Sultan read the letter, and had the bad one's head cut off. The good man returned to the King.

" What did he say? " asked the King.

" Ah, Sidi, I met a man who wanted to carry the letter. I intrusted it to him and he took it to the Sultan, who condemned him to death in the city."

THE CROW AND THE CHILD

A man had two wives. He was a rich merchant. One of them had a son whose forehead was curved with a forelock. Her husband said to her:

" Don't work any more, but only take care of the child. The other wife will do all the work."

One day he went to market. The childless wife said to the other, " Go, get some water."

" No," she answered, " our husband does not want me to work."

" Go, get some water, I tell you." And the woman went to the fountain. On the way she met a crow half dead with fatigue. A merchant who was passing took it up and carried it away. He arrived before the house of the woman who had gone to the fountain, and there found the second woman.

" Give something to this crow," demanded the merchant.

" Give it to me," she answered, " and I will make you rich."

" What will you give me? " asked the merchant.

" A child," replied the woman.

The merchant refused, and said to her, " Where did you steal it? "

" From whom did I steal it? " she cried. " It is my own son."

" Bring him."

She brought the child to him, and the merchant left her the crow and took the boy to his home and soon became very rich. The mother came back from the fountain. The other woman said:

" Where is your son? Listen, he is crying, that son of yours."

" He is not crying," she answered.

" You don't know how to amuse him. I'll go and take him."

"Leave him alone," said the mother. "He is asleep."

They ground some wheat, and the child did not appear to wake up.

At this the husband returned from the market and said to the mother, "Why don't you busy yourself looking after your son?" Then she arose to take him, and found a crow in the cradle. The other woman cried:

"This is the mother of a crow! Take it into the other house; sprinkle it with hot water." She went to the other house and poured hot water on the crow.

Meanwhile, the child called the merchant his father and the merchant's wife his mother. One day the merchant set off on a journey. His mother brought some food to him in the room where he was confined.

"My son," she said, "will you promise not to betray me?"

"You are my mother," answered the child; "I will not betray you."

"Only promise me."

"I promise not to betray you."

"Well, know that I am not your mother and my husband is not your father."

The merchant came home from his journey and took the child some food, but he would not eat it.

"Why won't you eat?" asked the merchant. "Could your mother have been here?"

"No," answered the child, "she has not been here."

The merchant went to his wife and said to her, "Could you have gone up to the child's chamber?"

The woman answered, "I did not go up to the room."

The merchant carried food to the child, who said: "For the love of God, I adjure you to tell me if you are my father and if your wife is my mother."

The merchant answered: "My son, I am not your father and my wife is not your mother."

The child said to her, "Prepare us some food."

When she had prepared the food the child mounted a horse and the merchant a mule. They proceeded a long way, and arrived at the village of which the real father of the child was the chief. They entered his house. They gave food to the child, and said, "Eat."

" I will not eat until the other woman comes up here."

" Eat. She is a bad woman."

" No, let her come up." They called her. The merchant
ran to the child.

" Why do you act thus toward her? "

" Oh! " cried those present, " she had a child that was
changed into a crow."

" No doubt," said the merchant; " but the child had a
mark."

" Yes, he had one."

" Well, if we find it, we shall recognize the child. Put out
the lamp." They put it out. The child threw off its hood.
They lighted the lamp again.

" Rejoice," cried the child, " I am your son! "

H'AB SLIMAN

A man had a boy and a girl. Their mother died and he
took another wife. The little boy stayed at school until
evening. The school-master asked them:

" What do your sisters do? "

One answered, " She makes bread."

A second, " She goes to fetch water."

A third, " She prepares the *couscous*."

When he questioned H'ab Sliman, the child played deaf,
the master struck him. One day his sister said to him:
" What is the matter, O my brother? You seem to be sad."

" Our schoolmaster punishes us," answered the child.

" And why does he punish you? " inquired the young girl.

The child replied: " After we have studied until evening
he asks each of us what our sisters do. They answer him:
she kneads bread, she goes to get water. But when he questions me I have nothing to say, and he beats me."

" Is it nothing but for that? "

" That is all."

" Well," added the young girl, " the next time he asks you,
answer him: ' This is what my sister does: When she laughs
the sun shines; when she weeps it rains; when she combs
her hair, legs of mutton fall; when she goes from one place
to another, roses drop.' "

The child gave that answer.

"Truly," said the schoolmaster, "that is a rich match."
A few days after he bought her, and they made preparations
for her departure for the house of her husband. The stepmother of the young girl made her a little loaf of salt bread.
She ate it and asked some drink from her sister, the daughter
of her stepmother.

"Let me pluck out one of your eyes," said the sister.

"Pluck it out," said the promised bride, "for our people
are already on the way."

The stepmother gave her to drink and plucked out one of
her eyes.

"A little more," she said.

"Let me take out your other eye," answered the cruel
woman.

The young girl drank and let her pluck out the other eye.
Scarcely had she left the house than the stepmother thrust
her out on the road. She dressed her own daughter and put
her in the place of the blind one. They arrive.

"Comb yourself," they told her, and there fell dust.

"Walk," and nothing happened.

"Laugh," and her front teeth fell out.

All cried, "Hang H'ab Sliman!"

Meanwhile some crows came flying near the young blind
girl, and one said to her: "Some merchants are on the point
of passing this way. Ask them for a little wool, and I will
restore your sight."

The merchants came up and the blind girl asked them for
a little wool, and each one of them threw her a bit. The crow
descended near her and restored her sight.

"Into what shall we change you?" they asked.

"Change me into a pigeon," she answered.

The crows stuck a needle into her head and she was changed
into a pigeon. She took her flight to the house of the school-
master and perched upon a tree near by. The people went
to sow wheat.

"O master of the field," she said, "is H'ab Sliman yet
hanged?"

She began to weep, and the rain fell until the end of the
day's work.

One day the people of the village went to find a venerable old man and said to him:

"O old man, a bird is perched on one of our trees. When we go to work the sky is covered with clouds and it rains. When the day's work is done the sun shines."

"Go," said the old man, "put glue on the branch where it perches."

They put glue on its branch and caught the bird. The daughter of the stepmother said to her mother:

"Let us kill it."

"No," said a slave, "we will amuse ourselves with it."

"No; kill it." And they killed it. Its blood spurted upon a rose-tree. The rose-tree became so large that it overspread all the village. The people worked to cut it down until evening, and yet it remained the size of a thread.

"To-morrow," they said, "we will finish it." The next morning they found it as big as it was the day before. They returned to the old man and said to him:

"O old man, we caught the bird and killed it. Its blood gushed upon a rose-tree, which became so large that it overspreads the whole village. Yesterday we worked all day to cut it down. We left it the size of a thread. This morning we find it as big as ever."

"O my children," said the old man, "you are not yet punished enough. Take H'ab Sliman, perhaps he will have an expedient. Make him sleep at your house." H'ab Sliman said to them, "Give me a sickle." Someone said to him: "We who are strong have cut all day without being able to accomplish it, and do you think you will be capable of it? Let us see if you will find a new way to do it."

At the moment when he gave the first blow a voice said to him:

"Take care of me, O my brother!"

The voice wept, the child began to weep, and it rained. H'ab Sliman recognized his sister.

"Laugh," he said. She laughed and the sun shone, and the people got dried.

"Comb yourself," and legs of mutton fell. All those who were present regaled themselves on them. "Walk," and roses fell. "But what is the matter with you, my sister?"

"What has happened to me."

"What revenge does your heart desire?"

"Attach the daughter of my stepmother to the tail of a horse that she may be dragged in the bushes."

When the young girl was dead, they took her to the house, cooked her, and sent her to her mother and sister.

"O my mother," cried the latter, "this eye is that of my sister Aftelis."

"Eat, unhappy one," said the mother, "your sister Aftelis has become the slave of slaves."

"But look at it," insisted the young girl. "You have not even looked at it. I will give this piece to the one who will weep a little."

"Well," said the cat, "if you give me that piece I will weep with one eye."

THE KING AND HIS SON

He had a son whom he brought up well. The child grew and said one day to the King, "I am going out for a walk."

"It is well," answered the King. At a certain place he found an olive-tree on fire.

"O God," he cried, "help me to put out this fire!"

Suddenly God sent the rain, the fire was extinguished, and the young man was able to pass. He came to the city and said to the governor:

"Give me a chance to speak in my turn."

"It is well," said he; "speak."

"I ask the hand of your daughter," replied the young man.

"I give her to you," answered the governor, "for if you had not put out that fire the city would have been devoured by the flames."

He departed with his wife. After a long march the wife made to God this prayer:

"O God, place this city here."

The city appeared at the very spot. Toward evening the Marabout of the city of which the father of the young bridegroom was King went to the mosque to say his prayers.

"O marvel!" he cried, "what do I see down there?"

The King called his wife and sent her to see what was this

new city. The woman departed, and, addressing the wife of the young prince, asked alms of him. He gave her alms. The messenger returned and said to the King:

"It is your son who commands in that city."

The King, pricked by jealousy, said to the woman: "Go, tell him to come and find me. I must speak with him."

The woman went away and returned with the King's son. His father said to him:

"If you are the son of the King, go and see your mother in the other world."

He regained his palace in tears.

"What is the matter with you," asked his wife, "you whom destiny has given me?"

He answered her: "My father told me, 'Go and see your mother in the other world.'"

"Return to your father," she replied, "and ask him for the book of the grandmother of your grandmother."

He returned to his father, who gave him the book. He brought it to his wife, who said to him, "Lay it on the grave of your mother." He placed it there and the grave opened. He descended and found a man who was licking the earth. He saw another who was eating mildew. And he saw a third who was eating meat.

"Why do you eat meat?" he asked him.

"Because I did good on earth," responded the shade.

"Where shall I find my mother?" asked the prince.

The shade said, "She is down there."

He went to his mother, who asked him why he came to seek her.

He replied, "My father sent me."

"Return," said the mother, "and say to your father to lift up the beam which is on the hearth." The prince went to his father. "My mother bids you take up the beam which is above the hearth." The King raised it and found a treasure.

"If you are the son of the King," he added, "bring me someone a foot high whose beard measures two feet." The prince began to weep.

"Why do you weep," asked his wife, "you whom destiny has given me?"

The prince answered her, " My father said to me, ' Bring me someone a foot high whose beard measures two feet.' "

" Return to your father," she replied, " and ask him for the book of the grandfather of your grandfather."

His father gave him the book and the prince brought it to his wife.

" Take it to him again and let him put it in the assembly place, and call a public meeting." A man a foot high appeared, took up the book, went around the city, and ate up all the inhabitants.

MAHOMET-BEN-SOLTAN

A certain sultan had a son who rode his horse through the city where his father reigned, and killed everyone he met. The inhabitants united and promised a flock to him who should make him leave the city. An old woman took it upon herself to realize the wishes of her fellow-citizens. She procured some bladders and went to the fountain to fill them with the cup of an acorn. The old man came to water his horse and said to the old woman:

" Get out of my way."

She would not move. The young man rode his horse over the bladders and burst them.

" If you had married Thithbirth, a cavalier," cried the old woman, " you would not have done this damage. But I predict that you will never marry her, for already seventy cavaliers have met death on her account."

The young man, pricked to the quick, regained his horse, took provisions, and set out for the place where he should find the young girl. On the way he met a man. They journeyed together. Soon they perceived an ogress with a dead man at her side.

" Place him in the earth," said the ogress to them; " it is my son; the Sultan hanged him and cut off his foot with a sword."

They took one of the rings of the dead man and went on their way. Soon they entered a village and offered the ring to the governor, who asked them for another like it. They went away from there, returned through the country which they had traversed, and met a pilgrim who had made the tour of the world. They had visited every place except the sea. They turned toward the sea. At the moment of embarking, a whale barred their passage. They retraced their steps, and met the ogress, took a second ring from the dead man, and departed. At a place they found sixty corpses. A singing bird was guarding them. The travellers stopped and heard the bird say:

"He who shall speak here shall be changed into a rock and shall die. Mahomet-ben-Soltan, you shall never wed the young girl. Ninety-nine cavaliers have already met death on her account."

Mahomet stayed till morning without saying one word. Then he departed with his companion for the city where Thithbirth dwelt. When they arrived they were pressed with hunger. Mahomet's companion said to him:

"Sing that which you heard the bird sing." He began to sing. The young girl, whom they meant to buy, heard him and asked him from whom he had got that song.

"From my head," he answered.

Mahomet's companion said: "We learned it in the fields from a singing bird."

"Bring me that bird," she said, "or I'll have your head cut off."

Mahomet took a lantern and a cage which he placed upon the branch of the tree where the bird was perching.

"Do you think to catch me?" cried the bird. The next day it entered the cage and the young man took it away. When they were in the presence of the young girl the bird said to her:

"We have come to buy you."

The father of the young girl said to Mahomet: "If you find her you may have her. But if not, I will kill you. Ninety-nine cavaliers have already met death thus. You will be the hundredth."

The bird flew toward the woman.

"Where shall I find you?" it asked her.

She answered: "You see that door at which I am sitting; it is the usual place of my father. I shall be hidden underneath."

The next day Mahomet presented himself before the Sultan: " Arise," he said, " your daughter is hidden there."

The Sultan imposed this new condition: " My daughter resembles ninety-nine others of her age. She is the hundredth. If you recognize her in the group I will give her to you. But if not, I will kill you."

The young girl said to Mahomet, " I will ride a lame horse." Mahomet recognized her, and the Sultan gave her to him, with a serving-maid, a female slave, and another woman.

Mahomet and his companion departed. Arriving at a certain road they separated. Mahomet retained for himself his wife and the slave woman, and gave to his companion the two other women. He gained the desert and left for a moment his wife and the slave woman. In his absence an ogre took away his wife. He ran in search of her and met some shepherds.

" O shepherds," he said, " can you tell me where the ogre lives? "

They pointed out the place. Arriving, he saw his wife. Soon the ogre appeared, and Mahomet asked where he should find his destiny.

" My destiny is far from here," answered the ogre. " My destiny is in an egg, the egg in a pigeon, the pigeon in a camel, the camel in the sea."

Mahomet arose, ran to dig a hole at the shore of the sea, stretched a mat over the hole; a camel sprang from the water and fell into the hole. He killed it and took out an egg, crushed the egg in his hands, and the ogre died. Mahomet took his wife and came to his father's city, where he built himself a palace. The father promised a flock to him who should kill his son. As no one offered, he sent an army of soldiers to besiege him. He called one of them in particular and said to him:

" Kill Mahomet and I will enrich you."

The soldiers managed to get near the young prince, put out his eyes, and left him in the field. An eagle passed and said to Mahomet: " Don't do any good to your parents, but since your father has made you blind take the bark of this tree, apply it to your eyes, and you will be cured."

The young man was healed.

A short time after his father said to him, " I will wed your wife."

" You cannot," he answered. The Sultan convoked the Marabout, who refused him the dispensation he demanded. Soon Mahomet killed his father and celebrated his wedding-feast for seven days and seven nights.